8/74

'When the sun rises, I go to work
When the sun goes down, I take my rest
I dig the well from which I drink
I farm the soil that yields my food
I share creation
Kings can do no more.'
—Ancient Chinese 2500 BC

FIRST-TIME FARMER'S GUIDE

Bill Kaysing's

THE EX-URBANITE'S COMPLETE & ILLUSTRATED EASY-DOES-IT FIRST-TIME FARMER'S GUIDE

A Useful Book

Straight Arrow Books

San Francisco

Library of Congress Catalog Card Number: 77-158518
ISBN 0/87932/047/8 (paperbound); 0/87932/008/7 (cloth)

Casebound: First printing, August 1971. Second printing, February 1972. Third printing, February 1973.
Paperback: First printing, February 1973. Second printing (revised), September 1973.

Straight Arrow Books
625 Third Street, San Francisco, California 94107

Distributed by Quick Fox Inc
33 West 60th Street, New York 10023

Printed by Levison McNally, Reno, Nevada
Production: Planned Production

Order no: 102047 (paperback); 102088 (cloth)

Other Writings of Bill Kaysing:

How To Escape The Rat Race/Paradise Publishers
Thermal Springs of the Western United States/Paradise Publishers
Twenty Five Ways Young People Can Make A Living in the Country/Paradise Publishers
How You Can Stop Smoking And Enjoy It/Now And Then Publications
Intelligent Motorcycling/Parkhurst Publishing Co
Automatic Servo Control Mechanisms/Rocketdyne Inc
Reliability of Thin Film Digital Modules/Intellux Inc
How To Live in the New America/Prentice Hall
The Robin Hood Handbook/Links Books
Great Swimming Holes of the West/Capra Press

Introduction and Acknowledgements

Writing this book was an enjoyable and rewarding trip in the best sense of the word. From the moment that Straight Arrow gave the high sign until the final illustration was agreed on at my ranch in the Sierra foothills, the project produced good vibes. For example, every single publisher we asked gave us permission to use copyrighted material. Free material poured in from garden equipment companies, complimentary seeds and stock from seed firms all over the US and dozens of people came forth to donate their prized bits of botanical or farmstead knowledge. In all, it was one of those fun tasks where everything goes right *plus*.

I hope that *you* the reader will capture some of this joyful enthusiasm from the pages of this book and use it to make a delightful, productive and enduring adventure of your own *first-time farm*.

And thanks. You've made it possible to bring the book up to date and reprint it once more. Keep those letters coming (c/o the Publisher) and we'll incorporate your findings in still another edition.

Peace, love
Bill Kaysing / September 1973

My warmest appreciation to the following people and companies who deserve much credit for creating this book:

Ruth 'The Gleaner' Kaysing (for typing & editing & watching like a friendly hawk, *every single word;* my daughters, Wendy & Jill for providing affectionate and encouraging words; Alan, Jon, Dian, Vickie, Tom, Kathy, Carol, and many others at Rolling Stone who extended the warmest of welcomes and the most diligent effort in doing the really hard work . . . producing the book; Burpee Seed Company; Harris Seeds; Rodale Press; Wine Advisory Board; Wood Heat Quarterly; John Deere Co; Whole Earth Catalog; Stokes Seed Co; The American Rabbit Breeders Assoc; Girard Nurseries; The Questers; University of Delaware; US Department of the Interior; Farmers Home Administration; practically all of the US Farming magazines; Garden Way Research Assoc; Countryside (Jerry Belanger); Mother Earth News (John Shuttleworth); Clear Creek (Don McCartney); The USDA; University of California, Division of Agricultural Science; World Health Organization; VITA; Rayner Seed Co; Aermotor Inc; Dempster Mill Co; Dept of State, Agency for International Development; Sears and Wards; United Farm Agency; Stark Farm Agency; Ford Motor Co; Stark Brothers Fruits; The Natural Development Company; Lane Publishing Co; Gurney's Seeds; JE Miller Nurseries; Economy Tractor Co; Gravely Co; Savage Farms; Park Seed Co; Nichols Garden Nursery; Interstate Nurseries; Troy Bilt Rototillers; Meals for Millions; Kelly Bros Nurseries; Waterwell Drillers; Valentine Equipment Co; Safe Buy Realty; Canadian Department of Agriculture; Saier Seeds; AI Root Co; Herb Products Inc; Brower Co; Strombergs; The Purina Co; William Vollmer, Vollmer & Sons and Tom Cole.

If you've been thinking along the same lines as Tom Jefferson, crystal pools reflecting bright blue skies and clear creeks ambling between hills crested with tall grass; warm afternoons sauntering through summery cornfields listening to the corn grow; the easy seasonal changes of tall apple trees from twigs and branches to bowers of blossoms to lush green leaves to red fruit hanging in bountiful clusters. If you've been thinking along these lines, then join the movement . . . the one that's headed towards the countryside.

Getting back to the land has many advantages. First there is fresh air and pure water to ensure your health. Then there's the green softness so necessary to the spirit. More mundane but important, it costs less to live. Things are more relaxed in the country. Your furnishings can be handmade, your clothes informal, leathery, homespun. You can build a cabin, a treehouse or live in a smial like the Hobbits do. Grow your own vegetables and fruit; keep a small flock of chickens, a pig or a goat. With electricity, you can enjoy city conveniences. Or, with an alternate source of power like wind, you can pump your water and grind your corn. Living in the country is like being on a year-round vacation. The blue lakes, quiet deserts, tall mountains and broad rivers . . . the best of everything worth seeing in America is in the country. And anyone who loves nature, trees, animals and growing things should be with them twelve months of the year instead of just two weeks. On a farm, every day can be a delight because every day something new happens.

Every age can enjoy a small farm. For those who have grown old in the city, a new life in more natural surroundings can be a rebirth of body and spirit. Those of middle age can enjoy a renaissance . . . a chance for a new and different life. For young people with the new consciousness, a small farm can be 'the place where it's at.' But most of all, farms and the country are where all of our children should be. Imagine the joy of a child who plants an apple tree and then sees the miracle of spring bring blossoms to its new branches. The free time that children enjoy on a farm is legendary. It's not too late to play Tom Sawyer and Becky Thatcher in the Twentieth century. Visualize children, your children, building a treehouse, damming a stream to make a swimming hole, digging a cave, riding the farm horse through an autumn cornfield.

For many reasons — political, economical, psychological — people are going back to the land. It's been a movement all along but lately it's become a floodtide. However, most city people don't know where to begin and that's what this book is all about. Farming isn't difficult . . . peasants are successful at it all over the world with no formal training, capital, or government subsidy. It's not that mysterious and it's not difficult, in fact it's easier than some of the things you already know how to do. We're just going to provide some simple facts and practical information and access to other information. This book will take away the mystery and point you in various directions, giving you many options, such as whether you just want to grow enough for yourself, start a little business, support your family or your commune, specialize in one crop, or get into something far out like fish farming or breeding wild game birds. With the information we're going to provide, you'll be able to:

Find a suitable farm or other country land.

Develop a water supply if one isn't available.

Improve the soil.

Obtain seeds, young trees and farm animals.

Plant and care for all kinds of vegetables and fruits.

First Time Farmer's Guide

Decide which of the many varieties of farm animals would be suitable and how to care for the ones you choose.

Learn many other useful, little-known tips and pointers on such things as finding free foods, making money from your farm, eliminating heavy labor and keeping yourself, your family, your gardens, groves and livestock healthy and happy.

With this guide you'll have all the information you'll need to be a mini-farmer on a one quarter acre plot or make a success with a 20-acre fish farm. You'll be able to grow enough vegetables and fruits for yourself and your family plus provide for a commune or a roadside stand.

We'll introduce you to a number of unique publications. With them, you'll discover what is worth getting and where.

So, in summary, our purpose is to help you obtain your own education, inspire enthusiasm, help shape your environment and invite you to share your outdoor adventures with those you love.

If Bill Schuler can do it, *anyone* can do it. (He flew the San Fernando Valley coop and lives with the pines in Twain Harte)

Land

'I have often thought that if heaven had given me choice of my position and calling, it should have been on a rich spot of earth, well watered, and near a good market for the productions of the garden. No occupation is so delightful to me as the culture of the earth.'

—*Thomas Jefferson*

By careful land selection, it's still possible to have your (country) cake and eat it too

Selection of the land on which to establish your first-time farm is easy. Just write down a list of qualifications. Here's a sampling of what we mean:

Fresh air.

Lots of elbow room.

No heavy traffic or industry near enough to cause noise, water or atmospheric pollution.

If you have school age children, suitable educational facilities.

A climate that invigorates your body and spirit.

Income possibilities.

Reasonable proximity to trading areas.

Suitability of land to grow crops (your local County Agent can provide this information or help you make a soil test).

Depending on the individual and specific needs of you and your family, you may want to add a number of additional qualifications. For example, if your 11-year-old son is having his teeth straightened, there should be an orthodontist within reasonable driving or flying distance. Further, if your spouse just *has* to see a first-run movie once a month, then by all means include a movie house within a day's journey. It's a fact that the people who make the best adjustment to rural living, take bits and pieces of their former environment with them or stay within a couple of hours flight of an urban area. This is one of the few instances where it's possible to have your cake and eat it too. Many people are enjoying the best of both worlds. With the proliferation of short range airline service, you can live amidst the sylvan delights of upstate New York and yet fly into Manhattan whenever you just have to see those bright lights again and breathe some of that thick air.

One young man who was brought up in a city and

learned to hate it with great passion, has made a compromise for himself that he claims is ideal. He lives in the rugged pioneering atmosphere of California's Mother Lode country. Whenever he wants to assure himself that the country is best, he rents a plane and flies over to San Francisco just two hours from his Amador County stomping grounds. He's always glad to get back — trading the dirt, noise and congestion of Third and Market Streets for the clean air, quiet and tranquility of pioneer.

How to suit your needs.

What you intend to do with the land will determine what type of land you should buy. If you've always had a desire to be a cattle rancher, then the great open plains that you'll find in Arizona, Montana, New Mexico, Wyoming, Colorado, Nevada and Western Oregon and Washington would be ideal. There are still vast reaches of grazing land that can be acquired quite reasonably. Although you would be using this land primarily for grazing cattle or sheep, it is possible that a fertile piece near a water source could be used for your vegetable garden and fruit and nut orchards. Speaking of orchards, the need for fresh fruit increases yearly with our expanding population. Therefore, fertile soil with an adequate supply of water would be a must if you intend to grow apples, pears, peaches, other fruits or nuts. There are suitable areas for fruit growing scattered throughout the United States. Georgia is noted for its fine peach growing climate, while the region just east of the Cascades in the state of Washington has become famous for the high quality of its apples. It follows quite logically that if your first-time farming efforts lean towards fruit and nut growing, you should look for a mature or young orchard, or land adjacent to existing fruit and nut growing regions.

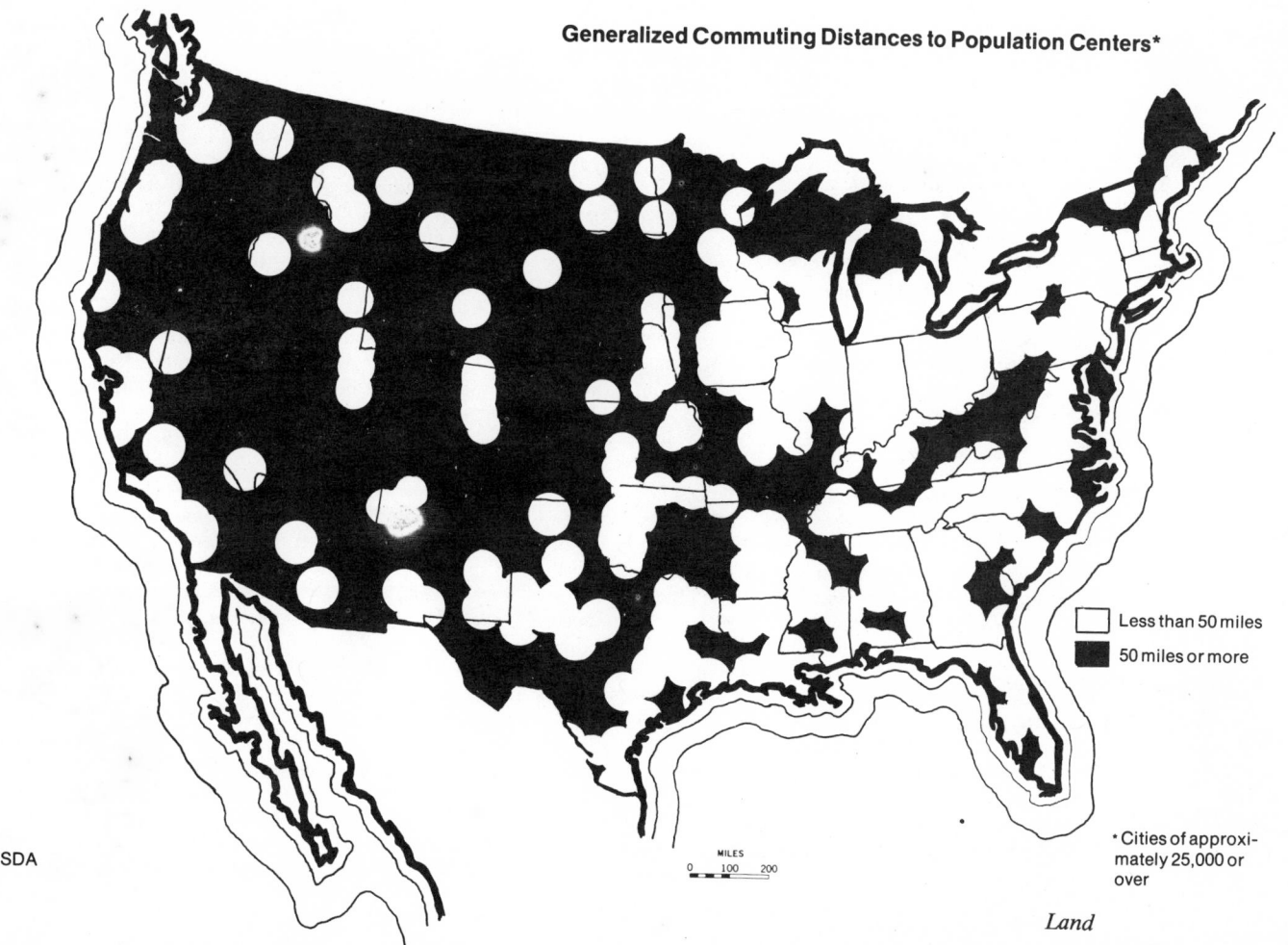

Generalized Commuting Distances to Population Centers*

Less than 50 miles

50 miles or more

MILES
0   100   200

* Cities of approximately 25,000 or over

USDA

Land 17

Opposite: tenacious,
resolute desert lovers
have carved a fertile
green empire out of
forbidding sage land
(note reservoir). If
fresh air and plenty
of elbow room mean
a lot to you, then
country land at *any
price* is a bargain

Until recently, much desert land was considered to be wasteland. However, with the development of water supplies, former desert land has been put to good use to grow alfalfa and other grasses, as well as crops that like a loose sandy soil, carrots, peanuts and melons. A new idea is the production of cactus. Cactus fruit and the young pads are suitable for human consumption while the mature cactus pads can be sold as cattle food after they are destickered. Since cactus requires little water, this would be an ideal crop for arid desert land previously held unsuitable for agriculture.

If you'd like to try your hand at the new enterprise of fish farming (more on this in Chapter 12) then you should seek land that has outlived its usefulness for conventional crops but has a plentiful supply of good water.

Many new forms of farming similar to fish farming are springing up. For example, the raising of game birds for food and hunting has grown tremendously in various parts of the United States. Land that would be considered poor for conventional agriculture could be used for this purpose. As an example, the rough and rugged regions in Nevada and Arizona that support only mesquite, sage and cactus would be ideal for the rugged little quail, feisty partridge or similar wild birds. They have been accustomed throughout the centuries to adapt to rigorous living conditions. Thus, if you provided them with food and water, they would consider the roughest of terrains a veritable paradise.

Another form of farming that can be conducted on poor land or, believe it or not, on practically no land, is the production of honey from bees. Hives placed on almost any kind of land that is adjacent to orchards, alfalfa fields, wild sage, or any other source of nectar from which bees make honey would be suitable. In other words, you don't need to own the land on which your little 'bee farmers' harvest their crop. In fact, many farmers will be happy to pay you to bring your hives close to where they are growing their crops.

Still another unique form of farming is tree farming. Much land considered too poor in nutrients, too rocky, hilly or mountainous could be easily adapted to crops of many different kinds of trees. In the South, several varieties of pine are grown for telephone poles, fencing, pulp or turpentine. Christmas trees are another crop that can be adapted to land unsuited for conventional farming. If you've always dreamed of a beautiful grove of deep green orange trees festooned with brilliant oranges then head for California, Arizona, or Florida. Here you'll find young orchards being planted by the hundreds of acres.

Breeding fine horses appeals to many people as a business or as part of a gentleman farmer enterprise. The bluegrass country of Kentucky or the rolling hills of California's Santa Ynez Valley would be just two of the many places where land and climate would be suitable.

The intensive culture of land is becoming popular in many parts of the country. By this we mean growing such crops as strawberries or blueberries in a small space. Did you know that it's possible to grow $1,000 worth of strawberries on just one quarter acre of good land? Thus, you might want to think in terms of owning just a small piece of land and devoting much attention to it.

But perhaps your desire is merely to live quietly, conservatively and independently on a small plot . . . an acre or two. If this is the case, then almost any land that meets your other needs and qualifications would be suitable. This is true because even poor land can become productive by adding nutrients to the soil. In summary,

There is one half
billion acres of
government
owned land

decide what characteristics your first-time farming efforts will have; then look for the land that will make your dreams come true.

Facts About Government Land

Almost a half billion acres are classified as public lands and are owned by the Federal government. There are two major ways that you can acquire some of this land: homesteading or public land purchase.

Homesteading was once a fabulous way to acquire land. All that was required was for the homesteader to occupy the land for a specific period of time, make some improvements such as a house, and till the soil. After fulfilling these requirements, the land was granted to him by the Government free of any cost. But now, nearly all of the land is gone and homesteading is just about a thing of the past . . . except in Alaska. Current rules governing homesteading are quite strict. Your investment in time and money for a homestead may easily run higher than if you purchased an existing farm on the open market. For further information on homesteading write the Land Office nearest you:

Alaska: 555 Cordova Street, Anchorage; and 516 Second Avenue, Fairbanks.
Arizona: Federal Building, Room 3204, Phoenix 85025.
California: Federal Building, Room 4017, Sacramento 95814; and 1414 Eighth Street, Riverside 92502.
Colorado: Federal Building, Room 15019, Denver 80202.
Idaho: Federal Building, Room 323, Boise 83701.
Montana (Includes North & South Dakota): Federal Building & Courthouse, Billings 59101.
Nevada: Federal Building & Courthouse, Reno 89505.
New Mexico (Includes Oklahoma): US Post Office & Federal Building, Santa Fe 87501.
Oregon (Includes Washington): 710 NE Holladay, Portland 97232.
Utah: Federal Building, Room 3216, Salt Lake City 84111.
Wyoming: 2120 Capital Avenue, Cheyenne 82001.
For All Eastern States: Robin Building, 7981 Eastern Avenue, Silver Springs, Maryland 20910

A more practical way to acquire low-cost government land is to buy it. Just write the Land Office nearest to your chosen area and ask them to tell you what is available. Typical lands currently for sale include rolling to hilly Arizona grazing country, high desert in California, isolated foothill land in Montana and some interesting big tracts in Nevada's White Pine County.

Some of this land wouldn't support two people on

First Time Farmer's Guide

Increasingly Less Pleasant Areas* in which to Live

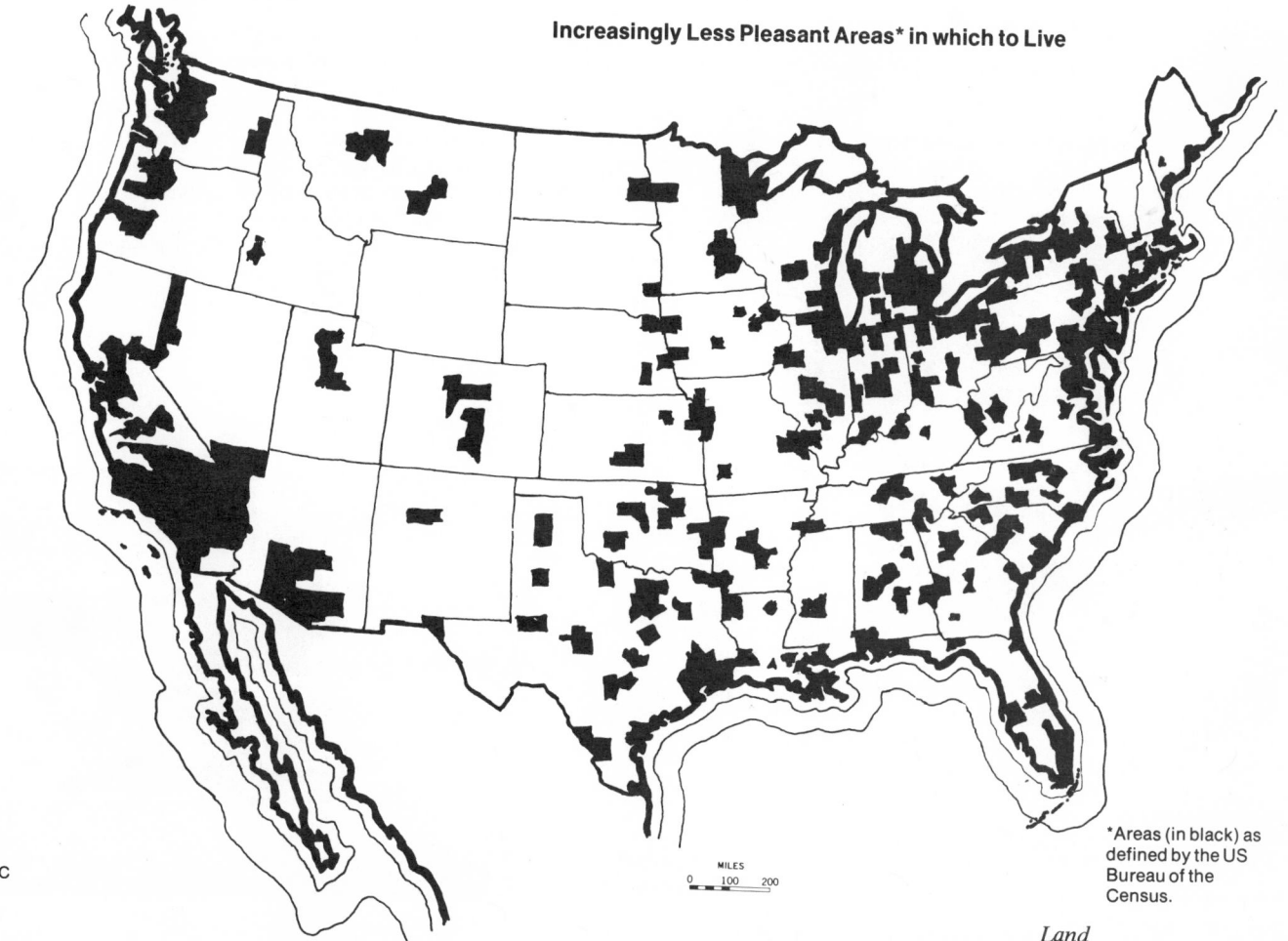

USDC

MILES
0   100   200

*Areas (in black) as defined by the US Bureau of the Census.

ten acres. Other parcels have lots of potential for the creative, imaginative farmer-to-be. As you will note, one thing is for sure, you can't beat government land in the low price department. However, keep this salient fact in mind when you consider the acquisition of public lands. Much of it has been passed over by hundreds of potential buyers as being inferior. Thus, even though it won't cost you much in the beginning, you may spend more in developing it than you would spend if you bought an existing 'spread'.

To keep abreast of public land sales, you can subscribe to 'Our Public Lands'. This little magazine is full of information about public lands and always lists what is currently for sale. For information, write Superintendent of Documents, Government Printing Office, Washington, DC 20402.

Finding Country Property

The positively best and easiest way to find out what's available in private rural land in America today is to send for the latest edition of land catalogs published by these firms:

United Farm Agency, 612 W 47th, Kansas City, Missouri 64112

Strout Realty, PO 2757, Springfield, Missouri 65803

Safe-Buy Real Estate, PO 589, Little Rock, Arkansas 72203

Stateside Realty, 507 Pyramid Building, Little Rock, Arkansas 72201

These catalogs will give you a good general idea of what's available *right now* in farm property. The catalogs show small pictures of the properties. Many of the photos show a view of the surrounding terrain. So if it

looks like the terrain has tall trees and rushing brooks and this is what you've always wanted, then you can concentrate on that region.

Opposite are some examples selected at random from the most recent catalog.

Once you've completed a comprehensive review of what you'd like, you're ready for the fine focus. Write to the Chamber of Commerce in the city nearest your chosen area. Ask them for the following kinds of information: climate, farm opportunities, names of local and regional papers that serve the area, names of land brokers and other general information. It's a standard ploy of Chambers of Commerce to present their area as though it were the Elysian Fields. Don't be fooled. Check their expansive allegations with the brutally candid maps and USDA climate descriptions which follow.

THE FOOL.

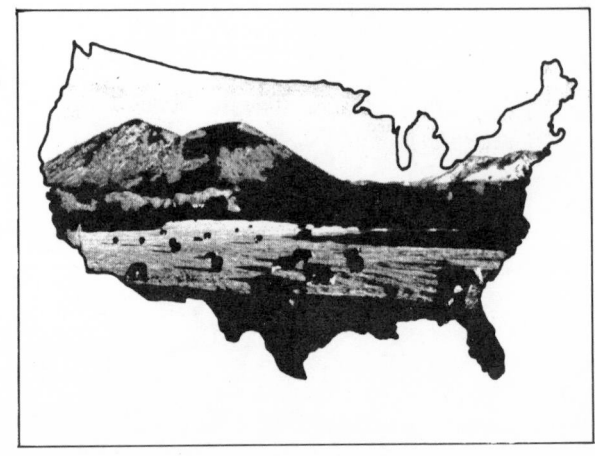

SECLUDED HIDEOUT

No.3153—17 acres, $4,900. Enjoy beautiful private setting on nice stream! 1,200-ft. frontage on water, fine area for deer, bear and good bird hunting. Within 3½ miles year-round fishing in lake for trout, bass, bluegill, catfish. 17 acres. Some could be tilled, some woodland, shade trees. Good homesites. On hardtop road, 8½ miles to town. This recreational hideout is all yours for $4,900, low down pay-

ment. UNITED, Cave Junction, Oreg.

A SITE TO BEHOLD!

No.617—2 acres, $3,500. Park a trailer or build a home on this oak-studded 2-acre parcel bordering pretty creek. Lovely park-like setting has good soil for gardening and flowers and also offers on-the-spot hunting for deer, quail and squirrel. Fronts hardtop road within 5 miles of store, church and school, 12 miles town. Easy drive to valley migratory bird shooting and mountain streams. Won't last long at $3,500, excellent terms. UNITED, Oroville, Calif.

LITTLE MAVERICK

No.280—56 acres, $20,000. Picturesque small ranch where you can have a few cows and a garden. Would also be good spot for horse stable operation. Comfortable 5-room home, 2 bedrooms, bath, beautiful lawn and flowers, hillside setting with view of Bighorn Mountains. Good 16x70-ft. log barn, corral, 800-bu. granary, 2-story storage and shop building. 56 acres, 26 tillable, 20 irrigated, 14 in al-

falfa, 6 irrigated pasture, some fruit and black walnut trees. City water to home, well in corral. On

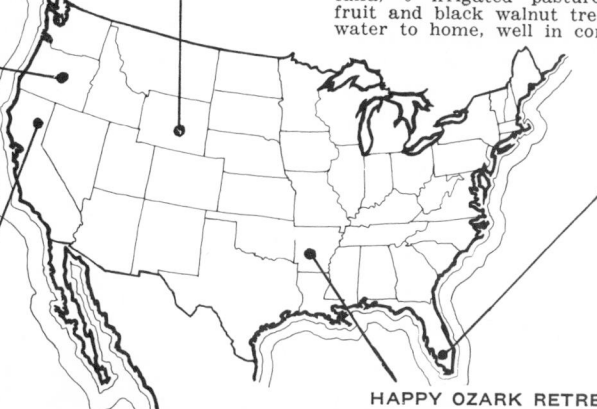

HAPPY OZARK RETREAT

No.3949—43 acres, $17,500. Beautiful log home is the jewel in this crown! In the scenic Buffalo River Country! Only 2 years old, ranch-style frame and log home is insulated, has oak floors, paneling, 2 bedrooms, bath, large living area with picture window, kitchen and dining area with picture window. Nicely-landscaped lawn, large oak shade trees. 20x30-ft. log barn, 12x30 and 10x12 storage buildings. 43 acres, mostly woodland with some tillable land, lots of water from deep drilled well, 2 stock

PRIVACY BECKONS

No.1543—10 acres, $7,950. Say good-bye to noise in the city, hello to peace and quiet of the countryside! Plenty of room to raise a garden, keep some animals, and still enjoy country living! Main 4-room home with bath, screened-in porch. Sec-

ond 2-bedroom home, bath, kitchen, screened-in porch, large utility shed. 10 acres, 5 tillable, in grass and fruit trees, balance native pasture and woodland, barb wire fencing. Secluded on county road yet within mile of town, fine fishing and hunting in area. Some furnishings included at LOW $7,950, good terms. UNITED, Palatka, Fla.

ponds, land fenced and cross fenced. On county gravel road within ½ mile of one of the most scenic state highways in the Ozarks, mile to Buffalo River, 4 miles town. Yours for fun and the future at $17,500. UNITED, Jasper, Ark.

Region 1 comprises the Pacific Coast west of the Coast Range, from Santa Cruz Bay to the Canadian line. Its characteristics are cool, dry summers with frequent fogs and heavy winter rainfall with lowest temperatures 8 to 10 degrees below freezing in the north to about freezing in the south.

Region 2 includes the Willamette Valley in Oregon and the region of similar climate north of it in Washington, including the shores of Puget Sound. The summers are warmer and drier than in region 1, and the average lowest temperatures are from 10° to 20° F.

Region 3 includes the Sacramento and San Joaquin Valleys in California. This region has hot, dry summers and mild winters with 10 to 20 inches of rainfall. The temperature drops to 8 or 10 degrees below freezing on the valley floor, with slightly higher temperatures on the hillsides.

Region 4 includes the Sierra Nevada and Cascade Ranges of mountains. Conditions here vary considerably according to elevation.

Region 5 comprises the coast west of the Coast Range from Santa Cruz to Santa Barbara, thence to San Diego, Redlands, and Riverside, including what is popularly known as 'Southern California'. The summers are dry, cool on the coast and warm inland; the winters are moderately rainy, from 30 inches in the mountains to 10 inches in the valleys, being nearly free from frost on the coast and in the foothills.

Region 6 is the Columbia River Valley in eastern Washington. The summers are warm; the winters have ordinary temperatures of 10° to 15° F, with extremes occasionally of zero. The annual rainfall varies from 7 to 20 inches, mostly in winter and spring.

Region 7 includes the plateau of the eastern part of the State of Washington and the valleys of northern Idaho and western Montana. The summers are warm, and the lowest winter temperatures range from zero to 15° F, with an annual rainfall of 10 to 20 inches.

Region 8 is the Snake River Plains and the Utah Valley. It is a semi-arid country with water available for irrigation. The summers are hot, and the winters often have minimum temperatures of zero to 10° below F, with a rainfall of 9 to 15 inches mostly in winter.

Region 9 is the northern part of the great arid interior plateau included in the States of Oregon, Nevada and Utah. Its characteristics are hot days and occasional frosty nights in summer with cold winters and about 10 inches of rainfall annually.

Region 10 includes all the Southwestern Desert, including portions of California, Arizona and a corner of Nevada. The climate is hot to scorching, with a rainfall of 3 to 10 inches.

Region 11 comprises the southern part of the great arid interior plateau included in New Mexico and Arizona. Its characteristics are the same as the plateau farther north (region 9), except that the temperatures are higher.

Region 12 is that part of the Rocky Mountains included in Idaho, Montana, Wyoming, Washington and Oregon. The temperature and rainfall vary greatly, depending on elevation and exposure.

Region 13 includes the Rocky Mountains of Utah and Colorado. It is similar to the region farther north, except that the temperatures for the same elevation are about 7 degrees warmer.

Region 14 includes the Rocky Mountains of Arizona and New Mexico. It is similar to the region farther north, except that temperatures for the same elevation average

First Time Farmer's Guide

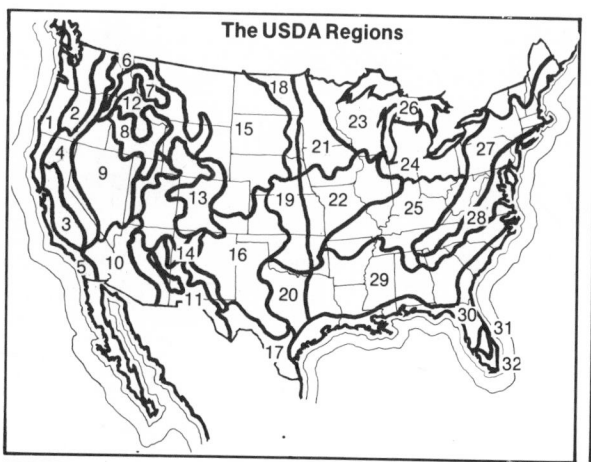

The USDA Regions

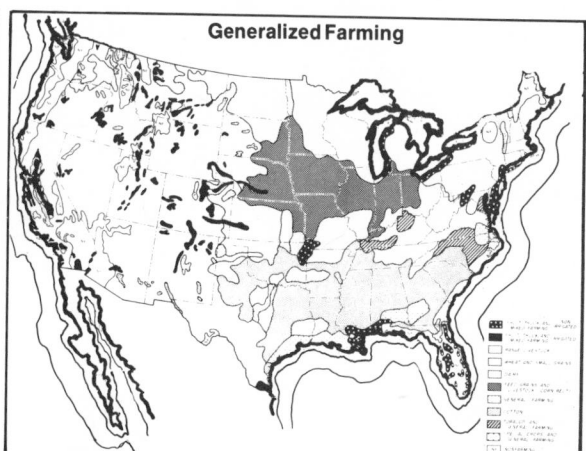

Generalized Farming

Four maps, available from the USDA, which provide essential background information

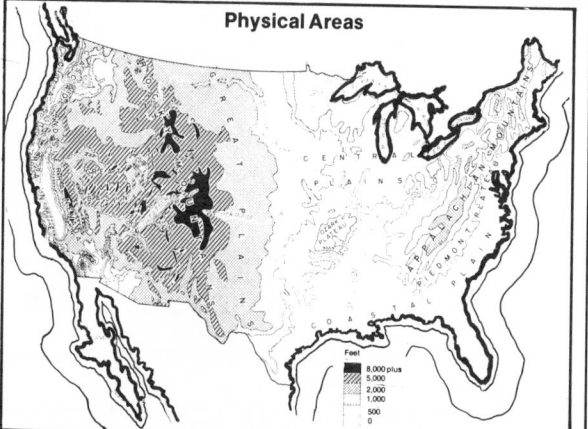

Physical Areas

Feet
8,000 plus
5,000
2,000
1,000
500
0

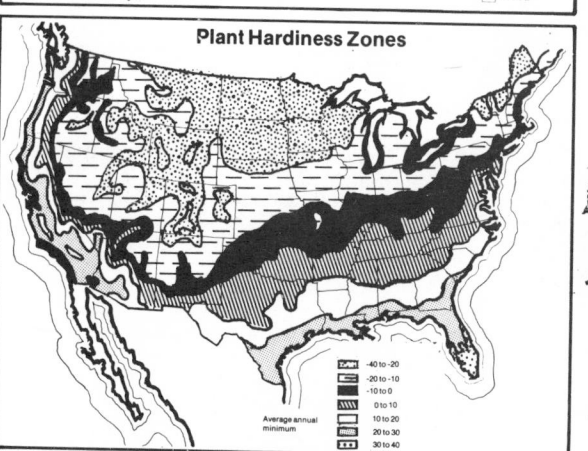

Plant Hardiness Zones

Average annual minimum

-40 to -20
-20 to -10
-10 to 0
0 to 10
10 to 20
20 to 30
30 to 40

Plant some sunflowers for good health.

25

Opposite: If the map
looks like an X-ray of
a bad disease it's no
coincidence. But just
look at pristine
Nevada!

about 6 degrees warmer than region 13 and 13 degrees warmer than region 12.

Region 15 is the northern Great Plains area south to Kansas and Colorado, extending from about the 5,500-foot contour on the west to the black soils on the east. It is extremely cold in winter in the northeastern portions, usually dropping to -30° or -40° F, while close to the mountains it is 20 degrees warmer. The summers are moderately warm. It is generally recognized as the northern part of the dry-farming area, with a rainfall of about 15 inches.

Region 16 is the central portion of the Great Plains, including the plains portions of Kansas, Oklahoma and New Mexico; also portions of the plains in Colorado and Texas. It extends eastward from about the 6,500-foot contour on the west to the black soils on the east. The rainfall varies from 12 to 22 inches. The climate is warmer and has greater evaporation than region 15. It is the southern portion of the dry-farming area.

Region 17 is the dry, hot portion of southwestern Texas, with 12 to 22 inches of rainfall, but excessive evaporation.

Region 18 is the subhumid black-soils country lying east of the dry-farming area of the northern Great Plains and is intermediate as to moisture between region 15 and the more humid area to the east of it. The winters are very cold and dry.

Region 19 is the subhumid black-soils area of Kansas, southern Nebraska and much of Oklahoma. There is more moisture than in the dry-farming country to the west of it and less than in the area farther east. It is a locality of sudden variation in winter temperatures and of hot winds in summer.

Region 20 is the subhumid or transition region of central Texas with black and chocolate-colored soils. In moisture conditions it is intermediate between the dry-farming regions farther west and the humid climate of eastern Texas.

Region 21 is in the northern part of the prairie country with frequent droughts of more than 30 days in the western portion and cold winters with drying winds. The rainfall is 20 to 30 inches, occurring mostly in the summer season.

Region 22 is that portion of the prairie country having higher temperatures than region 21, but subject to similar cold drying winds in winter. The rainfall is 30 to 40 inches.

Region 23 is the western part of the Great Lakes forest area. The eastern portion is slightly warmer and more humid than the western portion, the latter much resembling region 21.

Region 24 is largely that part of the country influenced by the Great Lakes, lying east of Lake Michigan, extending south into Ohio and eastward to Lake Ontario. There is considerable moisture in the atmosphere in addition to a rainfall of 30 to 40 inches rather well distributed through the year. The winter temperatures are more moderate than in region 23.

Region 25 includes the Ohio and lower Tennessee River Valleys and the Ozark Mountain region. The winter temperatures are rather moderate with much alternate freezing and thawing, while the summer is warm with a 30-day drought often occurring near its close. The rainfall is 40 to 50 inches.

Region 26 includes the colder sections of the eastern United States, comprising much of Maine, New Hampshire and Vermont, the mountainous portions of New York, and a portion of northern Michigan. It is character-

Population Density, Per Square Mile

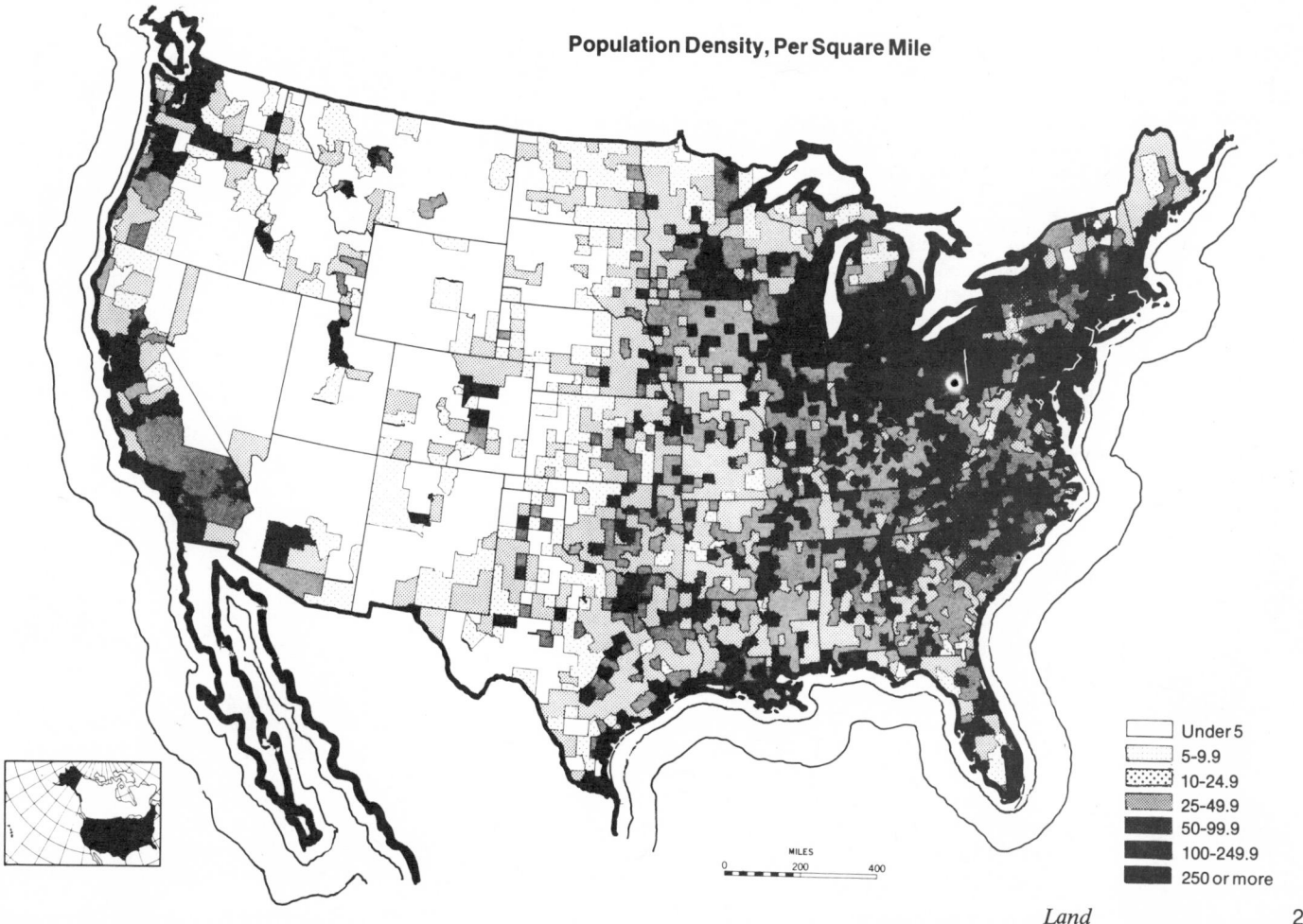

Under 5
5-9.9
10-24.9
25-49.9
50-99.9
100-249.9
250 or more

MILES
0 200 400

ized by cold winters with heavy snowfall and short summers of long days and cool nights.

Region 27 is the Appalachian Mountain country, including much of New England and New York, most of Pennsylvania, and the mountainous portions of the States southward. The rainfall is abundant, usually from 35 to 50 inches, and is well distributed through the season. In the colder parts the snowfall is abundant.

Region 28 lies just east of region 27 and includes the Piedmont and some adjoining sections with similar growing conditions. It extends from northern Alabama northeastward across the Carolinas and Virginia to New Jersey and the coast of Massachusetts. It is warmer than region 27, with abundant rainfall except in late summer, when 30-day droughts often occur. The winters are open, with much freezing and thawing, and there is but little snow protection to be relied upon.

Region 29 includes most of the cotton country, extending from what is known as East Texas eastward and northward to the Atlantic Ocean in North Carolina and Virginia. It lies between the Piedmont region and the swampy lower Coastal Plain that borders the Gulf of Mexico and the Atlantic Ocean. The rainfall is abundant, being from 45 to 60 inches, and is well distributed, except toward the last of the rather warm summer, when a long drought frequently occurs, particularly in the western portion.

Region 30 is the swampy Coastal Plain from Wilmington, NC southward along the Atlantic Ocean and westward along the Gulf of Mexico. It has moderate summer temperatures with hot sunshine, short winters, an abundance of rainfall (50 to 60 inches), except in the Texas portion, and is almost subtropical.

Region 31 is southern Florida, with the exception

of the subtropical fringe. It is subject to annual frosts, often becoming sufficiently cold to kill the tops of tender plants without killing their roots, and has rather warm summers and a rainfall of about 50 inches.

Region 32 is the tropical coast of southern Florida. It has slight range of temperature with no killing frosts and a rainfall of 50 to 60 inches.

Once you're familiar with the climate in the area of your choice, send for a subscription to both the local and regional newspapers. You can skip all of the glowing accounts concerning community 'progress' on the front pages of the Toonerville Bugle . . . this is window dressing again. Turn to the back where the classifieds are and look at 'Help Wanted' and 'Situations Wanted'. This will give you an instant readout on the employment situation in case you had planned to supplement your income with a job in town. Next turn to the real estate section for another fast flash on what things are really selling for and on what terms. Experts who evaluate regions can tell very closely what is happening in a community by reading the classifieds. For specific farm information on the region you select, write to your State Agricultural Experimentation Station.

State Agricultural Experiment Stations

Alabama
Auburn

Alaska
Palmer

Arizona
Tucson

Arkansas
Fayetteville

California
Berkeley
Davis

Colorado
Fort Collins

Connecticut
Storrs
New Haven

Delaware
Newark

Florida
Gainesville

Georgia
Athens
Experiment
Tifton

Hawaii
Honolulu

Idaho
Moscow

Illinois
Urbana

Indiana
LaFayette

Iowa
Ames

Kansas
Manhattan

Kentucky
Lexington

Louisiana
Baton Rouge

Maine
Orono

Maryland
College Park

Massachusetts
Amherst

Michigan
East Lansing

Minnesota
St. Paul

Mississippi
State College

Missouri
Columbia

Montana
Bozeman

Nebraska
Lincoln

Nevada
Reno

New Hampshire
Durham

New Jersey
New Brunswick

New Mexico
State College

New York
Geneva
Ithaca

North Carolina
Raleigh

North Dakota
Fargo

Ohio
Columbus
Wooster

Oklahoma
Stillwater

Oregon
Corvallis

Pennsylvania
University Park

Rhode Island
Kingston

South Carolina
Clemson

South Dakota
Brookings

Tennessee
Knoxville

Texas
College Station

Utah
Logan

Vermont
Burlington

Virginia
Blacksburg

Washington
Pullman
Puyallup

West Virginia
Morgantown

Wisconsin
Madison

Wyoming
Laramie

Opposite: Land that
has been carefully cul-
tivated for 15 centu-
ries (England) . . . still
highly productive and
well conserved.

Obtain the 'yellow page' directory for your new farm home region from your present telephone office. Few people know that you can have the yellow page directory for any part of the US either free or for a small sum, usually under $1. Write several (or all) real estate brokers and tell them your specific needs. You'll soon have your mailbox full of fascinating information about your chosen region. In many cases the broker will offer personal goodies about himself, his office, local contacts and that great little ten-acre spread that the Wilson's are selling now that the old man is planning to go live with his daughter-in-law. You'll gain a lot dealing with a knowledgeable broker since he can find property that's closest to your heart's desire a lot faster than you can. Furthermore, since his livelihood depends on making a sale or two once in a while, he'll be most anxious to get the seller and you go on a fair price and terms arrangement.

Some miscellaneous information concerning the property you'd like to buy could come from the local mayor, postmaster, sheriff, newspaper editor or other 'big man in town'.

Now that you've adjusted your sights for temperature and windage, you're ready to make a personal visit. It's advisable to do this during the 'worst-weather' season. Many people have been hornswoggled by a place by simply seeing it in the 'good old' summertime. Here's an example of what we mean. A young man from the San Fernando Valley decided it was getting too crowded there. He drove to the lushly forested region north of Flathead Lake in Montana in late July. He found the weather balmy, the rivers rushing clear and filled with trout, the air like vintage wine. He found an 80-acre ranch which bordered a river and sported the most weathered, picturesque log lodge that anyone ever photographed for a calendar.

He fell in love with everything and, like any lover, suffered the delusion that it would be this way forever. So he moved his family up to this piney paradise in September. By early November the cold truth descended in the form of four feet of icy snow which sat at his door step throughout the long and frigid winter. He wanted to hold out for the spring thaw, but his wife decided that she didn't want to become a frozen statue just yet (the temperature frequently dropped below -40°). They left on a blustery day in February, never to return. And so, by failing to gather firsthand information, this young man paid a high price — he lost every penny of his investment.

The moral is, visit your dream ranch at the nadir of its downcycle. Then you'll be assured that if you can hack it at that time, the rest of the year will be easy. To double-check yourself, take along the following checklist and rate your proposed farm.

Practical Ways of Making an On-Site Test

It's really easy . . . one way is to simply rent a house or a farm, or lease it with an option to buy. Live one year around and you'll know the best and the worst from personal observation. Another good way is to buy a secondhand trailer and tow it, or have it towed, to your Shangri-la-to-be. Incidentally, some natives get a bit huffy over strangers in trailers but you can usually obtain a permit on the basis that you will build later. It is practical to tow your own trailer up to about 35 feet, as long as you have a husky car and a good frame hitch. Trailers longer than this can best be towed by mobile home towing companies. If you're lucky, you may be able to buy or rent a mobile home that's in or near the region that you choose.

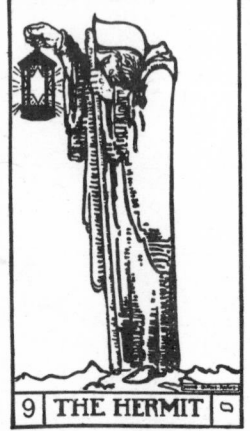

9 | THE HERMIT

First Time Farmer's Guide

Farmland has a won-
derful bonus...good
health

Check List for Rating Your Proposed Farm.

Air Purity—prevailing winds, climate, fog, etc; pollen counts.

Beauty of area — outstanding characteristics.

Honesty and efficiency of local and state governments.

Taxes—property, income, sales, etc; personal and business.

Housing and land availability and costs.

Cost of living—food and general.

Cultural and educational opportunities—university area?

Employment opportunities—economic profile of area.

Availability of help—skilled and unskilled and wage levels.

Medical facilities.

Population density and trends—especially predictions re future.

Transportation—air, rail, highway, to metro areas and otherwise; traffic conditions.

Suitability overall — soil, market for surpluses (resort areas, main-traveled highways, etc.), length of growing season.

Zoning, pollution control, water supplies, sewerage, etc.

Do the 'natives' lend a welcoming hand?

Financing Your Farm

Once you've located your farm, there are a number of ways to arrange financing. If you know what they are, you can save yourself a sizeable sum on interest rates, your payments can be· substantially less and you can avoid the usual finder's fee by arranging your own mortgage. Here's what is generally available:

The Farmer's Home Administration Farm Ownership Program
currently makes 40-year loans at 5% interest for the purchase, enlargement or development of farms no larger than family farms for persons unable to obtain required credit elsewhere. Maximum loan plus debts against the farm cannot exceed $60,000. To qualify, you must be certified by the local County Farmer's Home Administration as qualified to farm. 'Qualified' usually means that you have had farm experience. Veterans are given preferential treatment. Once you have enough equity in your farm through full-time operation, you are expected to refinance through a conventional mortgage. The Farmer's Home Administration also makes loans for the purchase of small farms if the applicant is considered eligible and has dependable off-farm income. The applicant must plan to continue farming part-time. If rural housing is desired, any individual who is unable to obtain sufficient credit elsewhere may qualify for a mortgage loan. For further specific information, contact the local Farmer's Home Administration office in your County Seat town or write to the Farmer's Home Administration, Department of Agriculture, Washington, DC 20250.

Federal Land Banks
make long-term farm mortgages through 700 local Fed-

eral Land Banks and their Associates. The Land Banks and Associations are owned cooperatively by their member-borrowers. Funds are obtained from the investing public through the sale of Federal farm loan bonds. First mortgage loans are arranged for persons who are—or will be—engaged in farming and who will derive a principal part of their income from farming. For more details, contact the Farm Credit Administration, Washington DC 20578 or a local Federal Land Bank or Association.

Life Insurance Associations

have broad investment powers and are often the best bet for financing an off-beat real estate transaction. Some of the smaller concerns deal almost exclusively with residential mortgages and the little private and fraternal insurance companies can lend at an extremely low interest rate.

Savings and Loan Associations

are the major source of mortgage funds for residential purchases. The usual loan limits are $40,000 with a maximum loan-to-value ratio of 90% and an average of 70%. However, since farmland is often bought at less than its appraised value on today's market and since it is possible to obtain maximum loans on exceptionally good purchases, you might finance your acreage with virtually no out-of-pocket cash through a S&L.

The New Federal Home Loan Mortgage Corporation has been set up to purchase both conventional and government mortgages with greater flexibility than in the past and to increase the supply of money available for home mortgages. Conventional financing has been encouraged to provide for lower down payments, longer payoff periods and lower monthly payments—particularly for low and middle income families. Authoritative sources indicate that new laws enacted by Congress should provide for even more federally subsidized housing at lower interest rates during the next few years.

Land Contracts

should be considered when there is little money for a down payment but funds may be available in the future for larger payments. Through a standard land contract agreement one can arrange an installment purchase. The seller may obtain the balance of the sale price over the existing mortgage by pledging his own credit for a loan with the land contract as security. The buyer assumes the existing mortgage payment plus payments due under the seller's loan. The seller retains title and is covered in case of default of buyer. Seller may also stipulate that all installment payments may be liquidated if the buyer defaults. In this manner, land contracts are encouraged without the risk of complicated foreclosure proceedings following default. The FHA does not insure installment sales but will continue to insure any existing FHA mortgage even though an installment purchase has been made. Once the buyer is able to refinance the total debt with an outside mortgage, he obtains title from the seller.

No money?

Then find someone with a farm and help farm it. Cooperative and communal "back-to-the-land" movements are increasing in scope and number!

Health has no price tag and there are no pockets in shrouds.

Water

'Everywhere water is a thing of beauty, gleaming in the dewdrop,
singing in the summer rain, shining in the ice-gems till the
leaves all seem to turn to living jewels, spreading a golden veil
over the setting sun or a white gauze around the midnight moon.'

There is no element
as important and as
delightful as water

Whether you've farmed or not, water is probably the natural resource with which you are most familiar. Here is a brief review of water, its cycle and its relationship to farming. All of us have had firsthand experience with it in its many forms; rain, hail, snow, ice, steam, fog, dew.

Water covers nearly three-fourths of the earth; most is sea water. But sea water contains minerals and other substances, including those that make it salty, that are harmful to most land plants and animals. Still it is from the vast salty reservoirs, the seas and oceans, that most of our precipitation comes, no longer salty or mineral laden. Water moves from clouds to land and back to the ocean in a never-ending cycle. This is the water cycle, or the hydrologic cycle. Ocean water evaporates into the atmosphere, leaving impurities behind, and moves across the earth as water vapor. Water in lakes, ponds, rivers, and streams also evaporates and joins the moisture in the atmosphere. Soil, plants, people, animals, and even factories, automobiles, tractors, and planes, contribute moisture. A small part of this moisture, or water vapor, is visible to us as fog, mist or clouds. Water vapor condenses and falls to earth as rain, snow, sleet, or hail, depending on region, climate, season and topography.

When water hits the ground some soaks into the soil and the rest runs off over the surface. The water that soaks into the soil sustains plant and animal life in the soil. Some seeps to underground reservoirs. Almost all of this water eventually enters the cycle once more.

Water management begins with soil management. A rainstorm or a heavy shower on bare soil loosens soil particles, and runoff, the water that does not soak into the soil, carries these particles away. This action, soil erosion by water, repeated many times ruins land for most uses. Erosion, furthermore, is the source of sediment that fills streams, pollutes water, kills aquatic life and shortens the useful life of dams and reservoirs. Grass, trees, bushes, shrubs, and even weeds help break the force of raindrops and hold the soil in place. Where cultivated crops are grown, plowing and planting on the contour, terraces, and grassed waterways to carry surplus water from the fields are some of the conservation measures that slow running water.

The Soil Conservation Service of the USDA can provide further information by mail or in person through one of its agents. Just write USDA, Soil Conservation Service, Washington, DC, 20502.

Water Is More Important Than Land

You can grow things without land (hydroponics) but you can't grow them without water. Water is so important that one nationally known real estate expert has made the following statement.

'The first thing we look at regarding a piece of property is the water situation. If it's OK, the land's OK. If there is no water there or it can't be brought in at a reasonable cost, then we just forget all about the land. We just pretend it never existed.'

A statement of finality to be sure but one that contains much truth. No matter what your farming activities will be, whether you intend to just grow enough peanuts for an occasional jar of homemade peanut butter or whether you're going to go into fish farming, water in appropriate amounts is an absolute must. Therefore, we're going to devote quite a bit of space to what we call the key to efficient land use . . . 'water in—water out'. This means that you must have a reliable source of usable water and a means for either recycling or otherwise properly disposing of used water.

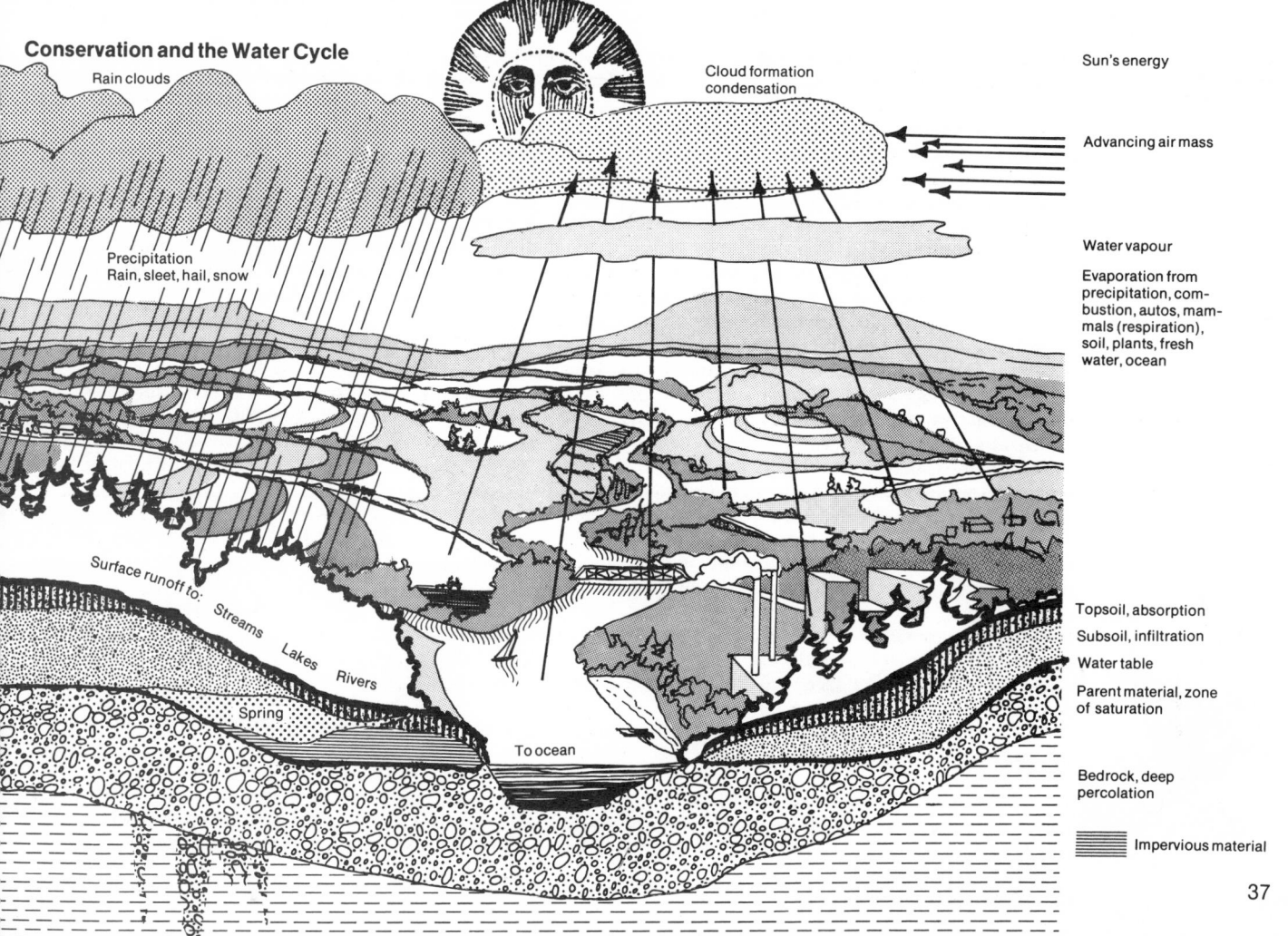

Conservation and the Water Cycle

Rain clouds

Cloud formation
condensation

Precipitation
Rain, sleet, hail, snow

Surface runoff to: Streams

Lakes   Rivers

Spring

To ocean

Sun's energy

Advancing air mass

Water vapour

Evaporation from
precipitation, com-
bustion, autos, mam-
mals (respiration),
soil, plants, fresh
water, ocean

Topsoil, absorption

Subsoil, infiltration

Water table

Parent material, zone
of saturation

Bedrock, deep
percolation

Impervious material

37

The average depth of
domestic water wells
in the US is less than
50 feet!

If you buy land that enjoys the proximity of water from a self-replenishing lake, a rushing all-year river, a stream, creek or spring that produces enough water for your needs, and you have the legal rights to use of this natural water, about 90% of your problems are solved. It is interesting to note that throughout the world, land has a human use factor very closely related to the amount of available potable water.

For example, in Baja, California, the number of families that can be supported in a canyon is determined directly by the amount of runoff or spring water per annum. If you travel through Baja and see an abandoned farm house, you are quite safe in assuming that the abandonment was due to the failure of the water supply. Thus, before you acquire a piece of rural land, make *absolutely certain* that you are guaranteed the indefinite, unrestricted use of adequate natural water resources. In some cases, water rights will be a part of the deed to the property. This means that a certain amount of water can be taken from a natural water source for use on your farm without cost. For example, if your farm borders a river, you will probably be granted riparian rights to take a specified amount of water for your own use. As another example, you may find that the land owners in your vicinity have formed a water association and charge an assessment based on over-all operating costs. Usually your ownership in the land will be associated with a membership in the water cooperative.

Finding Water

There are only a few places on earth where you can dig a hole with the *absolute certainty* that you will hit water. You will frequently find a dry hole surrounded by

producing water wells. You will frequently find a producing water well surrounded by dry holes. Fortunately for the well digger in the US, about 90% of all water beneath the surface of the ground occurs in the top 200 feet. Unless your area is famous for deep dry holes, the chances are that by a little exploratory digging you can find a good water vein at a modest depth. In fact, the average depth of all domestic water wells in the US is slightly less than 50 feet! So if you have as much as a city lot to search on, the odds of finding a good supply of water are in your favor.

The US Geodetic Survey of the Department of the Interior, Washington, DC, makes studies of ground water supplies in the United States. Write them and see if your farm is within their research scope. Ground water is found in three general types of formations: layers of sand, layers of gravel, and porous rock or a crack in rock. These are the only formations capable of holding water.

There is no single best source of water. Some people have the mistaken idea that the only good water comes from rock, but this is not true. In fact, some rocks have minerals that dissolve in water and these give the water an odd taste and sometimes an odor. As a general rule, the finest quality of water comes from layers of sand which filter the water naturally. Of course, this disputes everything you have ever heard about water wells, so let's take a closer look.

All underground water originates on the surface of the earth. It seeps into the ground and that is how we get ground water. So how does water get in rock? It enters through cracks in the rock and the point at which the water enters the crack determines the quality of the water. For example, the water may be filtered through a

Ground Water Areas

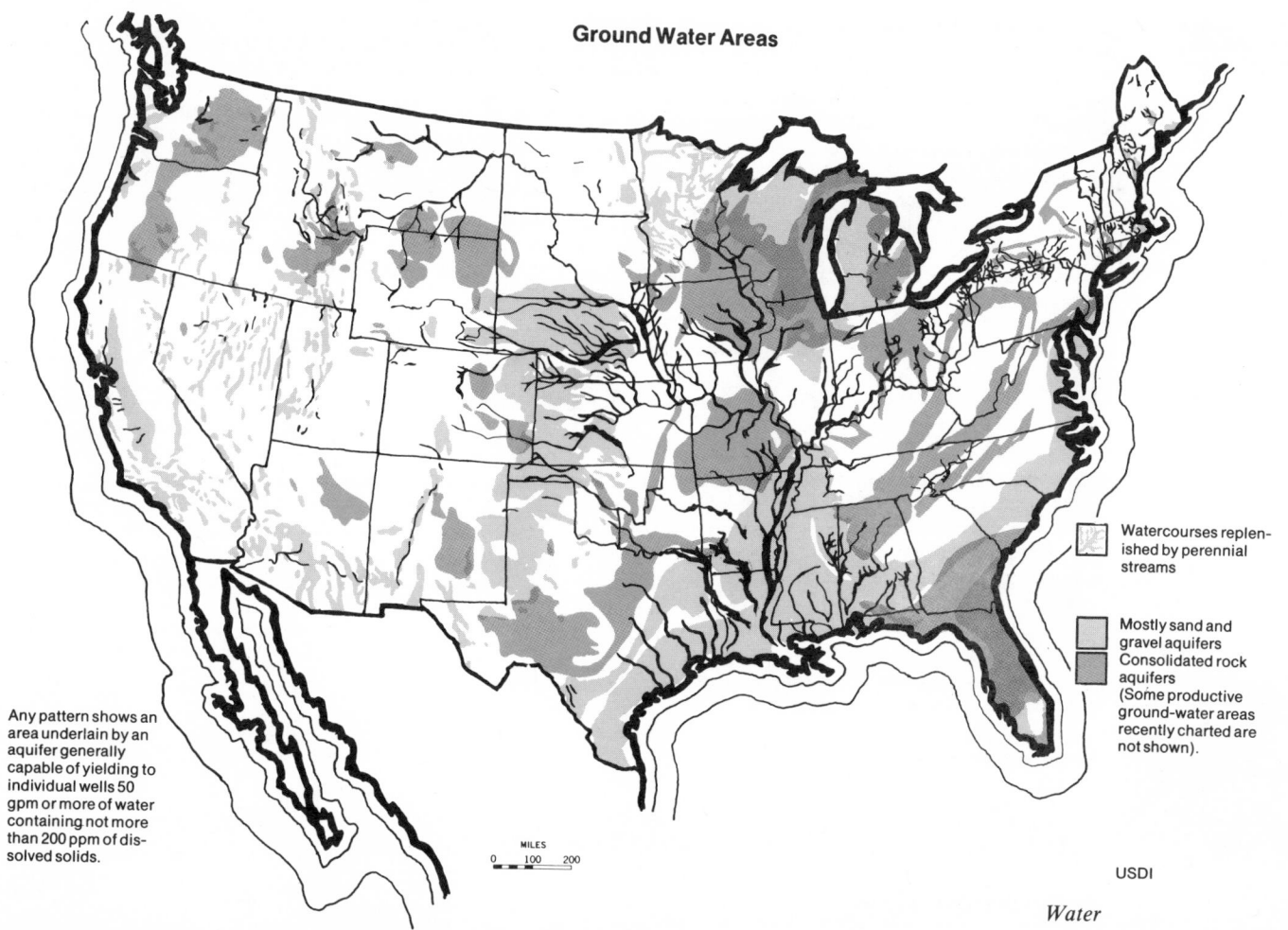

Any pattern shows an area underlain by an aquifer generally capable of yielding to individual wells 50 gpm or more of water containing not more than 200 ppm of dissolved solids.

MILES
0   100   200

Watercourses replenished by perennial streams

Mostly sand and gravel aquifers

Consolidated rock aquifers (Some productive ground-water areas recently charted are not shown).

USDI

Water

39

Vegetation usually indicates year-round water sources

The water table chart

Land surface

Zone of aeration

Water table

Surface water

Zone of saturation

layer of sand before it enters the crack. In that case, you would likely get a good quality water. However, the crack could open into the bottom of a creek or river. In this case, the water could be polluted the same as surface water. In the final analysis, good plentiful ground water is where you find it. It may come from layers of sand, layers of gravel, above rock, below rock, from a crack in the rock. As a rule of thumb, the best quality water and the most abundant supply of water is more likely to be found in layers of sand or gravel than in rock. This is fortunate, because as a rule you will hit layers of sand and gravel before you hit solid rock.

So now we are ready to take on the big question: exactly where are you going to dig on your property? First, let me tell you my own personal idea about picking a well site. I say there is no positive sign on the surface of

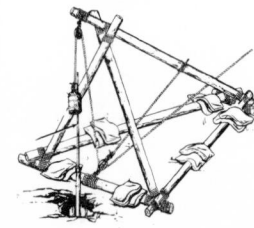

the ground that will lead you to a good water vein. Your first choice should be wherever you would like the well to be. The only other things to consider are the natural slope of the ground (you don't want your well site flooded by rain water) and, of course, you want to stay at least 50 feet away from waste water disposal systems such as septic tank leach fields and cesspools. Other than that, one site is just about as good as any other for your first place to try.

There are a great many successful well diggers who put great faith in digging near willow trees or other water-loving plants or trees. But the most popular, universal and controversial method of finding water is by divining. Some say it's a mystical magic trick — others can prove it works by showing you the wells they've found.

For anyone who wants to try it here's how some of the more skilled practitioners do it. Take a 12″ length of 1/16 brass welding rod (available from any welding supply store) and carefully bend it to form an 'L' shape with the short leg 4″ long and the long leg 8″ long. Make the angle as close to 90° as you can. Place the short leg in a plastic or glass tube which is closed on one end. Now you have an arrangement that looks like this:

Hold the tube so that the long leg is level and pointing straight ahead. Then very slowly walk forward. When you walk over a water vein the 'L' rod will swing to one side. Incredible? Perhaps, but before you scrap the whole idea it may be worth your time to make this experiment. With your 'L' rod check the area around your house for

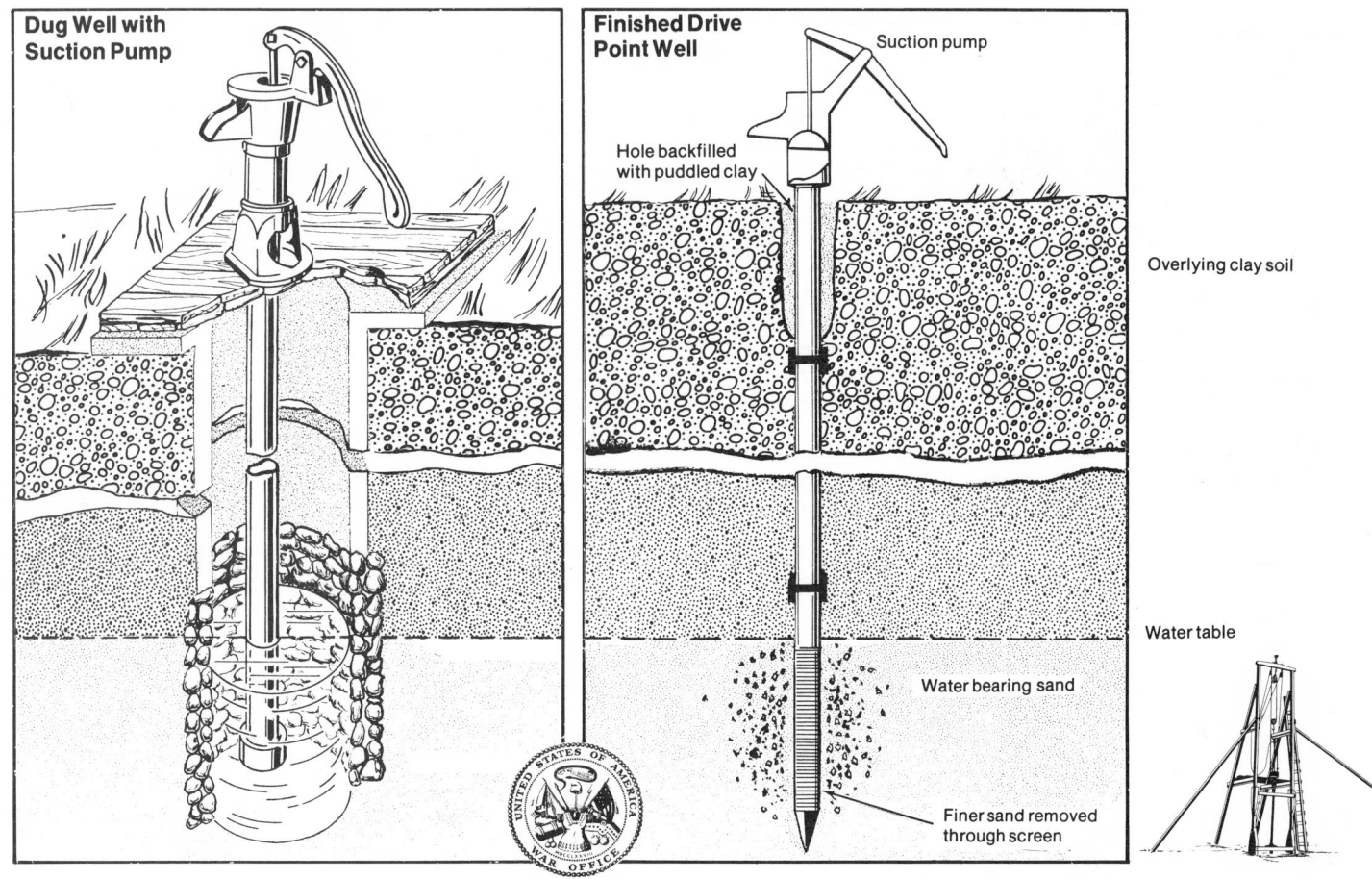

Dug Well with Suction Pump

Finished Drive Point Well

Suction pump

Hole backfilled with puddled clay

Overlying clay soil

Water table

Water bearing sand

Finer sand removed through screen

Water   41

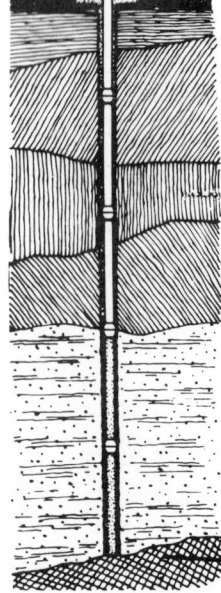

underground water pipes. Most people are shocked to find that underground water pipes can be located in this manner, and some of them can give you a very reasonable explanation of why it happens.

But let's say there are no willow trees or other water-loving plants where you want to drill, and you don't put much stock in the divining rod, and on top of that you have decided where you would like the well to be — okay, let's start digging! Other than the pick and shovel approach, there are several ways to put a hole in the ground to tap a water table or a water vein.

One popular method is driving a well point. In essence, this is simply driving or hammering a pointed 1½" pipe into the ground. It is economical but extremely hard work. The depth is limited to about 20 or 30 feet, the water production typically small, and again hard clay or rock stops it cold. For many years commercial drillers used 'churn' or 'spud' drills. The general idea can be copied in a small unit for home well-drilling. It consists of a hoisting arrangement to lift a heavy, chisel-shaped bit and then let it drop to the ground. This action is repeated over and over, and the bit goes deeper into the ground with each stroke. Periodically, water is poured down the hole to form mud, and the mud is bailed out of the hole. Churn drilling is slow but effective.

The most modern well drilling is 'rotary' which is the method developed and used to drill oil wells. It is fast and efficient, but until recently it was available only in big, heavy, truck-mounted models. Only in the last few years has it become available in a one-man portable model for do-it-yourself well-drilling. The rotary drill consists of an earth or rock cutting bit attached to a length of hollow drill pipe. The drill pipe and bit are rotated and water is pumped through the drill pipe. The bit cuts into the earth

and the water washes the cuttings out of the drill hole to the top of the ground. Additional sections of drill pipe are screwed on as the bit goes deeper.

Simplest and Easiest Well Drilling Rig in the World

Do you remember when you were a child and discovered that a hose with a nozzle on it made a fine hole digger? All you had to do was turn on the water full blast and point the nozzle into the ground. The force of the water stream blasted the dirt from in front of the nozzle. Not only was a hole created, the earth removed was turned into mud and pumped to the surface. This simple technique can be used to drill a well on your farm to virtually any depth. Here's a diagram to show you how it can be done.

If you have a plentiful source of high pressure water, merely connect the hose to pieces of steel pipe that can be connected with couplings to increase the length as the well deepens. Drilling consists of merely pushing the pipe into the ground while the water blasts its own hole. To prevent the creation of a big muddy mess around the drill site, dig a water disposal trench to drain away the used water.

If you don't have a lot of high pressure water available, then this method works fine. Dig a hole two or three feet in diameter and a couple of feet deep. Fill it with water. A couple of 50-gallon drums filled from your neighbor's supply or the nearest river will do fine. Then insert the screened pick-up of a high pressure gas or electrically driven high pressure water pump. The output of the pump is then used the same way as method number 1. As you see by the diagram, the water which comes back from the hole being drilled is drained back into the sump or supply hole. Modern pumps with tough plastic impel-

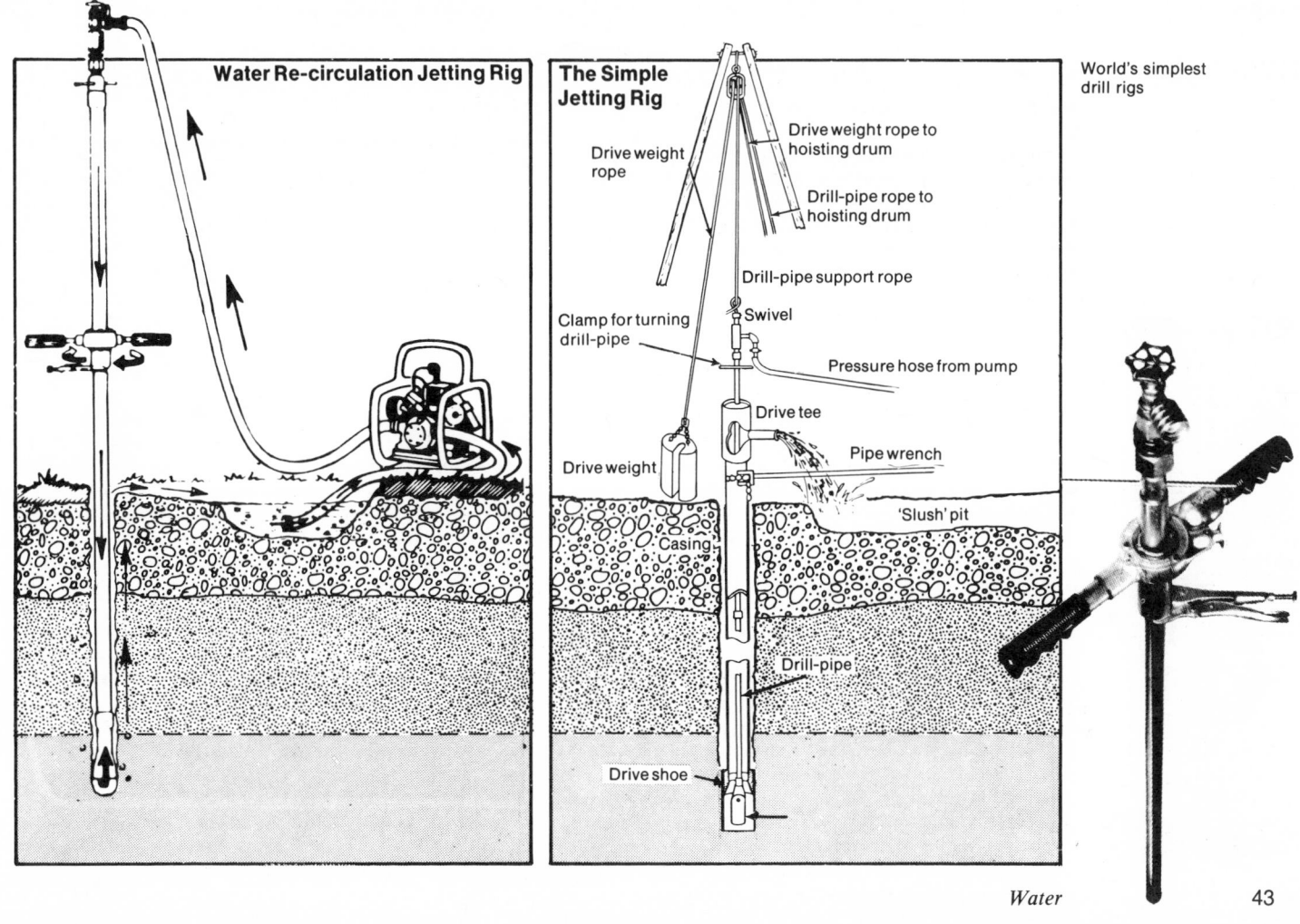

Water Re-circulation Jetting Rig

The Simple Jetting Rig

Drive weight rope to hoisting drum

Drive weight rope

Drill-pipe rope to hoisting drum

Drill-pipe support rope

Clamp for turning drill-pipe

Swivel

Pressure hose from pump

Drive weight

Drive tee

Pipe wrench

'Slush' pit

Casing

Drill-pipe

Drive shoe

World's simplest drill rigs

lers can handle the silt-laden water without damage.

What to Do When You Hit Water

If you are digging an open well with pick and shovel, you have the advantage of knowing when you hit water. The trouble, of course, is that you have to stop digging soon after you hit water, and that's why dug wells tend to go dry in the dry season. It is very difficult to dig very deep into a water vein or a water table. If you are drilling the well you have to watch for certain indications to know when you've reached water. However, you can drill deep enough to go all the way to the bottom of the water vein or water table so you won't run out of water in the dry season. Keep in mind that you are looking for something that will indicate a water-bearing formation: coarse sand, gravel, or a crack in the rock. If you are using a rotary drill, the cuttings will be washed to the surface as you drill. All you have to do is pick up a handful of cuttings and look at them (you don't have to be a geologist to tell the difference between sand, clay, gravel and rock). If you are drilling rock and the drill stem suddenly drops a few inches, you can be quite sure that you have hit a crack which could produce water.

After you have drilled down and found a promising looking formation, you 'case' the well which simply means inserting a pipe to keep the well from collapsing at some future time. If you have bottomed your well with something other than solid rock, you will use a 'well screen' or strainer to keep the sand and gravel out of your well. The next step is to flush the well with fresh water to get muddy drilling water out of the hole. Now you are ready to install the pump.

If you want to find out about pumps, look at a Sears or Wards catalog. Their prices are competitive so you can see what the cost should be even if you buy from someone else. Here's an important point: practically no new well will do its best when it is first pumped. Just about every new well will improve in both quality and quantity of water after a few hours (or even a few days in some cases) of pumping. Pumping gets rid of the last traces of any mud left over from the drilling and it gives the water veins a chance to open up and flow more freely. So don't be disheartened by what your well does the first few hours of pumping. It will probably get much better. Bringing the water you've found to the surface can be done with an electric or gasoline-powered pump. However there's a pollution-free method that has much romance in it . . . the classic windmill.

Windmills

'There was a sound to windmills. The Dempster that pumped faithfully in our corral during the years of my youth had all the usual sounds—the gentle sough of the breeze through the fans, the creak of the tower and rhythmic, metallic working of the gears and sucker rod, and finally the steady, soft pouring of the water into the tank.'—*Old Rancher*

Windmills have an appeal that far transcends their simple structure. There is something alluring about the phenomenon of wind bringing water. It's strange but true that many farm dwellers find themselves drawn to the windmill when they need spiritual rejuvenation. Countless farmers have taken their problems to the wind and water shrine, letting the cooling flow run over their hands. Farm workers have long considered the windmill spout as a cleanser of mind and body. Farm animals gravitate to the base of the windmill, indicating that they too know the source of life for them. In many parts of the

world where the land is flat or gently rolling, a windmill
stands as a lone beacon; the sole marker to indicate that
here people have drilled a well and put down both human
and plant roots. Many farmers who have long since converted to pumping water with an electric pump can't be
persuaded to part with the homestead windmill.

'Never can tell when we might need it again' they
say improbably. What they're really saying is that the
windmill means far more to them than a mere structure of
steel and wood and a giant windfan. If you have never
enjoyed an hour or two sitting beneath the creaking,
whispering, ever-turning mill, then one of the high points
of your life is still to come. What we're trying to tell you is
that windmills add much romance to a farm. They serve a
purpose far beyond pumping free water for your crops
and animals with free wind.

It's probable that many people think that windmills
have gone the way of iceboxes and steampowered tractors. Not true. There are still three manufacturers of
windmills in the United States: Aermotor, Dempster,
and Heller. Windmills are eminently practical wherever
the cost and difficulty of extending power lines would
preclude an electric pump. In the panhandle of Texas and
other vast regions, windmills are still the least expensive
solution to getting water to the surface. Aside from the
aesthetic value of the windmill, it would be useful where
water has to be pumped from a long distance. For example, if water supplies on your farm aren't sufficient,
it may be possible to drill a well on someone else's land
for a fee and pump or pipe the water by gravity feed to
your farmstead.

Windmills use the power of the wind to rotate the
fan. This is a circular structure from six to twenty feet in
diameter with vanes that catch the wind. As the air push-

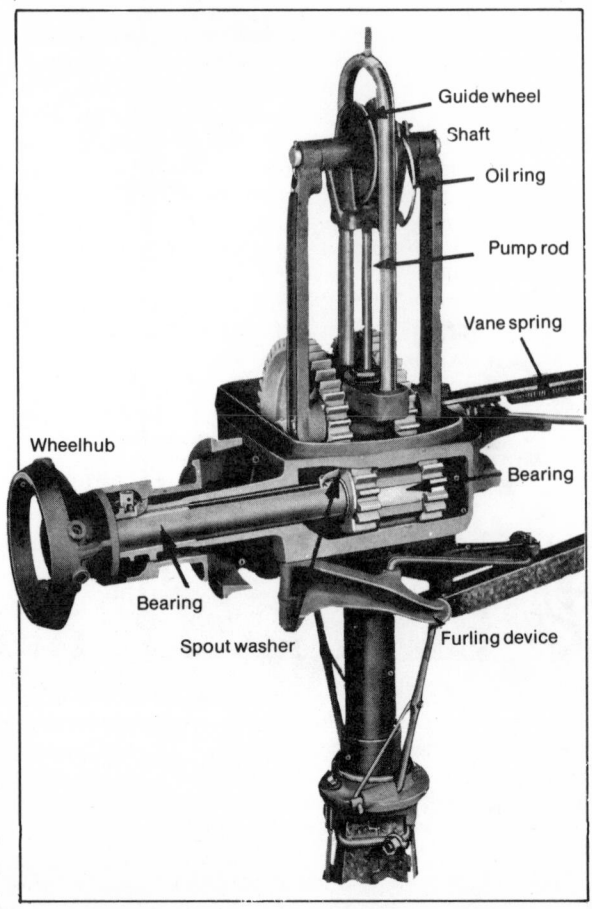

Guide wheel

Shaft

Oil ring

Pump rod

Vane spring

Wheelhub

Bearing

Bearing

Spout washer

Furling device

es against the vane, it tends to push it out of the way. With many vanes and lots of wind, the fan spins around, producing considerable power. The fan is connected to a geared shaft which in turn drives the vertical pump shaft. The small gear wheels are meshed with a larger gear, giving the fan a mechanical advantage. The large gear wheels are connected to an eccentric arm or connecting rod which translates rotary motion into up-and-down motion. The up-and-down motion is used to raise and lower a pump shaft. The shaft extends straight down through the windmill tower directly into the water well beneath. For convenience, windmill towers are always located directly over the drilled water well. In rare instances, windmills were placed where was a lot of wind but no water. The power of the windmill was then transferred by means of rods or wires to the well shaft and pumping mechanism. The rising and falling of the pump shaft creates a suction or lifting action to raise the water from the depths of the well and pour it into the waiting trough or pipeline.

Putting your windmill to work is a relatively simple task, once the well has been drilled. The tower and mill is assembled per the instructions and then placed on its foundation. A long line attached to the top and to the back of a truck will erect the tower quickly and easily. The next step is to hook up the sucker rod of the well to the equivalent up-and-down actuating rod of the windmill. Once this is done, you merely have to throw the lever which allows the weathervane of the windmill to bring the rotary fan at right angles to the wind direction. When those blades begin to turn, the mill starts pumping water and a fresh, clear flow comes out of the by-pass tap. Then you'll feel like you're really an authentic farmer.

Although as we stated previously, many farmers

Wind producing water just has to be one of earth's great benefits

are reluctant to part with their venerable mills, it's possible that you might be lucky and find one for sale. The important thing is to buy one for which parts are still available. This would mean that your purchase would have to be limited to those brands that are still being manufactured. If there is any doubt as to whether your model still has parts available, write the manufacturer. Pricing a used windmill is like pricing a used anything. Since a brand new mill with tower could cost upwards of $500, it would be logical to assume that a good used mill might be had for somewhere between $200 and $300. If the tower is steel and bolted together, there wouldn't be too big a problem in dismantling it and moving it to your farmstead. If the tower is wood and quite old, it would probably be wise to just purchase the fan and gear mechanism and put up your own new steel tower, or perhaps build a picturesque whitewashed wooden one.

If you have lots of money and a bright shiny windmill would make you happy on your first-time farm, then write to Aermotor, Broken Arrow, Okla. 74012 or Heller-Aller, Perry and Oakwood, Napolean, Ohio 43545—windmill companies still doing business in the US.

Windmill Specifications & Prices

With the vane spring set for maximum tension 6-foot and 8-foot fans, running at full speed, will wax about 32 strokes of the pump per minute; the 10-foot 26 strokes; the 12-foot 21 strokes; the 14-foot 18 strokes and the 16-foot 16 strokes. The smaller mills will attain this speed in winds blowing steadily from 15 to 18 miles per hour, and the larger ones in winds from 18 to 20 miles per hour when loaded according to the table.

Cylinder, Inches	Capacity per Hour, Gallons		Elevation in Feet to Which Water Can be Raised					
			Size of Fan					
	6-ft.	8-ft. −16-ft	6-foot	8-foot	10-foot	12-foot	14-foot	16-foot
1¾	105	150	130	185	280	420	600	1000
1⅞	125	180	120	175	260	390	560	920
2	130	190	95	140	215	320	460	750
2¼	180	260	77	112	170	250	360	590
2½	225	325	65	94	140	210	300	490
2¾	265	385	56	80	120	180	260	425
3	320	470	47	68	100	155	220	360
3¼		550			88	130	185	305
3½	440	640	35	50	76	115	160	265
3¾		730			65	98	143	230
4	570	830	27	39	58	86	125	200
4¼		940			51	76	110	180
4½	725	1050	21	30	46	68	98	160
4¾		1170				61	88	140
5	900	1300	17	25	37	55	80	130
5¾		1700				40	60	100
6		1875		17	25	38	55	85
7		2250			19	28	41	65
8		3300			14	22	31	50

Alternate Water Development Methods

Here are three other practical methods for developing water supplies on your farm. The first one assumes the existence of a small amount of water, perhaps a tiny spring that trickles out of the side of a mountain. The author recalls that in an arid canyon in northern Baja, a Mexican farmer had developed a rural homestead by using the output of a spring so small it would be thought worthless in many other parts of the world. This spring produced a flow of about a quart a minute. However, at 60 quarts per hour, or 15 gallons, this meant that he had a total water supply per day of 360 gallons. To bring this small flow to his farmhouse and garden, he built a miniature canal along the side of the rugged mountain canyons. Ferns and wildflowers decorated its hobbit-scale banks. The canal flowed directly into a large tank, painstakingly built of river cobblestones and cement. The tank supplied water for the house through a pipe and the balance was carefully metered to irrigate a good-sized vegetable garden and small fruit orchard. This small supply plus rainfall was sufficient to keep this one indomitable farmer happy and independent.

The moral is, no matter how small a water supply your land possesses, it can probably be nurtured and developed to yield enough to make you independent too. Where even a small trickle from a spring is not available, then you might look into the possibilities of saving rainwater.

Idea number two is quite old but has been brought up to date by new materials. In many parts of Europe, particularly on islands, water is collected from roofs and stone or cement catch basins. It is stored in large tanks called cisterns for use throughout the year. If your farm is in an area where water supplies are sparse or even nonexistent, but there is adequate rainfall, this method may be just what you need. It's certainly worth exploring, particularly where land is inexpensive enough so that your investment in a rain trap system would be economically sound.

A rain trap consists of a water-tight ground cover for collecting precipitation and a closed reservoir for storing the collected water. In arid and semi-arid regions of the Western United States, rain traps are practical and economical for providing water for livestock on the range. They are potentially useful for providing drinking water to farms and small communities. Much precipitation occurs as small showers which do not produce runoff. If, however, the precipitation is intercepted on a water-tight, nonabsorbent surface, large quantities of water can be collected even in arid and semi-arid lands. For example, if one square mile of land in a 12-inch rainfall area were covered with a watertight lining, enough water could be collected to irrigate 160 acres. Present cost of catchment liners makes rain traps impractical for providing irrigation water. They are practical, however, for providing water for livestock and they can be the key to better utilization and management of grazing lands. Normally, water harvested with rain traps will be more costly than water from wells or from ponds. However, there are areas in both low and high rainfall regions where the rain trap will be the most economic means of providing water for livestock, human consumption, and possibly irrigation. A rain trap installation to provide water for livestock is shown here.

The catchment liner is a square piece of watertight sheeting spread on the ground with one corner lower on the slope than the rest of the liner. Earthen dikes elevate

"...so you did drill a dry well. Well, here's hope for your first-time farm."

Hot Springs: There
are more than 1000
thermal or hot springs
west of the Rockies.
If you can acquire one,
you'll solve your
heating and water
problems simultaneous-
ly. For a book on the
subject plus maps, write
Capra Press, 631 State
St., Santa Barbara,
Ca. 93101

The power-free
horizontal well

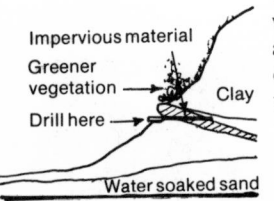

Impervious material

Greener
vegetation

Clay

Drill here

Water soaked sand

the edges of the liner to confine and direct water into a
hood at the lowest corner of the liner. The hood outlets
into a tube that leads to the intake of a storage bag located lower on the slope. When the trap is to provide water
for livestock, the storage bag is connected by pipe to a
drinking trough that is equipped with a float valve. If the
trap is to provide water for home use, the storage bag is
connected to the house by pipe. A pump and pressure
tank may be needed if the difference in elevation between
the storage bag and the house is insufficient to give desired water pressure. Complete information on how to
construct a rain trap is found in USDA Agriculture Information Bulletin No. 307 (10¢). Write USDA, Washington, DC, 20502.

Would you like to have a flowing spring on your
property? Water management experts describe the third
method of obtaining water as the most exciting water
idea to occur in the last 50 years.

This method entails horizontal drilling as a way of
creating an artificial spring. Instead of drilling straight
down for water, you drill *horizontally* into the side of a
hill or the face of a cliff until a water vein is penetrated.
Experiments by the University of Arizona over the last
two years completed 45 successful wells out of 53 tries!
The successful wells were relatively 'shallow' (40 feet or
so) despite the fact that conventional wells in the area
were about 400 feet deep. Production of the horizontal
wells ranged from a few gallons per minute to as much as
an amazing 60 gallons per minute! If you have a hillside
on your property, this new idea of drilling horizontally is
worth your consideration.

Water Needs

Daily use per person: 10 to 20 gals
Each bath: 30 gals
Daily domestic (kitchen) water: 20 gals
Daily laundry water: 10 gals
Toilet and other small use: 20 gals
This makes a total, for a household of four persons, of about 200 gallons per day so that a minimum storage capacity of some 600 to 800 gallons might be needed.
For agricultural purposes the following figures may be used as a daily basis:
Horse: 10 gals
Cow: 15 gals
Pig: 4 gals
Sheep: 1 to 2 gals
Poultry (per 100): 4 gals
Irrigation (1 acre-inch): 22,700 gals

These figures seem high to the author. It's a fact
that a couple of gallons of water will suffice any man in
the wilderness with ease. If a farm family practices water
conservation, the above water need figures could be lop-
ped in half, perhaps even quartered. There are many
ways to do this:

Turn off the water when you wash your hands.

Run sink water out to the vegetable garden. Be sure
when you do this that no strong soaps are used. If you install a valve under the sink, you can select which way the
water goes. For example, if you're just washing vegetables or rinsing out a t-shirt, let the water run into your
garden or orchard. When you are draining out soapsuds,
turn the valve so that the water goes into your regular

Rain Trap Installation

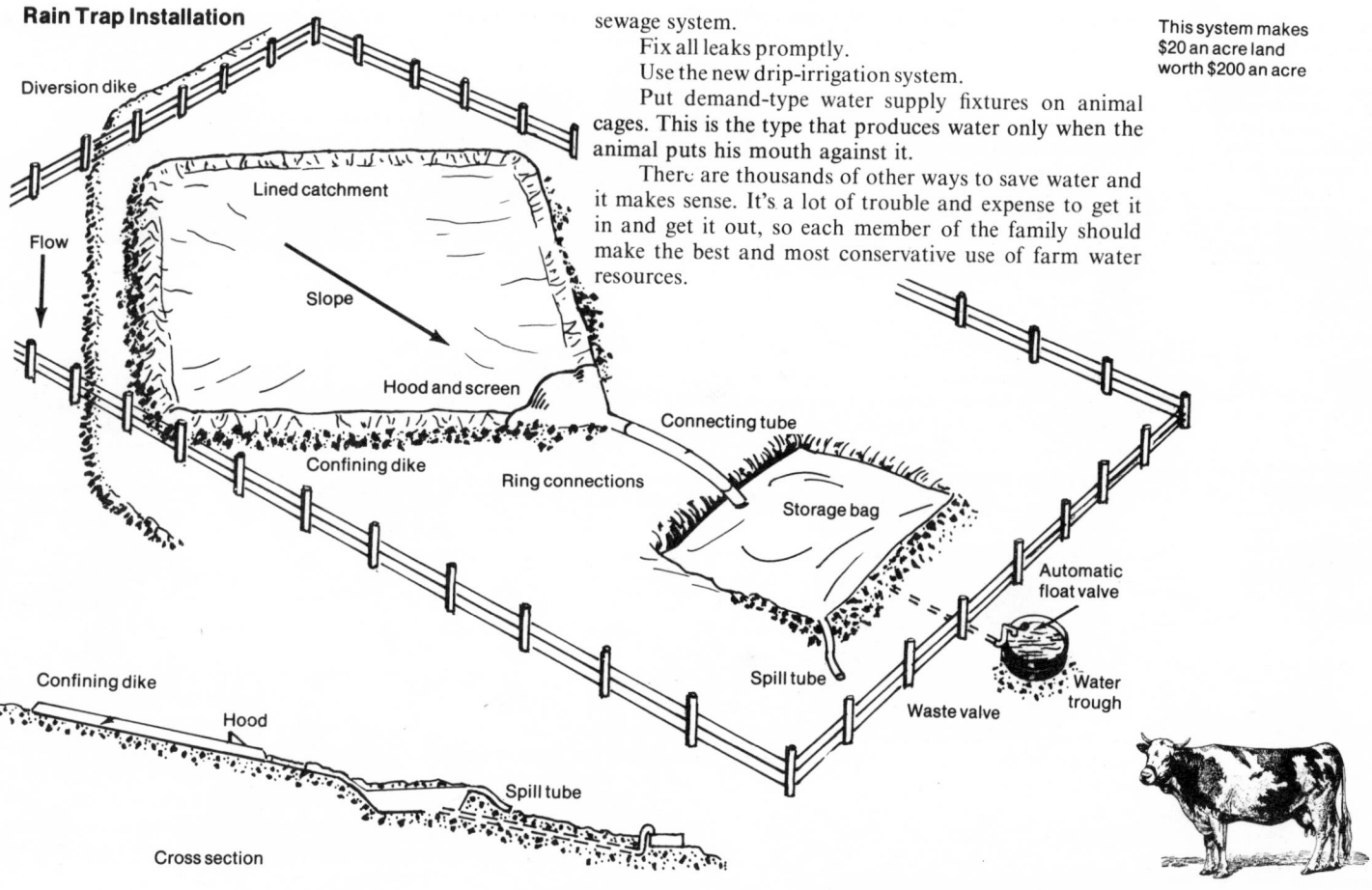

Diversion dike

Flow

Lined catchment

Slope

Hood and screen

Confining dike

Ring connections

Connecting tube

Storage bag

Spill tube

Automatic float valve

Water trough

Waste valve

Confining dike

Hood

Spill tube

Cross section

sewage system.

Fix all leaks promptly.

Use the new drip-irrigation system.

Put demand-type water supply fixtures on animal cages. This is the type that produces water only when the animal puts his mouth against it.

There are thousands of other ways to save water and it makes sense. It's a lot of trouble and expense to get it in and get it out, so each member of the family should make the best and most conservative use of farm water resources.

This system makes $20 an acre land worth $200 an acre

Soil

Behold this compost!
behold it well!
Perhaps every mite has once formed part of a
sick person—yet behold!
The grass of spring covers the prairies,
The bean bursts noiselessly through the
mould in the garden,
The delicate spear of the onion
pierces upward,
The apple-buds cluster together on the
apple-branches,

The resurrection of the wheat appears with
pale visage out of its graves.
What chemistry! That the winds are not really
infectious,
That all is clean, forever and forever,
That the cool drink from the spring tastes so good,
that blackberries are so flavorous and juicy,
that the fruits of the apple-orchard
and the orange orchard,
that melons, grapes, peaches, plums,
will none of them poison me.

That when I recline on the grass,
I do not catch any disease.
Now I am terrified at the Earth, it is that calm
and patient,
It grows such sweet things out of such corruptions,
It turns harmless and stainless on its axis, with such
endless succession of diseased corpses,
It distills such exquisite winds out of such
infused fetor,
It gives such divine materials to men, and accepts
such leavings from them at last.

—Walt Whitman

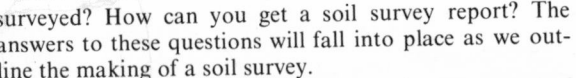

A farmer who had always been successful and whose neighbors respected his judgement on almost any farm problem bought another farm. Right away he had trouble. He decided to put a 17-acre field into alfalfa. He prepared, fertilized and seeded the field. The alfalfa came up, but then it just stopped growing. It turned yellow and didn't make a crop. The alfalfa didn't grow because the soil in that field stayed wet a few inches below the surface. The farmer knew alfalfa wouldn't grow under these conditions, but he hadn't known that the soil was like that before he bought the farm.

An urban dweller who lived in a new suburb decided he would like to grow his own fresh vegetables. He had almost half an acre of nearly level ground behind his house. The soil looked fertile, so he went ahead. When he started to work the soil he found it soggy, clayey, impossible to plow. A month of dry weather passed and he tried again. Still wet. He called the County Agent and found out that his septic tank was causing all the trouble. The soil was so tight that the liquid waste could not soak in.

'Septic tanks nearly always cause trouble in that kind of soil', the county agent said. There wasn't much this man could do. He was so far from the city mains that it might be years before he could hook on. Enlarging the tank would not help since the subsoil was practically impervious. The soil just wasn't right for a home needing a septic tank. The man was in for trouble, not only with his garden but also with his sewage disposal system. A soil survey would have indicated this tight soil immediately.

Soil Surveys

What is a soil survey? How is it made? Who does it? Who uses it? How can you find out if your land has been surveyed? How can you get a soil survey report? The answers to these questions will fall into place as we outline the making of a soil survey.

Soil, in the general sense of the word, covers most of the land surface of the earth. A soil, in the specific sense used here, is one particular part of this cover in one particular place. A soil is three-dimensional. It is bounded on the top by the surface of the land, on the bottom by rock material, and on the sides by other soils. The first job of the soil scientist is to distinguish between these separate soils. He then classifies them, describes them in great detail, and maps them. About 80,000 kinds of soils are recognized now. To find out whether a soil survey has been published for your farm and, if so, where you can find a copy, check with your County Agent, the local Soil Conservation Service Office, your Soil Conservation District (look under US Department of Agriculture in your phone book), or your State Agricultural Experiment Station. Published soil surveys can be purchased from the Superintendent of Documents, Washington, DC 20402. They may be seen in many libraries throughout the country.

Once you have obtained a soil survey for your farm, you can make decisions on how to use the soil and how it can be improved and protected. To help you in these decisions you can call in the local USDA Soil Conservation Service expert. His help is free. Here's a typical example of what a conservation man can do. He can advise a farmer that corn can be safely planted in a certain field if it is kept in grass the other three years to protect the soil from erosion. If the farmer needs to grow more corn, he might employ sloping land with a terrace system. In general, the conservation expert can help you because conservation of the soil and a good living are interdependent . . . one is

First Time Farmer's Guide

Soil survey laboratory data and descriptions for some soils of Montana. 1966. $2.00. SSIR 7

Soil survey laboratory data and descriptions for some soils of Tennessee. 1967. $1.50 SSIR 15

Soil survey laboratory data and descriptions for some soils of Colorado. 1967. $1.75. SSIR 10

Soil survey laboratory data and descriptions for some soils of Georgia, North Carolina, and South Carolina. 1967. $1.25. SSIR 16

Soil

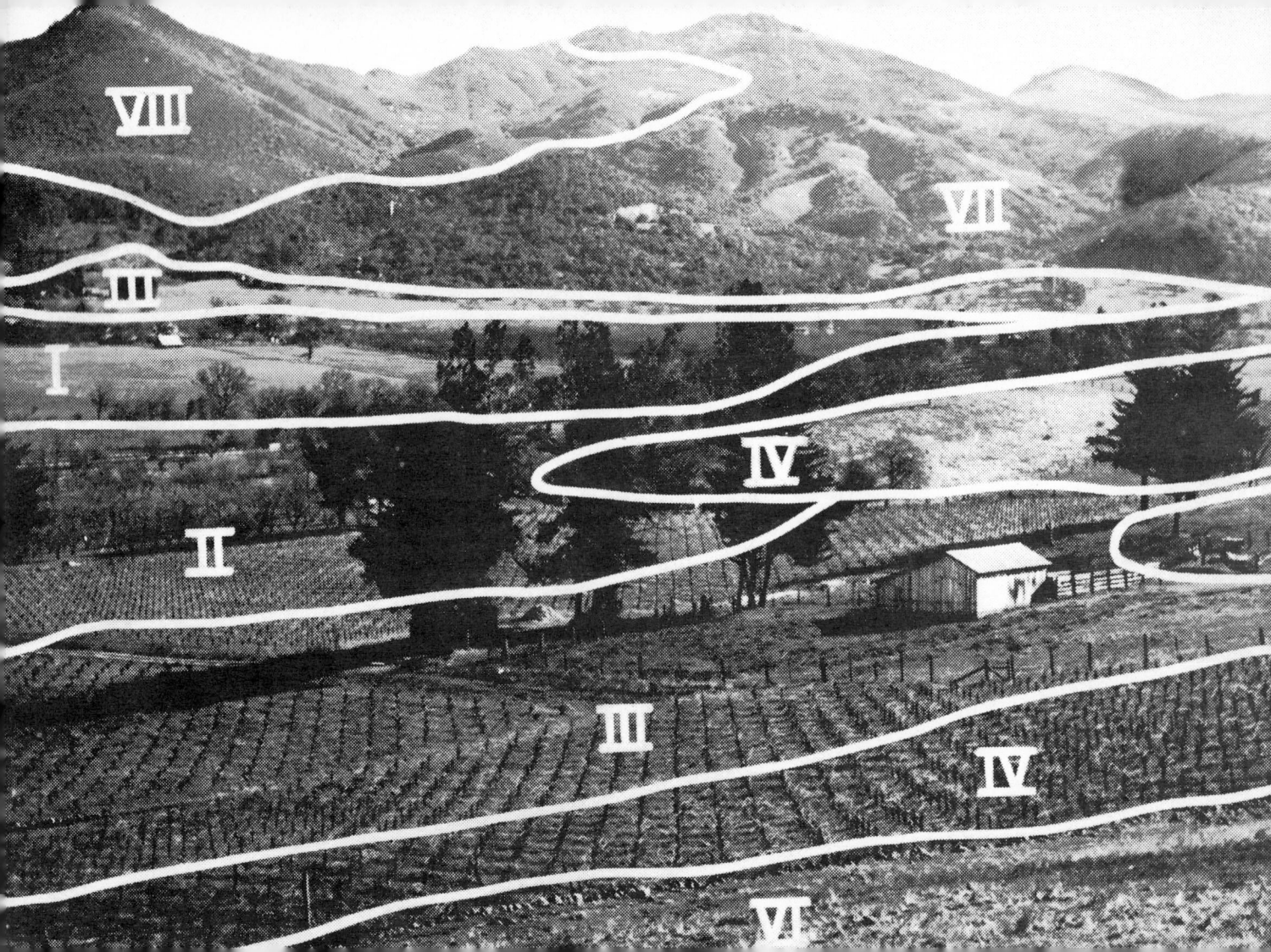

not possible without the other over a long period.

A widely used plan for making the best use of land is the Land Capability Classification. Here, the independent soils are classified according to what they are capable of producing. There are eight capability classes shown on land capability maps by Roman numerals. As you go from Class I to Class V your choices for use become fewer and the risks greater. Soils in Classes I through IV can be safely used for commonly cultivated crops which leave the soil bare part of the time. However, Class IV soils are borderline. Class V soils are not suited to ordinary cultivation because they are too wet or too stony but can provide pasture or trees where there is sufficient rain. Soils in Classes VI and VII are best used for permanent cover like grass or trees. Class VIII land is usually too steep, stony, rough or eroded to be used for any crop. However, it is useful for wildlife, recreation and protecting the watershed. Once you have established the land capability of your farm, you can adjust your focus to a finer view. This means that you will begin to look closely at the soil.

Soil Composition

Soil is composed of two major ingredients: inorganic material such as sand, clay and other small particles of the earth's original rock; organic material such as decaying vegetable matter and animal manure. The latter contains all the ingredients that plants need to grow. Of these ingredients, three are the most important: nitrogen, phosphorus and potassium. Again, these three major elements are present in almost all soil. Of course, the amount varies and this variance is what we call the 'richness or fertility of the soil.

To determine how fertile your soil is, you can plant a crop and observe how it develops, or you can make a soil fertility test. To do this, make a hole about six or eight inches deep. Then remove a sample slice with a trowel. Mail or take about 8 ounces of this soil to a State Agricultural Experiment Station or your County Agent. The report that you receive will indicate various characteristics and suitability of your soil. If you'd like to do your own testing, here are two soil tests that cost under $2.00.

Test for Soil Composition

Put about one pound of top soil in a quart milk bottle, removing any of the stones larger than the end of your little finger and pieces of roots or other foreign matter. Fill the bottle with water and shake vigorously. Then let it settle for a few minutes and you will see a clear picture of the composition of your soil. All coarse rocks and sand will be at the bottom. On top of this will be the slightly finer sand, and the very top layer will contain fine clay or silt and organic matter. Very fine clay will remain in suspension but will finally settle as the very top layer. If a soil has too much clay in it, it will be hard to work and have poor drainage. This can be remedied by adding sand, vermiculite (an expanded volcanic sand), leaves, ashes, straw, peat moss and other organic materials.

Test for Soil Acidity

Buy a roll of soil test tape from your garden or farm supply store. (It's available by mail from Perfect Garden Co, 14 E 46th Street, New York, New York 10017 for about $1.50). To test soil, a small amount of damp soil is placed on the tape. The change in the color of the tape is compared with a chart supplied with the test tape. This will tell you whether your soil is acid or alkaline. Most soils will test around pH 7. The hydrogen ion, (pH) content of

Free Soil Test... all you need is an empty bottle and some water

The Experts Agree...
Rodale, Howard,
Bromfield...
compost just has to
be the way

any compound determines its acid/alkali balance. The pH scale ranges from 0 to 14, acid to alkaline with 7 being neutral or the balance point. Different plants prefer different pH levels but most will do fine at pH levels from 4 to 8.

If you desire more alkalinity, add wood ashes from your fireplace or natural ground limestone, available at any farm or garden store. If you wish to make the soil more acid, add plenty of leaf mold. Ultimately you'll find that the best soil test of all is to simply grow something.

There is no question that the best route to go for a first-time farmer is the organic way. Therefore, to correct any deficiency in the structure or fertility of the soil on your farm, we recommend that you add compost that you make yourself. There is, of course, the possibility that your soil may be of the rich virgin variety which has done nothing but lie there accumulating layers of leaf mold and animal and bird droppings so that it would be unnecessary to add any nutrients to it before planting. In which case you would indeed be fortunate. Bear in mind, however, that after you have raised vegetables on it for a season or two, you should add compost to it.

How To Make Your Own Compost

Compost: A mixture of decomposed animal, mineral and vegetable matter that is vital to the health of all growing plants. This is the most important part of this chapter because if you read it and follow its instructions, you will be able to grow anything you wish with ease. Here is the exact method used by experts to create soil so rich you'll be able to grow the kind of bean stalks that Jack grew. Giant, flavorful tomatoes, heads of crisp lettuce as big as pumpkins, and yard-long cucumbers will literally leap out of the ground. (The latter really do exist and we'll tell you about them in a later chapter). Although it sounds like an exaggeration, when you plant a seed in this kind of soil, stand back! As Louis Bromfield, famous author/farmer said:

'Let no one ever deceive you: the greatest of soil builders, the most complete of fertilizers is organic animal manure. Fertilizer manufacturers will tell you that it is not a complete fertilizer and other elements not contained in manure or contained in too small quantities must be supplemented, that a corn crop cannot be raised without chemical fertilizers. I am less interested in chemical laboratory analyses than in the evidence of trial by practice; give me all the manure I want, so that I may plough under as much as the plough will cover year after year for three or four years, and I will show you the best crops you have ever seen anywhere.'

In his prophetic book *Pay Dirt,* the eminent organic gardening expert, JI Rodale, lists 36 reasons why compost farming is superior to farming or gardening with artificial fertilizers. A few of the 36 are summarized below:

By adding organically prepared compost to your soil, the general fertility level of your farm will be raised significantly.

Compost improves the structure of your soil so that it is easier to cultivate, earth worms multiply and move above easily and the soil has better aeration. Compost-soil mixtures increase water holding capability thus preventing soil erosion . . . the soil becomes soft and absorbent like a blotter.

Compost increases the valuable soil bacteria and fungi, which in turn permits compost to be made on a continuous basis.

Those plants grown in rich, compost-containing soil are healthy; there is less plant disease and fewer insect problems. Insects stay away from the healthy plants.

The foods that you grow in your composted soil will taste better, look better and give you better health.

Here is a step by step description of how to make a compost pile by a method originated in the 19th century by an English agricultural expert, Sir Albert Howard. It is also known as the Indore Process. This process involves mixing vegetable and animal waste products with earth and water. The mixture is prepared in such a way as to permit the natural bacteria to decompose the vegetable and animal wastes, transforming them into a useful, virtually cost-free, and highly valuable fertilizer for all of your gardening requirements.

Most home garden experts agree that one half acre will grow more than a family of four will need. Therefore we are suggesting a compost pile of the following dimensions: ten feet by ten feet by three feet. This equals 300 cubic feet or eleven cubic yards. A pile of these dimensions will give you five tons of compost, sufficient for your half-acre home garden. Obviously, you can adjust the size of your pile in proportion to suit your own home garden operation. For example, a one-acre home farm would require a compost pile twice as large, or ten

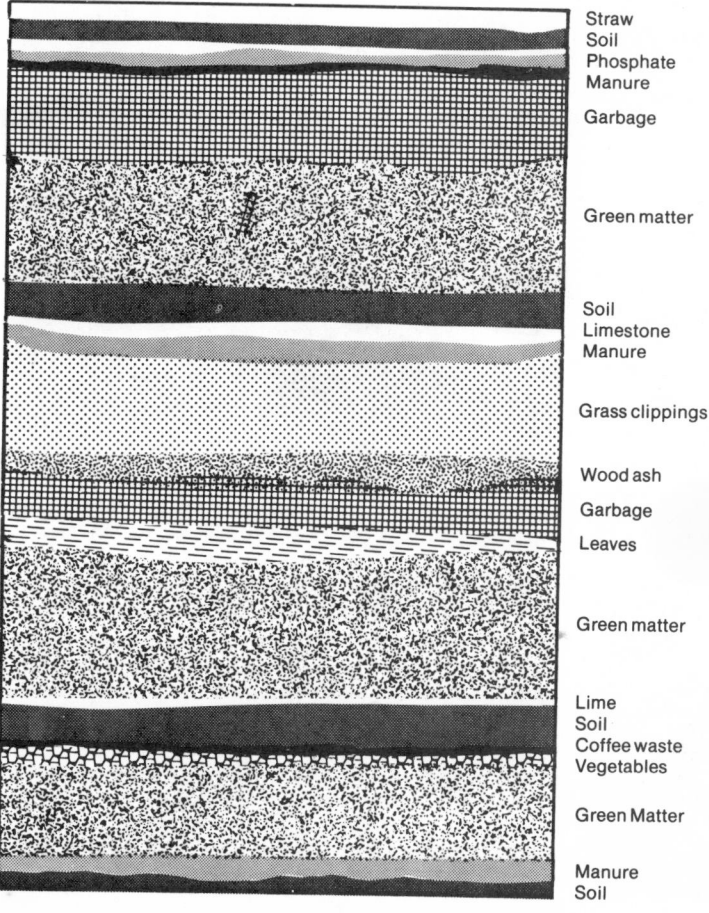

Straw
Soil
Phosphate
Manure
Garbage

Green matter

Soil
Limestone
Manure

Grass clippings

Wood ash
Garbage
Leaves

Green matter

Lime
Soil
Coffee waste
Vegetables
Green Matter

Manure
Soil

feet by ten feet by six feet. A one-quarter acre garden would indicate a compost pile ten feet by three feet. It is important to note here that as your garden becomes well fertilized with your home-made compost, the amount you will have to make each year can be less. As a guide, you might use half as much compost two or three years after you have started your compost-rich garden plot.

Most gardeners and farmers put their compost pile on the back of their property for aesthetic reasons. This is also a good location because you would be taking your lawn and garden trimmings, weeds, etc., to the rear of your property as a natural procedure. In addition, you will need space around your compost pile to store heaps of green matter so that they can age a little before adding them. If you will be bringing in materials in your pickup truck or garden trailer, provide access via a driveway. Another advantage of having your compost pile at the rear of your garden is that it will be close enough to make hauling the finished compost to the rows a simple matter. The site you choose should have good drainage on every side so that rains do not create a giant vegetative mud pie. Be sure that you can bring water via pipe or hose to the compost site. Some additional considerations are:

Choose a shady location. If this isn't possible, cover the heap with a thin layer of straw, hay or other suitable material.

The compost heap should be shielded from strong winds which stop fermentation.

Make the compost heaps orderly and neat with room to maneuver between them.

Try to use the same spot over and over again because the ground beneath will improve from the standpoint of bacterial life.

Making your own compost heap is something that you've done before whenever you've piled up layers of grass, hedge trimmings or other materials for eventual disposal. Here is the plan:

First spread a layer of green matter on the ground. This can consist of mown grass, leaves, weeds, vegetable scraps, a small amount of sawdust and any other reasonably fine vegetative matter. Over this spread a two-inch layer of manure. Cow manure is preferable but any animal manure will work. Next sprinkle a thin layer of the best soil from your farm. This layer should be sufficiently thick to cover the preceding layer. The last layer is ordinary lime (which you can buy from any farm or garden supply) or wood ashes. The latter is preferred as being a more natural, organic material and one readily available from your fireplace or barbecue. Then, simply repeat the process over again—until the pile has reached the desired height. Unless the materials that you use are quite wet, sprinkle each layer, but don't make the heap too wet. The amount of water to use will be a matter of trial and error for you until you get the 'feel' of it.

It's a good idea to taper the heap slightly so that it will be structurally sound. When the heap is finished,

First Time Farmer's Guide

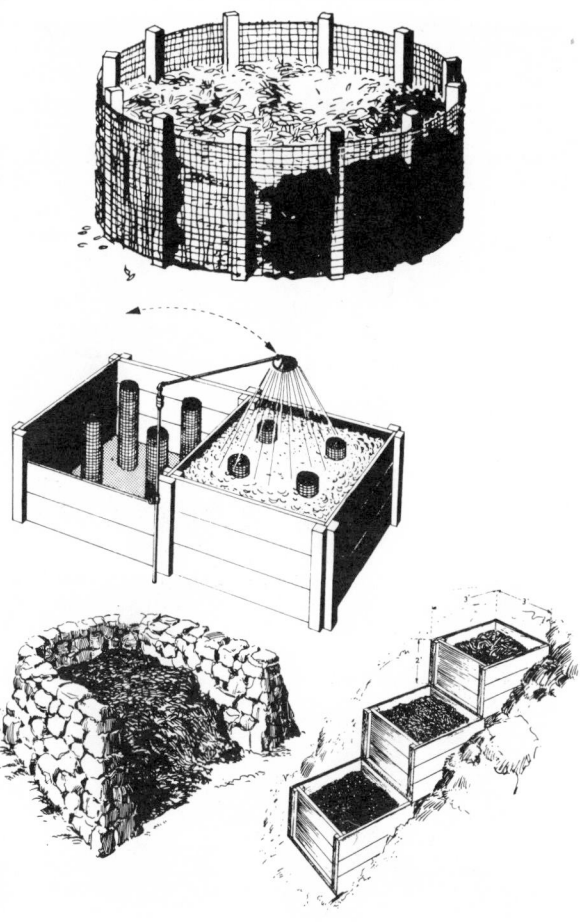

apply a covering of straw or hay to keep it moist. The final step is to punch holes through the heap with an iron bar. For a compost heap measuring 100 square feet, one half dozen holes five or six inches in diameter would be adequate. A clever way to make holes would be to put stove pipes in the ground and build your heap around them. When the heap is finished, simply pull out the pipes and there are your holes.

Although the time schedule would vary, depending on the conditions, let the pile work by itself for approximately three weeks. Then take a pitchfork and turn the heap so that all parts are thoroughly mixed. About five weeks later, turn it again. That's all you have to do. Four weeks later, or about three months after you started, the compost is ready to use. Certainly a lot easier than a two-hour drive on a crowded freeway every day, wouldn't you say? As soon as the heap has become compost, you can apply it to the soil where you intend to plant. For the small garden, simply haul wheelbarrow loads and dig it into the upper four or five inches of the planting rows. Experts agree that compost should be worked in so that it is covered, thus preventing the valuable chemicals from evaporating.

Some ingenious methods of composting. Four hay bales in a square works too

Instant Compost

Although the methods we have described are simple and effective, they may not be fast enough for those who can't wait to crunch a crispy carrot. It is now possible to turn organic waste matter into compost in just *14* days! The secret is *shredding*. Experimentation at the famous farm of Organic Gardening magazine has proved it can be done. In fact, some compost has been made in as little as *six days!* Isn't that the most heartening news? Here are the items you'll need.

Nitrogen Sources

Nitrogen is needed for the fast compost process. Animal nature, as specified in the slower methods is the best source because it will heat up the compost heap quickly. However, if fresh animal manure isn't available, use dried manure, cottonseed meal, dried blood or bone meal.

Shredder

The material from which you make the compost must be shredded. Fortunately there are a number of shredders on the market. Here's a typical one made by the Kemp Company of Erie, Pa. Other models both larger and smaller may be obtained from the following manufacturers:

Amerind-MacKissic Inc.
Box 111, Department 0
Parker Ford, Penn 19457

Red Cross Mfg Corp.
Bluffton, Indiana 46714

California-McCulloch Equipment Co.
Box 3068
Torrance, California 90510

Gilson Bros Co.
P.O. 152, Department C
Plymouth, Wisconsin 53073

W W Grinder Corp.
2957B No. Market
Wichita, Kansas 67219

Shredders are simple to use, fairly inexpensive to buy and will last a long time if properly maintained. If the noise and fumes of gasoline motors bother you, then buy an electric model. If no electricity is available, then check the chapter on power sources for the small farm. Incidentally, rotary mowers often sell for less than $50 in their simplest form. Secondhand ones sell for a lot less. Either a new or a secondhand rotary power mower makes a fine pulverizer and shredder to create either compost

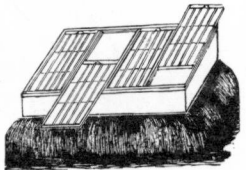

First Time Farmer's Guide

material or mulch. To use it, simply spread the leaves, twigs, straw and other vegetable matter on the ground and run the rotary mower over it several times. You can make it as fine as you want by making as many passes as are needed. If you do this work near the point of use, all you have to do is rake the finished product into the compost pile, or, if to be used as mulch, into your garden.

Moisture

To speed up the composting process be sure to water it liberally as it is made. Check it occasionally to make sure that it has sufficient moisture so that the composting process will continue. It's just as important to prevent the compost pile from being too soggy as it is to let it dry up. Again, this aspect of compost making is one that you will learn from experience.

A Wooden Bin With Solid Sides

For a more permanent structure you can use cement blocks with or without mortar. For a really fast compost bin, buy four bales of straw (it's cheaper than hay) and arrange them in a square. You can always use the straw later for mulch or as part of the compost, so it's a good investment.

A quaint little group called the Auckland Humic Club of New Zealand devised a simple structure that you can make from scrap lumber. As you can see, the box has a sliding front so that it can be removed and the compost loaded into your wheelbarrow, wagon or truck with ease. The New Zealanders suggest that you toss the green matter, manure, soil and ashes in the box, watering them so that they are as moist as a filled sponge, and then mix them up furiously—no layering required. Next make one air hole down the center with a crowbar and turn the mixture on the same schedule as the previously men-

A check on moisture level in the compost heap...also a source of valuable elements

tioned plan. Keep the box covered with burlap or straw matting.

Now that you have the components, go to it! First use your shredder to grind up all of the grass, leaves, garden trimmings, weeds, and kitchen scraps around your farm. If you need more vegetable matter, just drive around the countryside and help yourself to fallen leaves, chunks of bark and similar organic good things. Dump the proceeds of your shredding activity into the bin. Incidentally, it's really a gas to watch all of these odd things become a beautiful, finely pulverized heap of organic matter. Add about one-third as much manure, a small amount of soil and a sprinkling of wood ashes. The exact amounts are a matter of judgment and experience, which you will soon acquire in becoming a compost expert. Water as you mix until the whole batch is thoroughly wet.

18 THE MOON P

Soil   63

Even more variations on the compost heap
Opposite: A fast way to mix up compost ingredients and your garbage

Now go climb the nearest apple tree or relax in a sunny haystack because from here on out the compost will do its own thing.

The best test of a finished compost is that all of the ingredients have turned a rich dark color and the texture of the compost has become crumbly rather than soggy. Add it to your garden rows in the same manner as explained previously.

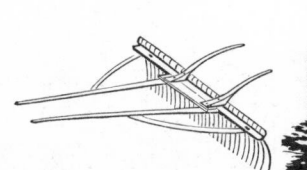

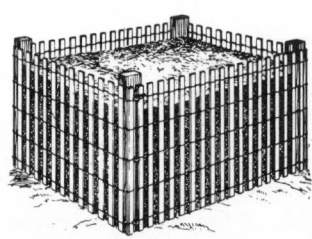

First Time Farmer's Guide

Seeds & Stock

'A sower went out to sow his seed, some fell by the wayside and it was trodden down and the fowls of the air devoured it. And some fell upon a rock and as soon as it was sprung up, it withered away because it lacked moisture. And some fell among thorns and the thorns sprang up with it and choked it. And others fell on good ground and sprang up and bore fruit a hundredfold.'
— *St. Luke, Chapter 8, V5*

Have you ever really given much thought to what a fantastic storehouse of information a seed really is? You've probably got some seeds in your house as you are reading these words . . . celery seed for salads, carroway to bake with rye bread, whole dill seed for pickling, and many others. Pick up one of these seeds right now and visualize the incredible complexity of its internal organization. There amidst the protons and electrons of the atomic structure, concealed from view by the unimaginably complex molecular design, are all of the instructions needed to germinate the seed, put down roots, erect a stem and leaves, become a complex chemical factory using light, water and myriad chemicals from the soil to build another plant like the one from which this seed stemmed. Think of it! An entire world of planning, design and potential execution, all in a speck so tiny that for many plants *thousands* of them weigh *less than an ounce.*

It is this miracle of regeneration, of periodic renaissance that will make farming infinitely fascinating for you.

Seeds

As you dig deeper into the field of farming, you'll find that many so-called farming chores will turn out to be more fun to do than the entertainments for which you had to pay in the city. A good example of this is the joy of choosing your seeds, seedlings and stock. The whole family can participate since what you grow will be consumed by all. If little Mary has a thing for marigolds or if Cynthia digs cymbidiums then by all means add a 35-cent packet to your vegetable seed order. If your wife, or husband, is a health devotee, then buy a half pound of those wonderful giant sunflower seeds.

One of the greatest pleasures that you'll come to

know as a first-time farmer is to sit by your own crackling hearth on a chilly winter night with your arms entwined about your favorite seed catalog. Seed catalogs have had a fascination for gardeners and farmers since they were first published back in the 19th century. In those days, seed purveyors allowed themselves a little poetic license with the prose concerning the size of carrots and turnips and fudged a little on the illustrations showing watermelons too big to put in a wheelbarrow. But then a harmless exaggeration (and maybe it isn't so exaggerated) is of no great consequence. Every farmer believes that he will grow snap beans longer and tomatoes bigger than anyone else in the country, and the seed catalogs help him sustain this belief, with their glorious color pictures and vivid descriptions.

Come and take a tour through some of the most colorful catalogs available today. Here's one as big as a Sunday supplement magazine and at least ten times as colorful. On the cover they exhort you to 'grow your own groceries' and 'save $500 a year.' Over on the side of the front page is a special offer for kids only. For just *one cent* children can buy the giant Jumble Packet containing 100 seeds of every kind imaginable—both vegetable and flower. What a lot of fun your children would have surprising themselves when this mixed-up garden starts growing. As you open this catalog, the impact of the brightly colored fruits and vegetables is overwhelming. Over here are climbing tomatoes with the tops much higher than a nearby roof. Then there's a hamburger onion that grows up to four inches across. A watermelon called New Hampshire Midget just fills a man's hand, while Mrs. Lucille Buckwheat is pictured holding three cabbages she grew that total 54 pounds. Here's a whole page of salad vegetables, blackseeded Simpson lettuce,

First Time Farmer's Guide

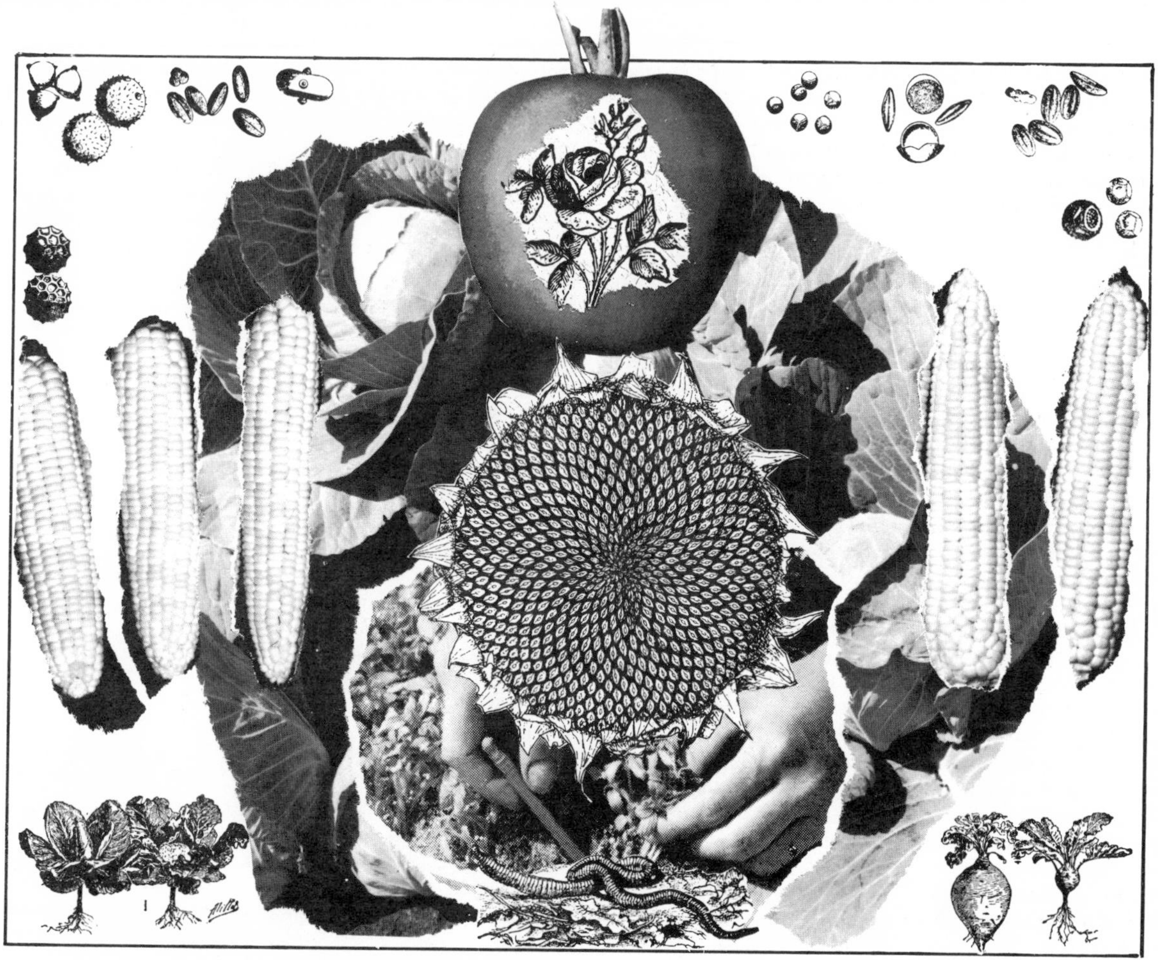

Seeds like ideas, can
produce fantastic
results

U.S.E. SEEDS

25¢ 25¢

Seeds and Stock

a dark green romaine that branches itself, tender spinach rich in vitamins, calcium and iron, and the 'Aristocratic' cabbage. Then there's kohlrabi—the catalog proclaims it a novel member of the cabbage family with a mild nutty flavor all its own. One whole page of mouth-watering melons makes you wish that your vines were well along and the yellow casabas, golden Champlain cantaloupes and big Gurney's mammoth muskmelons were ready to pick and eat. Following the more conventional items are exotic vegetables and small fruits. There are mangels or sugar beets that yield 40 tons per acre, guinea beans that grow to astounding lengths and citron, a green melon used for perserving or pickling.

Then page after page of wonderful seed bargains— ten packets for three dollars that will let you grow a garden full of 40-pound watermelons, a 50-pound squash, a 20-pound cabbage, or a 2½-pound tomato. At the opposite end of the spectrum is a collection of six midget vegetables, all six packets for $1.50, including corn, cucumbers, tomatoes, watermelons, lettuce and carrots. The lettuce produces heads the size of a tennis ball, while the midget sweet corn never grows longer than four inches . . . perfect for a window box garden. To put some surprises into your first-time farm garden, try a few seed packets of things like three-foot long cucumbers, Aladdin's Turban squash, blue potatoes and a tomato that's almost *white* when ripe. We promise you that you'll have lots more fun reading about the 12-year old girl who picked enough berries from her mother's strawberry patch to buy a pony than you will about how many cars piled up on the freeway just four miles from your old suburban crackerbox.

With your land and water standing by and your seed order ready to mail, there's no question that you'll

be excited with the prospect of seeing *your* farm garden produce these wondrous botanical specimens . . . just one of the joys of being your own first-time farmer.

Sources

To get you started, here is a list of firms that will send you their free catalogs for just a five-cent postcard request:

W. Atlee Burpee Company, 4061 Burpee Building, Philadelphia, Pennsylvania 19132; (Exceptionally fine catalog!)

Burrell Seed Company, Box 150-G, Rocky Ford, Colorado 81067.

Farmer Seed and Nursery Company, Ellicott Street Station, Buffalo, New York 14205.

Girard Nurseries, Geneva, Ohio 44041.

Gurney Seed and Nursery Company, 2642 Page Street, Yankton, South Dakota 57077; (Splashy, colorful, delightful!)

Joseph Harris Company, Inc., 48 Moreton Farm, Rochester, New York 14624; (Very professional. Quantity wholesale prices).

Harry E. Saier, Dimondale, Michigan 48821. (50¢).

Hemlock Hill Herb Farms, Litchfield, Connecticut 06759.

Henry Field, Shenandoah, Iowa 51601.

J.W. Jung Seed Company, Station 23, Randolph, Wisconsin 53956.

Mellingers, North Lima, Ohio 44452; (Dozens of unique items).

Natural Development Company, Bainbridge, Pennsylvania 17502.

Nichols Garden Nursery, 1190 N. Pacific Highway, Albany, Oregon 93721; (Strong on herbs and oddities—

entertaining).

Parks Seed Company, Inc., Greenwood, South Carolina 29646.

Robson Quality Seeds, Inc., 18 Hall, New York, New York 14463.

Stark Bros., Louisiana, Missouri 63353.

Stokes Seeds, Inc., Box 15, Ellicott Street Station, Buffalo, New York 14205.

Tennessee Nursery Company, P.O. 111, Cleveland, Tennessee 37311.

Vita Green Farms, P.O. 878, Vista, California 92083.

Although the cost of seeds will be negligible, there are a couple of sources of seeds which will eliminate even this miniscule expenditure. For example, many plants will produce seeds if they are not harvested. Carrots, cabbage or onions will display beautiful seed plumes. Gath-ering these seeds is a simple process. For those that are plainly visible, simply shake over a plain piece of paper and store. Seeds from tomatoes, melons, apples and similar fruits and vegetables can be extracted from the pulp, dried and preserved. When you buy seed, buy enough to last for several seasons within the predicted life of the seed because it's less expensive that way. A small supply of seed is a great hedge against any sort of earthly catastrophe. It's truly 'money' in the bank that money couldn't buy if for some reason seeds were no longer available as easily and readily as they are today. Seed life is usually indicated in the catalog. Storing seeds is simple. Any cool, dry place where it would be impossible for seeds to germinate is adequate. They should be kept from any possible raids by hungry, unscrupulous mice. Coffee cans with tight-fitting lids are ideal.

Keep good supplies of seeds—in large glass jars—you can even sprout and eat them...

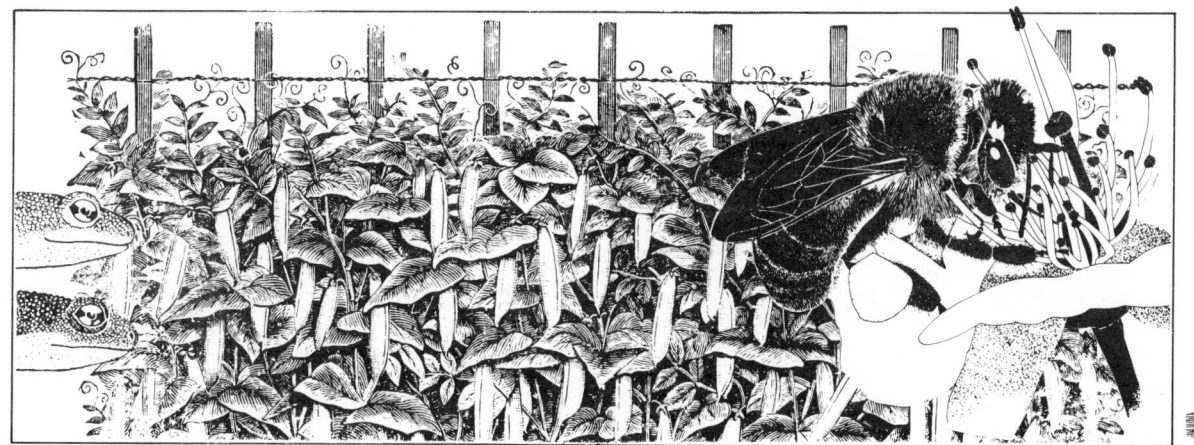

Stock

It's customary to refer to seedlings (which are small plants), roots, cuttings (sometimes called slips), bulbs and rooted plants and small trees as stock. So after you finish making your seed tour, continue on through the stock section of your seed catalogs. The most popular items bought in stock farms are the *perennial* plants, such as rhubarb and asparagus. By *perennial* we mean a plant that is established in the ground and every year thereafter produces a crop until it dies. Asparagus is a perennial that lives as long as 15 years. Therefore, an investment in high quality asparagus plants will be one of the most rewarding investments you can make on your first-time farm. Three or four dollars will buy a couple of dozen asparagus plants from your local nursery or through your mail order seed and stock supplier. The price goes down as the quantity goes up. If you bought 100 of them, they would cost about a dime each. Asparagus is easy to grow and once it's started it will come up year after year, providing you with a delicious vegetable for your table. Another item frequently purchased in mature plant form is rhubarb, which has the same year after year characteristic as asparagus. Additional plants that fall into the stock category are currants, gooseberries, horseradish, all types of small trees, many varieties of berries and grapes, and from one supplier an interesting, authentic, native fruit garden. This would include wild plum, wild blackberry, chokecherry, buffaloberry, sand- and compassberry. An assortment of eight of these wild plants that gave our forefathers delightful provender for their tables costs about three dollars.

One of the most common vegetables that's grown in almost every garden, and nearly always purchased as a seedling plant, is the tomato. These are usually obtained

Wild Rhubarb

from your local nursery.

When considering your choices for seeds and stock for your farm, don't forget that most seed catalogs will overwhelm you with fantastically beautiful color pictures of gorgeous flowers—roses, mums, peonies, asters, carnations, delphiniums, pansies and lilies. Every farm should have a goodly splash of color throughout the growing season. The cost can be only a few dollars for a magnificent garden. Here are some examples of package offers. For less than three dollars postpaid you can establish a garden of lovely, long-lived perennials, including red phlox, yellow carnations, red cushion mums, blue delphiniums and pink baby's breath. They'll even throw in a free perennial sweet pea. For this small investment and a few moments of garden time, you'll have years of beauty.

While the emphasis in this book is on a self-supporting farm, remember that bread alone won't provide all you need for a complete life. So as you browse through your seed catalog, make room on your order blank and in your budget for an exquisite early bloomer like Virginia bluebells, yellow double daffodils and fragrant two-tone clove pinks.

No-Cost Seed And Stock Sources

In his famous book 'Stalking the Wild Asparagus' Euell Gibbons describes dozens of wild plants that are available throughout the world free for the picking. He often points out that the seeds of these wild plants may be gathered and eaten. However, what's wrong with creating a home garden of wild plants? After all, every single one of our domestic plants from asparagus to watermelons originally were wild and went through a domesticating process.

A common wild vegetable is purslane. This is a small

First Time Farmer's Guide

ground-hugging annual that grows in many parts of the wilds. It's seldom over two inches tall, although it may be a foot or more in diameter. It is most easily identified by tiny yellow flowers that open in the morning. The young leaves and stems are the tastiest part, although if you're really hungry, the entire plant is edible. It can be eaten raw or cooked. It has a pleasant salad-like taste. As Gibbon suggests, if you pick only the young purslane tips, a few plants will supply a family for an entire season.

Seeds

Doesn't this sound like a handsome and free addition to your garden? If so, find yourself some wild purslane and keep an eye on it until it goes to seed. The seeds appear in a small sphere in the fork of the stems. Gather as many as you wish and plant them in an outer fringe of your garden. Then when someone sees your lush growth of purslane and asks you about it, you can boast that your garden is so diversified that you're even growing wild plants for food.

This is but one of thousands of examples of wild plants that could be easily domesticated at no cost. Keep in mind that there are more than 300,000 classified plants that grow on the earth's surface. Of this number, about 120,000 are edible. Here is a list of a few wild plants that Mr. Gibbon mentions in his book from which seeds could be gathered and a crop grown in your garden: wild rice, milkweed, poke (or poke salad), wild sunflowers, watercress, pigweed, wild onions, ground nut or Indian potato, wild cranberries, Jerusalem artichoke, cattails, calamus, great burdock, wild ferns, marsh marigolds, cow cabbage, cow peas, wild tomatoes, wild pie plant, arrowhead, and wild oats.

As mentioned previously, there are many more edi-

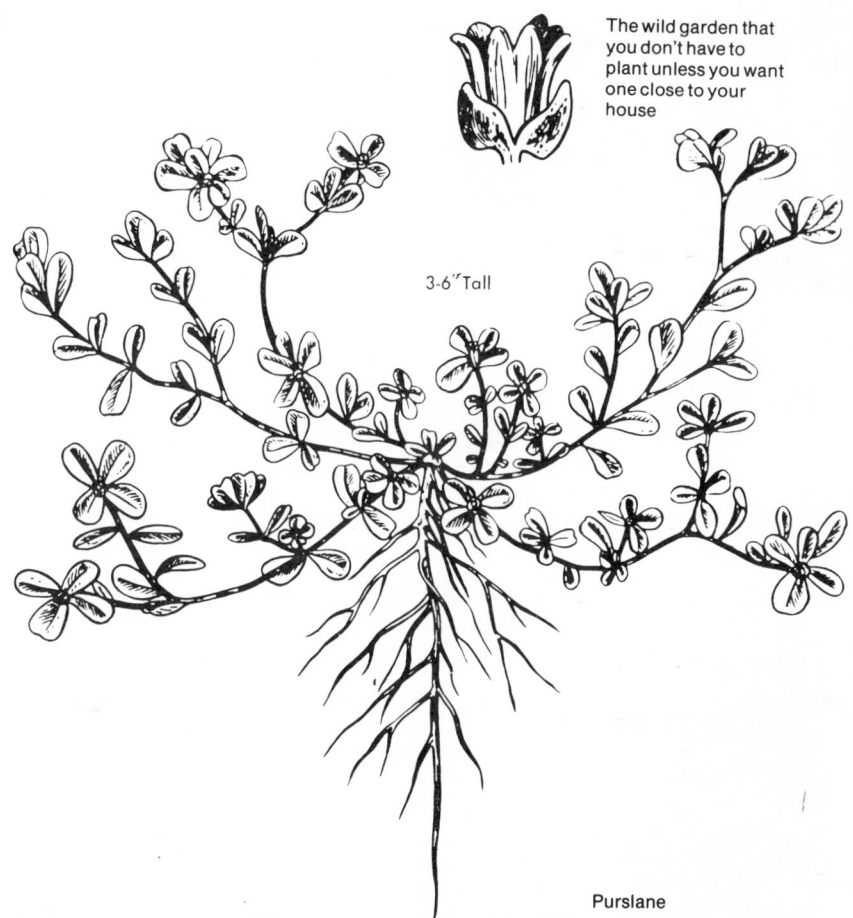

The wild garden that you don't have to plant unless you want one close to your house

3-6" Tall

Purslane

The supermarket that
grows out of your
farm pond

ble wild plants from which seeds could be obtained as an added feature and food supply for your farm garden.

Stock

You are probably even more familiar with the many wild plants that can be propagated from slips, cuttings, roots, or runners. For example, every visitor to the rural regions of America has seen enormous berry vine tangles. Blackberries, raspberries and blueberries abound in wild form in many parts of the United States and the rest of the world. Gathering blackberry canes (cuttings of blackberry vines) requires only a pair of stout clippers and a pair of gloves. Incidentally, it is best to gather these canes in the spring rather than after your plant has borne fruit. Other stock that you can gather are forest seedlings of oak, all types of evergreens, wild cherry, apple or persimmon, wild nut trees, such as walnut and hickory, sassafras, mulberry and sweet birch. Wild rose that produces the vitamin rich rose hips grows in many parts of the country. Wild grape vines are another choice and completely free stock item. Simply cut canes or slips from a healthy looking wild grapevine. Wild asparagus and wild onion are two other plants that can be propagated from roots that you dig where you find them.

Mr. Gibbon has called cattails the supermarket of the wilderness since so many of its parts are edible, raw or cooked. Almost every marshy meadow, swamp and riverside in America has its stand of cattails. Take off your shoes and wade around with a small shovel and collect yourself a healthy plant. Bring it home and put it in your own farm pond and within a few years you'll have your own private supply of cattail foods. Other rooted crops that can be dug and transplanted are: arrowhead, great bullrush, Jack in the pulpit or Indian turnip, crin-

kle root (a Dentaria), ground nuts, man of the earth (cousin of the sweet potato which has roots that sometime reach twenty pounds), and prairie turnip.

Few people are aware that many types of cactus are edible, both leaves and the fruits. The prickly pear is one that is familiar to people because of its brightly colored but highly stickery fruits. Incidentally, a fast way to desticker them is to hold them with a fork and rotate over a flame. This burns off the stickers and permits you to peel them as easily as if they were an apple. Cactus grows throughout the American Southwest that can be grown in many other parts of the country. Propagation is from the thick slab-like leaves. Another edible cactus plant is the yucca or God's candle. Its stalk can be roasted while the flower buds boiled make a fine dish.

Again, the possibilities of roaming the countryside near your farmstead to find free stock items is unlimited. Don't forget that if you live in a mountainous or semi-mountainous region, your regional forest ranger may be able to provide you with free seedlings of many types of evergreens. These fast-growing trees are great for windbreaks, erosion control and general farm beautification.

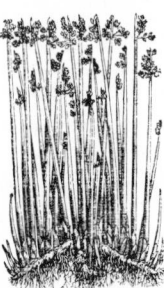

First Time Farmer's Guide

Far left to right:
Bull-rush, Mulberry,
Wild asparagus
(doesn't normally
droop like this),
Dentaria and Scotch
pine

Tools & Equipment

'Pickaxe, shovel, spade, crowbar, hoe and barrow,
Better not invade, Yankees have the marrow.'
—Samuel Woodworth,

In his book *The Golden Age of Homespun, a Story of Authentic Pioneer Farming Life,* Jared Van Wagenen, Jr says:

'To advance upon a piece of tall timber and prepare the ground for the first crop, the pioneer needed, besides his own high courage and skill, three—and only three—tools, to wit, his keen axe, his firebrand and his trusty ox team.'

The axe was used to cut down the trees, the team to drag them into a pile and the fire to burn them. This land clearing operation was basic to any early American farming enterprise. It is doubtful whether you'll ever own an ox. You'd never get a permit to pollute the air with ten acres of burning logs. But it is likely that you will make good use of a keen axe. It's just the thing for chopping up saplings for livestock fencing, cutting up some deadwood for your fireplace and, if you're really energetic, creating a log cabin for your farm homestead deep in the wilds of Canada or Alaska.

Minimum Farming Tools

Much research into small scale farming indicates that the total picture is much like we've just described . . . only a few basic tools are needed to carry on a successful small scale farm adventure. For example, if your initial efforts are restricted to gardening, here are the tools you may need: an ordinary shovel for mixing and moving soil. A spade for excavating. A wide blade hoe for light cultivation. A two-pronged seeding hoe for seeds—what else? A Warren hoe which has a triangular shape and will make and fill seed drills (a drill is a furrow in which you plant your seeds). An ordinary garden rake for breaking up clods and smoothing seed beds. A grass rake, bamboo or steel, for removing leaves. A three-pronged cultivator

for breaking up soil crust. A spading fork for uprooting potatoes and other underground goodies.

It's very possible that you already have all or most of these garden tools if you've been a suburban gardener and landscaper. If not, you can buy the whole works for under $50 and a lot less if you buy them used. If you hire someone to do the initial soil tilling (providing it's at all necessary), you won't have to invest in a fancy rototiller or garden tractor. This will save you lots of money right at the start when it's so important to conserve capital. As Henry Tetlow says in his excellent book, *We Farm For A Hobby.*

'It's neither necessary nor desirable to invest a great deal of money in farm production nor—and this is at least equally important—to do it all at once.'

Henry goes on to point out that on his rather large Pennsylvania farm which was a complete operation with cows and chickens, pigs, fruit trees and a large garden, he got along with the following equipment in addition to normal home equipment:

Set of butchers' tools—knives, saw, cleaver, block & tackle for hoisting carcasses, lard press, sausage stuffer.

Hand-operated cream separator (to separate milk from cream).

Small motor-driven mill for grinding cereals.

A spraying outfit mounted on a hand barrow.

A pressure cooker: absolutely necessary for canning all meats and some vegetables.

An eighty-four-egg electric incubator (to hatch chicken eggs).

Two electrically lighted and heated brooders for small chicks (to keep chicks warm).

One finishing battery brooder for birds six to six-

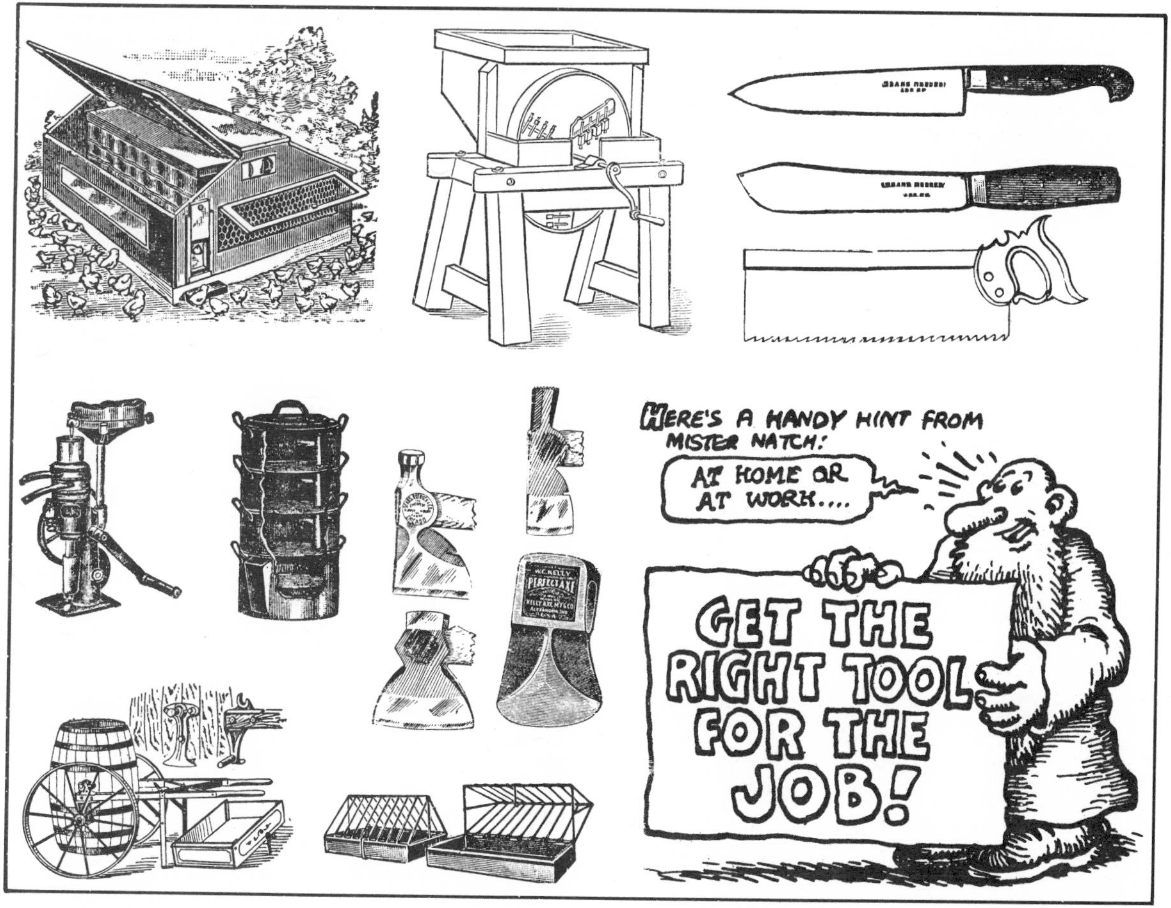

'The right tool makes the job easy'

HERE'S A HANDY HINT FROM MISTER NATCH:

AT HOME OR AT WORK....

GET THE RIGHT TOOL FOR THE JOB!

Tips on how to cut
your capital invest-
ment to an absolute
minimum

teen weeks old (for slightly older chicks).

Miscellaneous feed troughs for chickens and pigs. Sixteen galvanized iron trap nests.

Five galvanized iron ash cans to store stock feeds out of reach of rats.

Two scales: one for grading eggs by weight, and one for weighing milk in the barn.

Apparatus for testing the butterfat content of milk.

According to Mr. Tetlow, this vast array cost him less than $200. However, these were depression prices, but even at a three or four times rise in prices, you could duplicate all of this equipment for about $800 — less if some of it were used, war surplus or improvised. Remember that this sum would be needed *only* if you were operating a *full-scale* livestock and vegetable-fruit farm.

The Careful Tool Buyer

So go easy and acquire what you need as you go along. Send for Sears (Chicago, Illinois) and Wards (Oakland, California) farm equipment catalogs. Also get surplus catalogs from:

The Surplus Center	Airborne Salvage
P.O. 82209	8501 Stellar Drive
Lincoln, NB 68501	Culver City, California 90230

These four catalogs will give you a good idea of what is available and at what prices. But weigh every decision to buy a piece of machinery carefully. Here are some of the considerations prior to making any purchase:

Do you really need it or are you buying it just to have fun with it (many garden tractors fall into this category).

Since much farm equipment is used only once or twice a season (things like seeders, plows, cultivators and

harvesting equipment), try renting. Along these lines, you may be able to work a trade-off with another first-time farmer. You buy the cherry pitter and he buys the apple parer and you exchange when the crops get ripe.

If it's a large capital investment, will you be able to amortize its cost against the value of the crop? We've all seen rusting pieces of elaborate equipment that some farmer thought he had to have to do something complicated to the corn. As Thoreau pointed out, any venture that requires new clothing should be looked upon with skepticism. We can paraphrase this by substituting 'expensive farm machinery' for 'clothes'.

In these days of heavy air pollution, resist the impulse to bring a lot of petroleum-burning monstrosities to your homestead. After all, one of the reasons you left the city was to escape breathing all that exhaust gas.

If you can buy it cheaper than you can grow it using a piece of equipment, then use the money to buy the food item. Whole grain wheat at even $10 a sack can be purchased for many years before you could defray the cost of a single item of mechanized grain production.

So think before you buy. Don't fall into the trap that engulfs city and country people alike — having to pay for and maintain more things than they really need. On a more positive plane, there are lots of small, inexpensive new items that will make your farm productive with little labor. Take the soaker hoses that you've probably used for shrubs and lawn when you lived around a big city. At three or four dollars for 50 feet these soakers can be used to provide effortless irrigation to strawberry patches and rows of blueberries. Couple the soaker hose with a seven dollar water timer and you can turn on the water and forget it.

Then there's the brass fogger that will break water

into a fog-like spray. They can be used to cool your livestock in the summer time by installing one in the barn, or you can use it to water your seed beds. They also make a fine fire fighting tool. A few dollars invested in foggers can return many times that amount in real farm assistance. For about three dollars you can buy an earth auger to fit your ¼ inch electric drill. It will drill an inch and a quarter diameter hole in the ground to help you fertilize your trees or to determine the amount of moisture in any part of your farm land. The new contour sprinklers permit you to set a spray pattern and follow the contour of any pasture. These put water just where you want it and with good pressure will reach for forty feet. So take the advice of the Volkswagen people and think small. Keep your farm operation under close scrutiny from an economic standpoint.

Whatever you buy, buy top quality and keep it in top shape. For example, a bucketful of oiled sand will keep your shovels and hoes rust-proof. A small shed which you can build to suit your farm equipment would be a worthwhile investment to protect everything you own from the elements or rip-offs. Here are some plans for facilities you can build yourself.

In time you may wish to add tools and equipment. If so, here is an extensive suggested list of tools which you might wish to consider *as you gain experience and know-how*. The list that follows is classified into major work areas.

A Check List

The following is a suggested list of tools which you might wish to consider in equipping your farm shop.

The One Dollar Air Conditioner...a fog spray unit

Robinson Crusoe did
it with a lot less . . .
and Sylvan Hart *made*
most of his tools

Your selection of tools depends on the activities you plan to undertake. Some prefer to do complete overhaul jobs on power units, tractors and machinery; others expect to do only the simpler maintenance tasks. It is not possible to give a complete list of tools for all purposes, because special tools are needed for certain machines.

The tool lists that follow are classified into major work areas. It is granted that the tools may be used in areas other than the ones in which they are listed.

Number	Name of Tool	Description
1	nail hammer	16 oz. curved claw
1	combination square	12″ grooved blade
1	steel tape	50′ metallic
1	jack plane	length 14½″, 2″ cutter
1	cross cut or panel saw	26″, 8 point, skew-back
1	rip saw	26″, 5½ point, skew-back
1	brace	10″ sweep, ratchet
1 set	wood auger bits	¼″ to 1″ by 16ths with tang or ½″ round shank for power drill
1	hand drill	capacity to ⅜″
1 set	drill bits with stand	high speed steel, 1/16″ to 1/2″ by 32nds
1	combination oil stone	1″ x 2″ x 7″ coarse and fine
1	wood file or rasp	12″, half round
2	screw drivers	electrician's 3″ and 6″

Number	Name of Tool	Description
1	lineman's side cutting pliers	7″ insulated
1	long nose pliers	6″
1	oblique cutting pliers	6″
1	anvil	100 or 150 lbs., ½″ steel face
1	blacksmith's sledge	4 lbs., cross peen
1	machinist's vise	6″ jaws
1	blacksmith's hammer	2½ pounds
3	cold chisels	½″, ⅝″, ¾″
1	hack saw frame	adjustable 8″ to 12″
2	files	10″, mill bastard
1	drill press vise	2¾″ x 7¼″
1	electric soldering iron	200 to 300 watts
1	tinner's snips	combination 13″, 3″ cut
1	starter punch	½″ body, 3/16″ point
1	wheel and gear puller	medium duty, interchangeable jaws
1	socket wrench set ½″ drive	12 point, 17 sockets ⅜″ to 1¼″ with 7 attachments
1 set	combination box and open-end wrenches	12 sizes, ⅜″ to 1¼″
1 set	Allen wrenches	set, sizes 3/16″ to ¾″
2	"vise-grip" type wrenches	7″ and 10″
1	slip joint plier	10″
1	lever grease gun	1 lb. capacity, high pressure

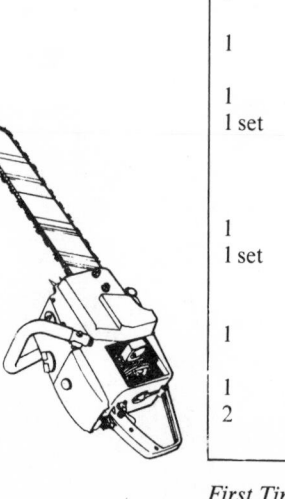

Number	*Name of Tool*	*Description*
1	piston type oil can	½ pt.
1	spark plug socket set	½″ to ⅞″ by 16ths
1	water pump pliers	capacity 3/16″ to 1⅝″
1	first aid kit	bandages, gauze "Bandaids," adhesives, antiseptic, burn dressing, scissors, tweezers
1	fire extinguisher	Foam — 2½ gallons (will freeze)
1	shop broom	4″ x 18″ head, stiff bristle

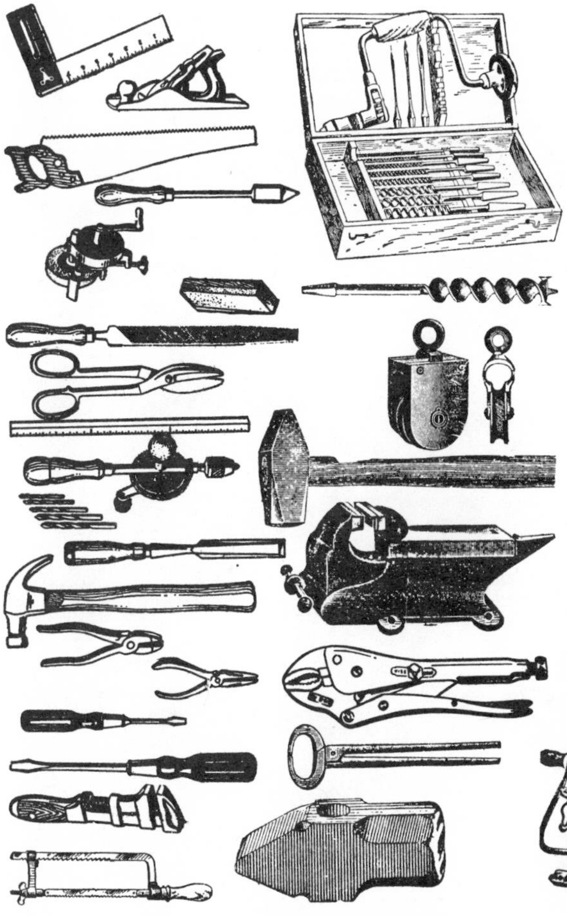

Sharp tools require less labor—an old fashioned pedal-grinding wheel is a must for a well-operated first-time farm.

THE
"CYCLONE"
TRADE MARK REG.
SEED SOWER

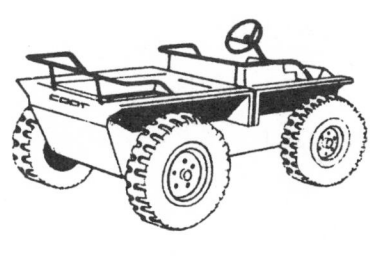

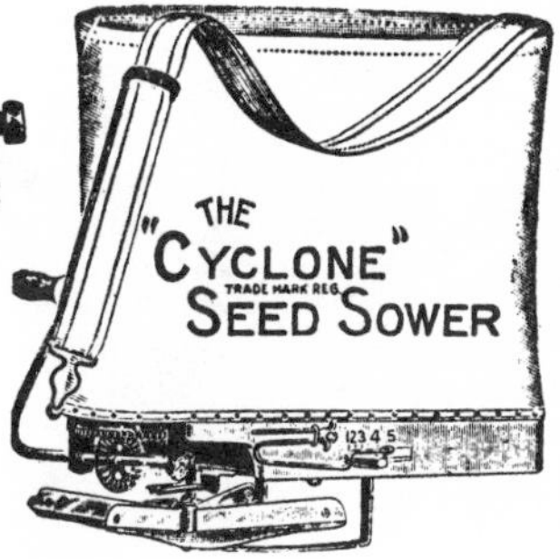

Tilling the Soil

'We can recreate Soil wherever good soil
formerly existed' — *E. H. Faulkner*

The most traditional way of showing a farmer at work is to show him with his plow. Plowing the soil preparatory to planting is a mistake that farmers have been making for many centuries. Mistake? Yes, mistake, and here is some proof based on observations that you can make yourself at any time. Travel (preferably by foot or bicycle) to the nearest field, meadow, wood or forest . . . a natural one of course. Now sit down on the ground and think about what you see. In the field and meadow tall grass is growing. In the wood or forest stand magnificent trees. Nature planted all these wonderful growing things and *she surely didn't use a plow.*

One of the most graphic examples of this is demonstrated every year in the wilderness behind Santa Barbara. There, in a region not far from the beautiful Mono River, are some rolling hills. In the summer these hills are covered with wild oats—some over six feet tall. The author has visited this region many times for many years and, if anything, the oats seem to grow higher each summer and no one has *ever* plowed there!

The No-Plow Theory

This theory is based on a remarkable book titled *Plowman's Folly* by E.H. Faulkner. With permission we are reprinting a review of this book which contains the basic tenets of the theory. This review was originally published in 'Wood Heat Quarterly,' a most admirable, spiritually oriented 'back-to-the-land' publication. For a sample copy of this valuable magazine, send a dollar to Lowther Press, RD 1, Wolcott, Vermont 05680.

Plowman's Folly is a revelation. No one who wants to work positively and harmoniously with the land should be without it. In the author's words:

'Briefly this book sets out to show that the mold-

board plow . . . is the least satisfactory implement for the preparation of land for the production of crops . . . The truth is that no one has ever advanced a scientific reason for plowing. Mr. Faulkner clearly demonstrates with evidence he gained from his own almost life-long experiments that plowing is the first mistake farmers make, and that nearly all other activities after that are an effort to remedy the first error, for plowing is contrary to the laws of nature. He points out that our endeavors should be undertaken with 'a field where the plow has not disturbed the soil' for in these areas vegetation thrives. "This evidence that trouble stops where the plow stops, has been almost universally overlooked."

The damaging effects of plowing are as follows: Plowing turns the surface soil and vegetation upside-down and buries this vital organic matter out of reach of the plant roots. This rotting organic matter forms a layer which, because of its highly absorbent quality, acts as a barrier to capillary water rising from below; thus depriving the crops of a steady supply of water. Plowing loosens the soil which, besides stopping the capillary action of water (the soil must be tightly packed for capillarity to take place), allows air to enter the soil which dries it out still further. Because the spongy organic matter is buried, the surface of the soil is left defenseless against rain and wind. Plowed land is particularly subject to erosion and leaching away of vital minerals. Soil that contains only inorganic particles cannot absorb water, so much of it runs off. In contrast, soil that has a large amount of organic matter in its surface pulls water into itself like a blotter.

'Volume for volume organic matter can hold many times as much water as can any kind of soil mineral; for organic matter is chiefly open space internally . . .' Plow-

First Time Farmer's Guide

Opposite: Plowing
has created dust
bowls; there were no
dust bowls until the
plow

ing buries weed seed where, in the future, it can sprout, thus making weed control an endless problem. In short, plowing causes numerous problems which require expensive and time consuming efforts to solve them. Instead of these practices, Faulkner recommends the use of only one piece of farm equipment: the disk harrow. This he finds the best tool for incorporating organic matter on a large scale with optimum efficiency. His method is to plant a green manure crop, such as rye, and disk it into the surface just before planting; or simply to disk in whatever weeds and grasses may have taken hold on the land to be cultivated. He also invented a special tool called a 'marker.' It is made from two wooden wagon wheels, and its purpose is to restore capillary action at specific points after the disking operation, as in the following:

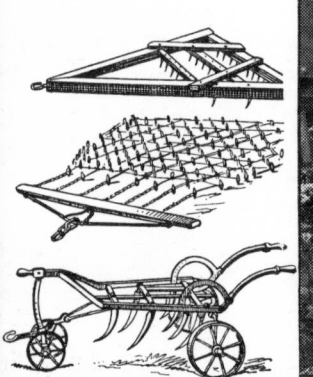

'At the outset, the soil was disked thoroughly in order to destroy whatever vegetation was at that time growing on it. In the spring of 1939, there was little but a scattering stand of weeds. In 1940, rye fully three feet tall—a fair stand all over the surface—had to be disposed of. The disk harrow so completely mixed in even the rye crop that little sign was left of any vegetation cover. Following the mixing in of this decayable material, the land was marked off in rows. To do this marking, a specially designed implement was used which simply 'tramped' over the field—behind the tractor, of course—firming the soil together at points where plants were to be located. By exerting considerable pressure at each such point, this implement reconnected the capillary contacts which the disking had broken up. (To visualize the effect of pressing the soil together again, just recall what would be the effect of snipping the lamp wick above the oil level; then later sewing the pieces together again). The natural wicking action of the soil—destroyed temporarily by the disking—was restored in the vertical column of soil just under the point where a plant was to be set. That this actually was the effect of this pressure we have plenty of evidence. Even though the soil surface was dry and the weather hot in 1939, the bottom of a great many of these 'tracks' showed moist even in the middle of the day. Unless the capillary connection had been restored, this could not possibly have been true.

Transplanting was done in the simplest possible manner. The roots of each tomato plant, after being freed of all clinging soil, were laid in the prepared track, covered with as mellow earth as could be found near by, and firmed in place by tramping. No attempt was made to place the plants upright. That is something that nature will attend to. Thus, the plants were left lying flat on the

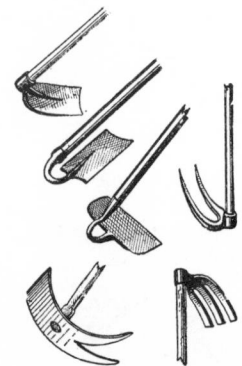

ground; but they did not lie there long. By late afternoon every plant set in the forenoon was pointing its tip toward the sky; by the following morning every plant without exception was standing upright. No water was used in transplanting or afterward. Capillary water already in the soil was brought in from below—through the compressed column of soil beneath the site where the plant stood—and provided a dependable, continuous supply of moisture. No watering that could have been done at transplanting time could possibly have equalled this inherent natural supply. So, instead of going through a wilting period after transplanting, these plants (even though in some cases they were wilted when set), straightened up and never again, regardless of dry weather, showed signs of trouble from lack of water. And, which is additional proof of the validity of the method, blossoms which were on the plants when set often produced fruit. Any experienced gardener will recognize this as unusual.'

In another experiment, Faulkner restored an area of rock-hard clay to productivity by mixing large amounts of rotting leaves into its surface. This process loosened the soil to a fine, granular condition after only one season. He says, *'We can recreate soil wherever good soil formerly existed . . . The satisfying truth is that a man with a team or a tractor and a good disk harrow can mix into the soil, in a matter of hours, sufficient organic matter to accomplish results equal to what is accomplished by nature in decades!'* (our italics).

Faulkner's procedure has numerous practical advantages. Fertilizers are unnecessary. Decaying organic matter produces abundant carbon dioxide which, in combination with water (which is always amply supplied) forms carbonic acid. Carbonic acid is 'the best solvent for plant food minerals'. In the presence of water alone, these minerals dissolve very slowly. Plants are enabled to take all their nitrogen from the air, thus eliminating the need to apply it to the ground. This is accomplished by bacteria that work in the air and eat organic matter. When the organic matter is at the surface where air may reach it, the bacteria have access to the nitrogen in the air and can fix it in the soil.

'Moreover, the nitrogen gathered has no chance to be lost, for the crop roots are present to make use of it as soon as the bacteria die and become part of the decaying mass.'

Faulkner's crops showed little if any damage from insects. He suggests that this may be because the plant sap, in being richer in minerals, is at the same time lower in sugar and that insects are not attracted to these unpalatable plants.

Besides being highly instructive, *Plowman's Folly* is enjoyable to read. Written in clear language that anyone can understand, it is lightly sprinkled with Mr. Faulkner's wit. To get the full details on how to go about crop production the right way, we strongly emphasize that you read this book. It is available in many local libraries or by ordering through a bookstore.

About the author: 'Edward H. Faulkner is an agricultural expert who has carried on his own experiments during recent years. Trained in agriculture at Willamsburg Baptist Institute (now Cumberland College) and at the University of Kentucky, he has been a County Agent in Kentucky and Ohio, a Smith-Hughes teacher of Agriculture, and a soil and crop investigator in private employment. He recently has carried on his experiments in a garden plot and on a farm scale near Elyria, Ohio; his

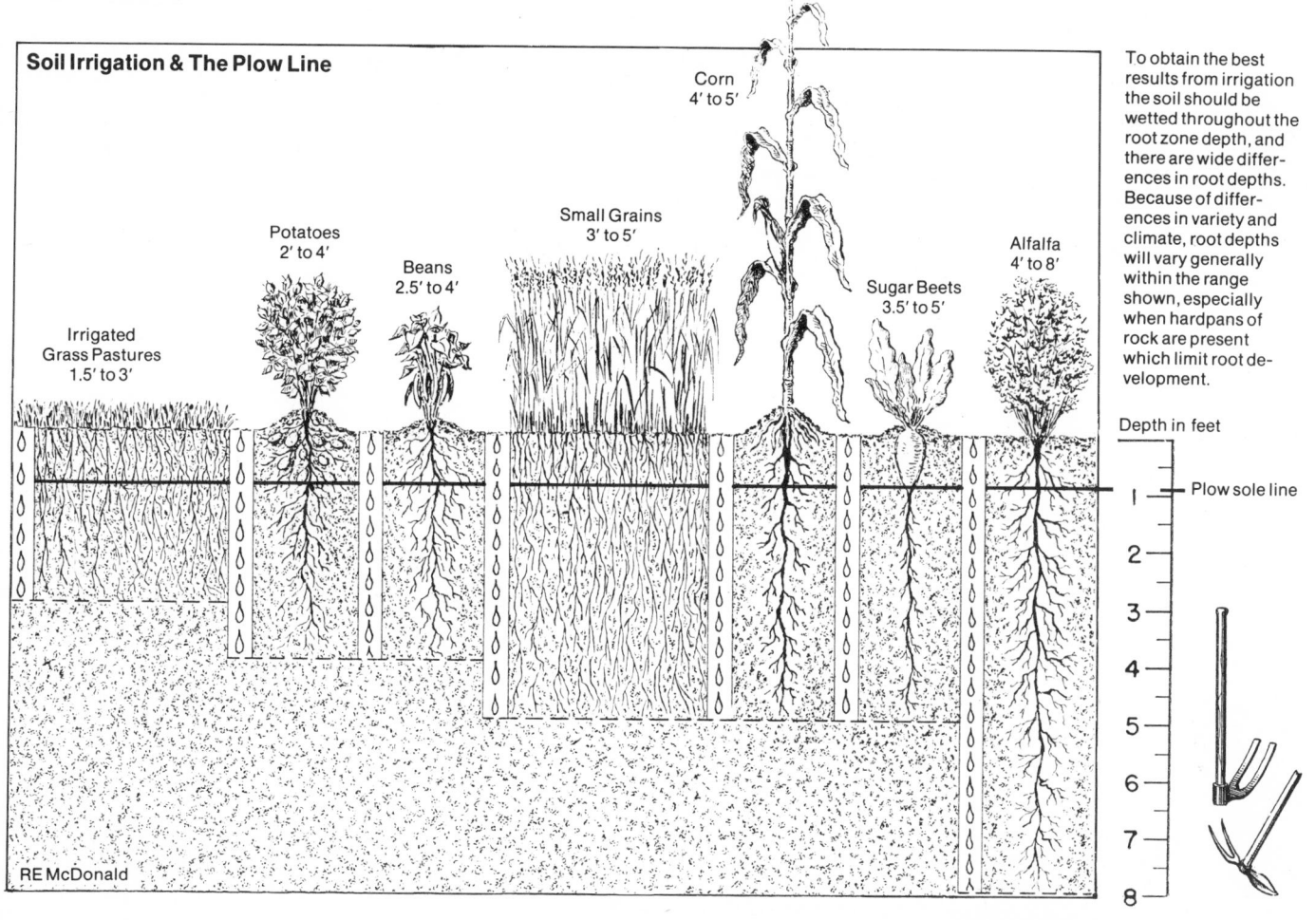

Soil Irrigation & The Plow Line

Corn
4' to 5'

Small Grains
3' to 5'

Potatoes
2' to 4'

Beans
2.5' to 4'

Sugar Beets
3.5' to 5'

Alfalfa
4' to 8'

Irrigated
Grass Pastures
1.5' to 3'

To obtain the best results from irrigation the soil should be wetted throughout the root zone depth, and there are wide differences in root depths. Because of differences in variety and climate, root depths will vary generally within the range shown, especially when hardpans of rock are present which limit root development.

Depth in feet

Plow sole line

1
2
3
4
5
6
7
8

RE McDonald

Opposite: A method
that disturbs the
natural conditions
the least is harrowing

almost unbelievable yields make his experimental plots commercially profitable.'

The Editor of 'Wood Heat Quarterly' comments: 'We have been fortunate to be able to employ Mr. Faulkner's methods on a small scale for two seasons. Both seasons produced surprising results on land that has not been tilled in over forty years, and we are currently reaping the fruits that all can expect by working in cooperation with nature.'

As noted in this review, the *only* piece of equipment suggested is the disk harrow shown here. This equipment can be purchased from a number of sources, including:

John Deere & Company, Moline, Illinois 61265.

Case, Racine, Wisconsin 53404.

Allis Chalmers, 864-57th Street, Milwaukee, Wisconsin 53213.

Often they are available secondhand from farmers who have given up farming, or from farm equipment companies. The sole use of the disk harrow that Faulkner recommends would be to mix in compost where necessary. For example, if the soil you intend to till is hard clay or has been mistreated by inorganic farming methods, then the addition of copious quantities of organic compost would be necessary and the harrow would be the best means of performing this operation. The power needed to pull a disk harrow through your fields is dependent on the number of disks and the condition of your soil. The best way to find out what you need is to check with a farm equipment dealer, a nearby farmer, or simply use the trial and error method.

If you don't have a tractor, there is another way of having your fields harrowed. It is called contract plowing. This means that you simply hire someone who has the equipment to come in and do the work on a per job, per acre or per hour basis. This is a most advantageous method because you don't tie up your capital in heavy equipment that is used once or twice a year at the most. Moreover, the work is done by a professional who knows all of the shortcuts. And you'll be able to devote your time to other more important tasks, such as compost making, livestock tending, or sitting underneath your windmill listening to its rhythmic creaking. If you have visions of driving a tractor and pulling a plow, forget them and join the insiders who know how to farm for real!

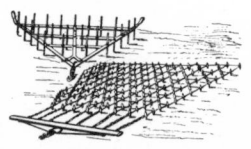

Starting to Grow

'The countryman has a provident and gainful
family, not one whose necessities must be furnished
out of a shop. His provision is always out of his
own stores and agrees with the season of the year.

— *Don De Guevara, The Praise and
Happiness of the Country Life*

Now that you have acquired land, water and seeds, you are ready to embark on the great adventure—seeing whether you, as a first-time farmer, can really combine these three natural elements and grow a living plant. It's not a formidable operation; nature does it all the time without any help whatsoever from first- or even last-time farmers. Trees drop their acorns, winter rains soak the outer hull and soon it splits, permitting the seed kernel to extend leaves up and roots down to create a new oak. Those lush fields of weeds and grass that you see when you drive through the country were, for the most part, self-sown. Seeds of each variety fell from the mother plant. They lay on the ground, vulnerable to field mice and the fowls of the air. If they escaped, then the rains came and the seeds did what comes natural to any seed—they germinated, pushed roots into the soft ground and extended their stems above the dry stalks of their ancestors. And so nature repeats the cycle of birth, growth and death endlessly. Your part in all of this is just to help things along . . . to be a director so to speak of where and how many plants are going to grow.

Beginning Seeds:
Flats, Cold Frames, Hotbeds and Greenhouses

The simplest way to get started is to propagate seeds in what is called a flat. A flat is a wooden box which has been standardized by the people who set gardening standards. It measures 14½ inches wide by 23 inches long and is three inches deep. It can be made of any kind of wood, but cedar, redwood or other long lasting woods are preferred. When filled with soil it resembles a miniature garden, which indeed it is. Flats are available at most nurseries, or if you are handy with a saw and hammer, make your own. If you like, stop by a grocery store or

fruit and vegetable market and pick up some wooden lug boxes. Line these with cardboard, aluminum foil, plastic or any other material to seal up the holes. Then fill with a mixture of seed compost. This is composed of:

one part good top soil, the best you have;
one part of the compost that we told you about;
and one part clean sand.

Mix these ingredients up, making sure that they are fine and free of lumps. Sprinkle the seeds that you wish to start early onto the smoothed surface of your flat. Then cover them with a fine layer of additional seed compost and sprinkle gently by using sufficient water to ensure that the seed bed and the seeds are thoroughly moistened.

You can place this flat in any warm part of the house, maintaining a temperature of about 70° (which you probably will do anyway). Within a few days you will be

First Time Farmer's Guide

greatly encouraged by the sight of tiny green things poking their heads through the fine earth. And that's all there is to it, first-time farmer! You have grown your first plants from scratch without any hassle whatsoever, and nature did 99% of the work for you, which is well and good. There are many variations to this simple sequence. For example, you could create rows in your flat so that each variety of seed would be with its neighbors. If you are starting mostly seeds like beans or squash, you could divide the flat into square sections and poke a seed in the center of each. When the seedlings appear, select the strongest one and remove the rest, giving them to your chickens.

Cold Frames

All of these variations are simply frosting on the initial cake. Once you have started seedlings in a flat, you'll be able to handle any of the other slightly more

Selection of the strongest

complex methods and techniques. For example, if you want to make an early start with a large number of plants, enough to feed your family for example, you may want to build what is called a cold frame. Cold frames are used in many parts of the country to permit plants to grow without danger of being killed by frost. Cold frames also permit you to keep a close control on seedling growth and protect them from marauding dogs, cats and hungry birds, and speed up growth by providing optimum growing conditions. Think of a cold frame as simply a large flat with higher sides and a glass top. You could build one in miniature by simply placing a piece of glass or plastic over the top of that lug-box flat we talked about. This unit would then become a true cold frame. If you want a larger cold frame, here's how to build it.

Because of the glass sash that is used for the cover, cold frames are built to standard size. Cut two boards (redwood or cedar are preferable but ¾" exterior ply will work fine) six feet long, sloping them from about 18 inches at one end to about 8 inches at the other. If you cannot find boards 18 inches wide, then nail two together with cleats. These provide the sides of your cold frame. Next cut two boards, the first 18 inches by three feet and the second 8 inches by three feet. These provide the back and front boards of your cold frame. Nail the four boards together in a rectangle and then top with a standard cold frame sash three feet wide by six feet long. That's all there is to it. If you don't want to invest in a standard cold frame sash, you can make a covering from a large sheet of clear plastic.

To use your cold frame, install it so that it slopes toward the south. Then fill it with the same compost soil that you used for the flat. This cold frame functions by collecting the heat of the sun during the day and holding

First Time Farmer's Guide

it during the night. You can help it out by covering the transparent top with a canvas or cardboard at dusk, removing it in the A.M. The cold frame also preserves the moisture and protects the young seedlings from damage by wind, animals or birds. In some areas cold frames are constructed with a bottom lined with bricks or stones shown here. These are called solar frames and are more efficient because the sun heats the bricks below the planted area and supplies heat during the night.

You can use a cold frame continuously letting the sun provide free heat

Hotbeds

The solar frame is a simplified version of a variation of the cold frame called, appropriately, a hotbed. A hotbed is defined as a cold frame that has been adapted to some form of heating. Many years ago hotbeds were heated by manure. Your farming ancestors learned that manure heats up as it decomposes. They took advantage

The dehydrated peat pellet

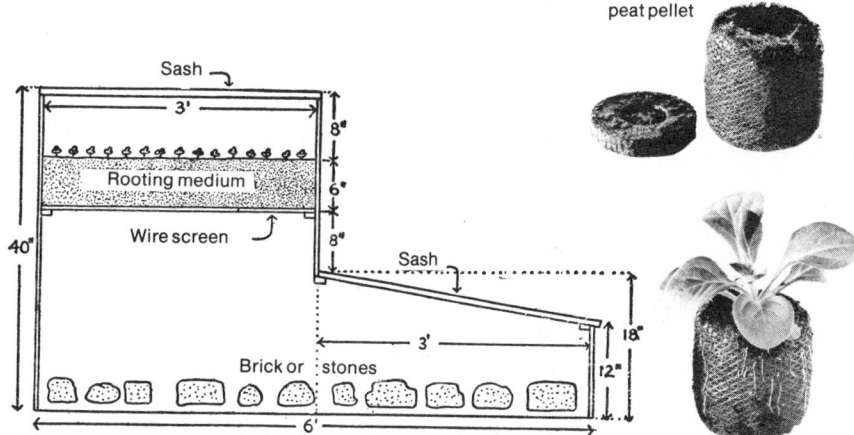

Building a hotbed
from scrap lumber is
an easy project

of this fact by placing a layer of manure under the soil which propagates seedlings. The amount of manure is a matter of trial and error since it depends on the animal from which the manure is obtained, the ambient temperature around your manure-heated hotbed, and the length of time that you require heat. Placing an inexpensive thermometer in the ground that is manure-heated will be a good way to keep tabs on its heating action.

There are several other ways that you can create heat for your early-start hotbed. One lucky small farmer in west central Nevada enjoyed free heat from hot springs over which his house had been built. An unlimited supply of 120° water permitted him to circulate it under a large seedling bed. How's that for the intelligent use of natural resources? Although we'll discuss it in detail in the chapter on alternate power sources for your farm, you might consider using methane gas which

can be generated from farm animal wastes. This gas is almost identical to the gas you have used in your stove for years. It could be piped from its generator to a small burner, which would keep your hotbed hot. As shown in the illustration, some clever gardeners build their hotbeds as an extension of the home, particularly extensions from a cellar where the furnace is located. Thus, the heat from your own living quarters extends into the outdoor hotbed and the temperature can be controlled within narrow limits by opening or shutting a sliding partition. To a died-in-the-wool pioneer type, electrical hotbed heating is downright heresy. However, it is downright easy too. All you have to do is buy a length of heating cable from your local farm, garden or nursery supply. Many companies sell it by mail. It consists of a plug with a heavy duty cable containing a resistance wire which heats when connected. Placed in a bed of clean

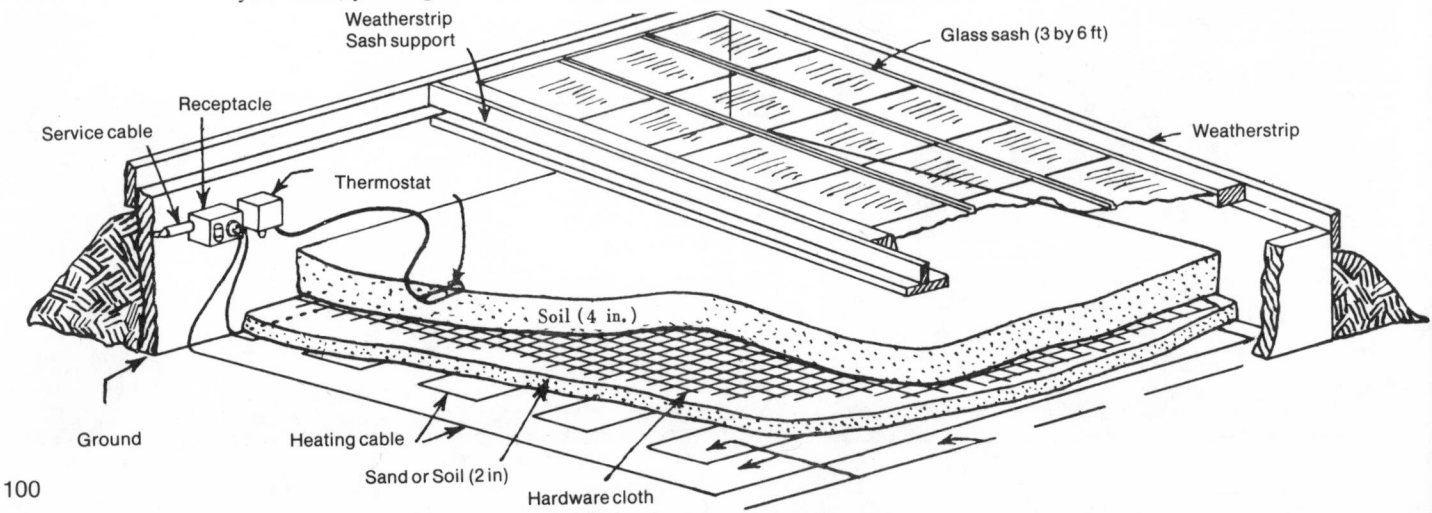

Weatherstrip
Sash support
Glass sash (3 by 6 ft)
Receptacle
Service cable
Weatherstrip
Thermostat
Soil (4 in.)
Ground
Heating cable
Sand or Soil (2 in)
Hardware cloth

sand under the soil in which you plant your seeds, it maintains the proper hotbed temperature by means of a thermostat.

Cold frames and hotbeds are started in the same manner as the simple flat that we first discussed. Here are some of the things that would require your attention when using a cold frame or a hotbed.

An inexpensive thermometer can be placed in the soil to insure that the temperature stays within the proper limits . . . as close to a constant 70° as possible. If the temperature drops, provide more heat by means of a kerosene lamp, several light bulbs, or other convenient means. Of course, if you use the electrical system, the thermostat will take care of the temperature problem. If temperatures exceed the limit, prop the sash open and let in some air. If this doesn't do it, cover the sash to shield the plants from the sun. As the seedlings mature, the sash can be kept partly open at times and finally removed to adapt the plants to the outside environment.

Watering is an art that must be learned by experience. Too little water will let the plants wilt and wither. Therefore watch them closely. Too much water can cause the death of the small seedlings through 'damping off', an ailment brought on by too much moisture. Thus, you should water the plants gently with a sprinkling can and *only enough* to keep them thriving. Judgment will come with experience.

Cold frames and hotbeds can be used to start all of your plants, although they are usually used only for those that require a good head start. Tomatoes, peppers, melons, and cabbage are typical of those plants that will do best by coming to life under controlled conditions. However, if the area in which you are going to farm stays cold until well into the growing season, build lots of hotbeds and start all of your plants under glass.

Greenhouses

If you live in a North Pole-type climate then consider building one or more greenhouses. A greenhouse may be defined as a giant hotbed . . . one big enough to walk around in and do your gardening work. With the advent of low cost transparent plastic film, it has become possible to build large greenhouses for relatively little money compared to the old-fashioned glass type. Greenhouses can be built to any size you wish from a small lean-to, which uses the side of your house for one wall, to a giant measuring twenty by forty feet or twice the size of a double garage.

Greenhouses are built by erecting a frame similar to that of a conventional house. Then the entire structure is covered with polyethylene film. There is a big catch in

The old-fashioned glass greenhouse that invited rock-throwers has been displaced by the modern, low-cost poly-film unit. (You may not love plastics, but here's one place where it can be quite useful)

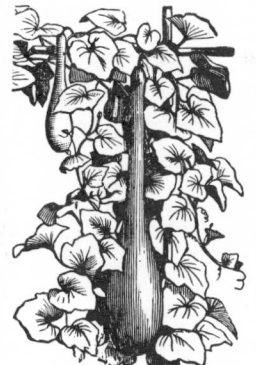

greenhouses and that is they must be heated where climates are very cold. Recently a breakthrough in greenhouse design permitted a substantial reduction in the amount of fuel needed to keep the temperature to the desired level. This method involves using two layers of film separated by a cushion of air. The air is pumped into the space between two films and maintained there by a small electrically-driven blower. In addition to fuel savings, the double thickness film helps the snow to slide off quickly. The originators state that once you have tried a double film greenhouse, you'll never go back to conventional covering. For more information, write to Dr. Ray Sheldrake, Jr, a professor at Cornell University, Ithaca, NY. An article concerning this method was published in the January, 1971 issue of 'The American Vegetable Grower' (37841 Euclid Avenue, Willoughby, Ohio 44094).

No matter how your plants are started, whether in little flats indoors, cold frames, hotbeds or greenhouses, you'll need to know how to transplant them to the open garden. Here are some guidelines to enable you to perform this simple but important first-time farming task. When removing the seedling from its original home, take as much soil with it as possible. A small trowel, putty knife or old table knife make good tools to do this. Where plants have been grown in rows or squares, divide up the space between them equally . . . in other words cut them as you would a square pan of brownies or fudge.

Stretch a string to the length of the planned row to make it easy to set the plants in an orderly fashion. A stick cut to the length desired between plants, can be used to measure the distance apart. Remember, leave plenty of room between plants so that they can all develop to their maximum growth. Crowding them because your garden is rather small is not advisable. It's better to

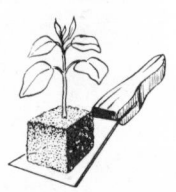

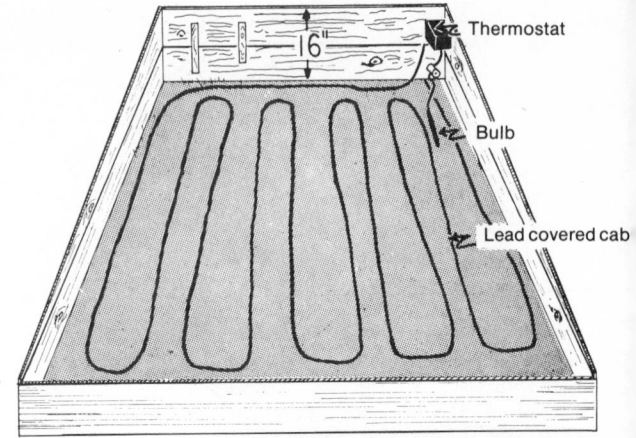

102   *First Time Farmer's Guide*

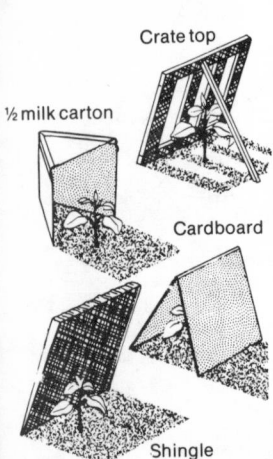

WATER

½ milk carton

Crate top

Cardboard

Shingle

have one melon vine producing lots of big melons than two scrawny ones producing much less because of their competition for nutrients, water and sun.

Dig a hole large enough to receive the root ball with some left over to add loose soil all around the new transplant. If soil is dry when you plant, fill the planting hole with water.

If the plant will need support, as tomatoes and peppers do, put in the stick when you plant it. Then you won't hurt the roots later. Then add plenty of water to settle the plant into its new home and, finally, add a protective mulch of straw, sawdust or similar mulch materials.

Your seedlings will look mighty lonesome and vulnerable in that big garden and that's exactly what they are. To keep them from being cooked by the sun, gobbled by the bugs, blown over by the wind, mashed by dogs

and cats or eaten alive by hostile birds, create some shelter for them. Many seed catalogs list tiny houses made from paper or plastic. They go by various trade names, such as Hotcaps, Hotents and Titantents.

After taking all that time to germinate the seed, helping it through its first weeks in the earth and making the effort necessary to transplant it, it's well worthwhile to give it the protection it needs from late frosts, heavy rains and all of the other plant enemies we mentioned previously. In quantities of 100, a typical protective cover would cost about 10¢ each . . . inexpensive insurance to guarantee that a tomato plant, for example, will produce three or four dollars or more worth of tomatoes. If you do not want to invest in commercial plant protectors, start saving your milk cartons and similar containers. A quart milk carton cut through the middle will make two fine hothouses for your young peppers or cabbage. You can

use your ingenuity to make protective housing for your new plants. Scraps of cloth supported by twigs, branches of heavy brush, two shingles or pieces of cardboard make a fine tent, and old window screens, fishnet or burlap could all give the protection needed to let the plant progress to its next stage of development.

Your Vegetable Garden

As an ex-urbanite, first-time farmer your efforts to grow vegetables will probably be 'for real'. You will want to be successful the first time out because the vegetables you grow will be those you'll use for family meals throughout the year. Before you plant even one carrot seed, you'll need a solid, practical, workable plan. Intelligent planning of your vegetable garden involves several important considerations such as:

What and when to grow; the size and location of

The productive, diversified, vegetable garden

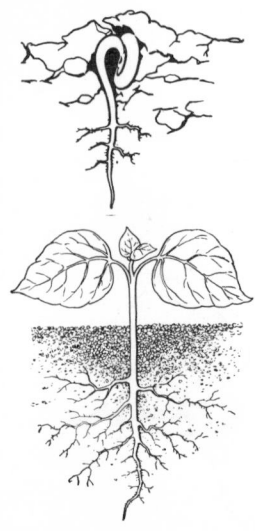

your garden; expected yields; planting procedures; mulching, irrigation, and the harvesting.

A productive diversified vegetable garden is the real key to rural independence. While it is important to keep livestock, food animals require as much as ten times the land needed for a nutritionally equivalent supply of vegetables and small fruits. A nutritional survey which covered representative households in five income groups revealed that 95% of the people surveyed consumed protein at or above recommended levels. On the other hand, nutrients most likely to be below recommended levels were vitamin A and vitamin C . . . all readily available from vegetable sources.

The conclusion was drawn that many Americans rely too easily on meat as a protein source. In addition, this reliance is expensive because one dollar out of every three spent for food in America is spent on meat, whereas only one out of five goes for vegetables and fruits.

The average household, urban or suburban, could save as much as fifty percent on its food bill provided the home garden supplied vegetables and fruits. Even more important, this saving could occur at the same time that the imbalance between protein surplus and vitamin deficiency could be corrected.

'Garden Ways Research', which has provided much of this information, points out that by relying on vegetables for the major source of protein and other food value, meat could be relegated to a far less prominent position in the family diet. Beans and peas, which are easy to grow, provide excellent vegetable proteins. A plan suggests itself in which meat would be used mainly for its flavor value. For example, a little beef can go a long way to give flavor to a big steaming kettle of pinto beans, viz., chili con carne with beans. A big soup bone

with some scraps of meat adhering can flavor a fine stew or soup of fresh vegetables. Milk, eggs and cheese could then fulfill the remaining animal protein requirements while legumes, nuts and grains could provide the bulk of the over-all daily protein requirement.

Here's a good example of what we've been discussing. A hard working farmer can receive one third of his daily protein requirement (23 grams) from only a few cents worth of pinto beans which can be grown in any home garden. The cost of the same amount of protein in the form of pork roast purchased in a market would be 20 times greater. While prices may change, the relationship would stay about the same.

It's been well established that vegetables lose much of their food value and flavor after they are picked. Thus, if there were no other reason for a garden and even if it cost more than buying vegetables in a market, you would

First Time Farmer's Guide

still come out ahead by enjoying fine flavors of fresh-picked vegetables plus benefiting from the higher vitamin and mineral content of home grown produce. The feeling of satisfaction and security that you will get from growing your own foods is truly priceless. As you walk between the rows of chunky carrots, big, green leafy cabbage and bright red strawberries, you will be able to appreciate the real significance of the poem we've used to start this book which ends 'Kings can do no more.'

When and Where to Grow

When to plant is almost as important as what to plant since timing is a corollary of success in gardening. You'll naturally want to start each vegetable as early in the season as you can without having it damaged by cold weather. No matter where you live in the United States, you can determine when to plant any crop by using the

Earthworms—your most valuable ally

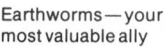

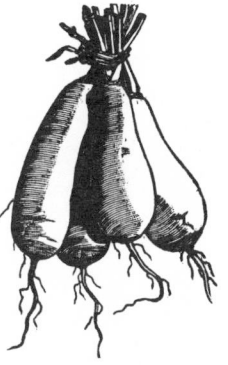

Starting to Grow   107

Doughty medieval
farmer about to clout
his wife for nagging
him about planting too
early. Note the saint
about to intercede.

the map and the table which follows. The map*, provided by the US Weather Bureau, shows the dates of the last expected frost in spring. From these dates, planting times can be determined by using the table. For example, if you live in the region around San Francisco Bay, the last time that frost may kill a planting is between January 30th and February 8th, (based on an average from studies of temperature in that region for more than 40 years). The first frost could be November 30. By referring to the table, you will find that the latest date that it's safe to plant a 'cool-weather' crop such as lettuce would be in the range of late September 1 to December 1. A hearty plant like turnips could be planted as late as November 15.

As you use the map and table   remember that you must time your plantings to escape not only cold but with certain delicate crops, to escape the heat of the later season. Thus, rather than sew your heat-sensitive plants too early (leafy vegetables that could be scorched), plant them in late spring so that their maximum development would occur in the cooler weather of late summer or early fall. Another consideration is that some hardy plants may be sewn in late fall (six to eight weeks before the first fall freeze), so that their basic development will take place before it becomes too cold.

Remember that the information presented in this map and table is very general. Use it with plenty of common sense. For example, if you're still wearing your long underwear every day and your pussycat refuses to go outdoors because of the snow on the ground, forget the fact that the table says it's OK to plant sweet potatoes. Throw another log on the fire and start your sweet potatoes in a flat of damp sand over the stove.

There's evidence that
the phases of the moon
affect planting. Consult
your local astrologer.

* *Further map & table guides available in Bulletin No. 9, from the USDA*

In summary, take everything that you read with lots of grains of salt, including everything you read in this chapter. As the title of the book indicates, all of this is just a *guide*.

First Time Farmer's Guide

Last Expected Date of Spring Frosts

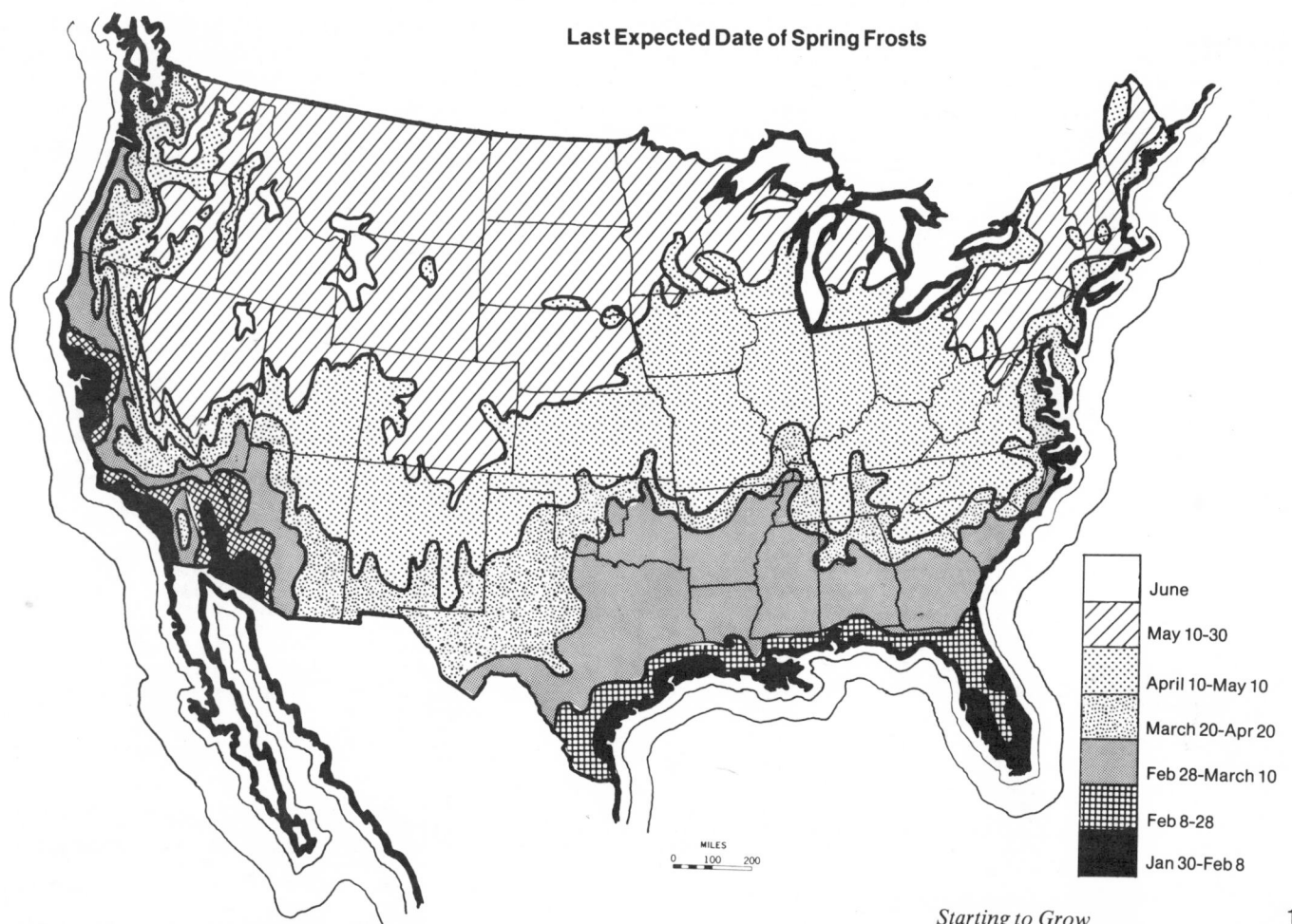

Legend:
- June
- May 10-30
- April 10-May 10
- March 20-Apr 20
- Feb 28-March 10
- Feb 8-28
- Jan 30-Feb 8

MILES
0 100 200

The Frost Planting Table

Planting dates for localities in which average dates of first freeze is —

Crop	Aug. 30	Sept. 10	Sept. 20	Sept. 30	Oct. 10	Oct. 30	Nov. 10	Nov. 30	Dec. 10	Dec. 20
Asparagus[1]					10.20-11.15	11.15-1.1	12.1-1.1			
Beans, Lima				6.1-15	6.1-15	7.1-8.1	7.1-8.15	8.1-9.15	9.1-30	9.1-10.1
Bean, snap		5.15-6.15	6.1-7.1	6.1-7.10	6.15-7.20	7.1-8.15	7.1-9.1	8.15-9.20	do	9.1-11.1
Beet	5.15-6.15	do	do	do	6.15-7.25	8.1-9.1	8.1-10.1	9.1-12.15	9.1-12.31	9.1-12.31
Broccoli, sprouting	5.1-6.1	5.1-6.1	5.1-6.15	6.1-30	6.15-7.15	7.1-8.15	8.1-9.1	8.1-10.1	8.1-11.1	Do.
Brussels sprouts	do	do	do	do	do	do	do	do	do	Do.
Cabbage[1]	do	do	do	6.1-7.10	6.1-7.15	8.1-9.1	9.1-15	9.1-12.31	9.1-12.31	Do.
Cabbage, Chinese	5.15-6.15	5.15-6.15	6.1-7.1	6.1-6.15	6.15-8.1	8.1-9.15	8.15-10.1	9.1-11.1	9.1-11.15	9.1-12.1
Carrot	do	do	do	6.1-7.10	6.1-7.20	7.1-8.15	8.1-9.1	9.15-12.1	9.15-12.1	9.15-12.1
Cauliflower[1]	5.1-6.1	5.1-7.1	5.1-7.1	5.10-7.15	6.1-7.15	7.15-8.15	do	8.15-10.10	9.1-10.20	9.15-11.1
Celery[1] and celeriac		5.15-6.15	5.15-7.1	6.1-7.5	6.1-7.15	6.15-8.15	7.1-8.15	8.1-12.1	9.1-12.31	10.1-12.31
Chard	5.15-6.15	5.15-7.1	6.1-7.1	do	6.1-7.20	6.1-9.10	6.1-9.15	6.1-11.1	6.1-12.1	6.1-12.31
Chervil and chives	5.10-6.10	5.1-6.15	5.15-6.15	(2)	(2)	(2)	(2)	11.1-12.31	11.1-12.31	11.1-12.31
Chicory, witloof	5.15-6.15	5.15-6.15	do	6.1-7.1	6.1-7.1	7.1-8.10	7.10-8.20	8.15-9.30	8.15-10.15	8.15.10.15
Collards[1]	do	do	do	6.15-7.15	7.1-8.1	8.1-9.15	8.15-10.1	9.1-12.1	9.1-12.31	9.1-12.31
Cornsalad	do	5.15-7.1	6.15-8.1	7.15-9.1	8.15-9.15	9.15-11.1	10.1-12.1	10.1-12.31	10.1-12.31	10.1-12.31
Corn, sweet			6.1-7.1	6.1-7.1	6.1-7.10	6.1-8.1	6.1-8.15			
Cress, upland	5.15-6.15	5.15-7.1	6.15-8.1	7.15-9.1	8.15-9.15	9.15-11.1	10.1-12.1	10.1-12.31	10.1-12.31	10.1-12.31
Cucumber			6.1-15	6.1-7.1	6.1-7.1	6.1-8.1	6.1-8.15	7.15-9.15	8.15-10.1	8.15-10.1
Dandelion	6.1-15	6.1-7.1	6.1-7.1	6.1-8.1	7.15-9.1	8.15-10.1	9.1-10.15	9.15-12.15	10.1-12.31	10.1-12.31
Eggplant[1]				5.20-6.20	5.15-6.15	6.1-7.1	6.1-7.15	7.1-9.1	8.1-9.30	8.1-9.30
Endive	6.1-7.1	6.1-7.1	6.15-7.15	6.15-8.1	7.1-8.15	7.15-8.15	8.1-9.1	9.1-11.15	9.1-12.31	9.1-12.31
Fennel, Florence	5.15-6.15	5.15-7.15	6.1-7.1	6.1-7.1	6.15-7.15	7.1-8.1	7.15-8.15	do	9.1-12.1	9.1-12.1
Garlic	(2)	(2)	(2)	(2)	(2)	(2)	8.1-10.1	do	9.15-11.15	9.15-11.15
Horseradish[1]	(2)	(2)	(2)	(2)	(2)	(2)	(2)	(2)	(2)	(2)
Kale	5.15-6.15	5.15-6.15	6.1-7.1	6.15-7.15	7.1-8.1	7.15-9.1	8.1-9.15	9.1-12.1	9.15-12.31	9.15-12.31
Kohlrabi	do	6.1-7.1	6.1-7.15	do	do	8.1-9.1	8.15-9.15	do	9.15-12.31	Do.
Leek	5.1-6.1	5.1-6.1	(2)	(2)	(2)	(2)	(2)	9.1-11.1	9.1-11.1	9.15-11.1
Lettuce, head[1]	5.15-7.1	5.15-7.1	6.1-7.15	6.15-8.1	7.15-8.15	8.1-9.15	8.15-10.15	9.1-12.1	9.15-12.31	9.15-12.31
Lettuce, leaf	5.15-7.15	5.15-7.15	6.1-8.1	6.1-8.1	7.15-9.1	8.15-10.1	8.25-10.1	do	do	Do.
Muskmelon			5.1-6.15	5.15-6.1	6.1-6.15	7.1-7.15	7.15-7.30			
Mustard	5.15-7.15	5.15-7.15	6.1-8.1	7.15-8.15	8.1-9.1		8.15-11.1	9.1-12.1	9.1-12.1	9.15-12.1
Okra			6.1-20	6.1-7.1	6.1-7.15	6.1-8.10	6.1-8.20	6.1-9.20	8.1-10.1	8.1-10.1

First Time Farmer's Guide

	Aug. 30	Sept. 10	Sept. 20	Sept. 30	Oct. 10	Oct. 30	Nov. 10	Nov. 30	Dec. 10	Dec. 20
Onion[1]	5.1-6.10	5.1-6.10	(2)	(2)	(2)		9.1-10.15	10.1-12.31	10.1-12.31	10.1-12.31
Onion, seed	5.1-6.1	do	(2)	(2)	(2)			9.1-11.1	9.1-11.1	9.15-11.1
Parsley	5.15-6.15	5.1-6.15	6.1-7.1	6.1-7.15	6.15-8.1	8.1-9.15	9.1-11.15	9.1-12.31	9.15-12.31	9.1-12.31
Parsnip	5.15-6.1	do	5.15-6.15	6.1-7.1	6.1-7.10	(2)	(2)	9.1-11.15	9.1-12.1	9.1-12.1
Peas, garden	5.10-6.15	5.1-7.1	6.1-7.15	6.1-8.1	(2)	8.1-9.15	9.1-11.1	10.1-12.31	10.1-12.31	10.1-12.31
Peas, black-eye					6.1-7.1	6.1-8.1	6.15-8.15	7.1-9.10	7.1-9.20	7.1-9.20
Pepper[1]			6.1-6.20	6.1-7.1	do	6.1-7.20	6.1-8.1	6.15-9.1	8.1-9.15	8.1-9.15
Potato	5.15-6.1	5.1-6.15	5.1-6.15	5.1-6.15	5.15-6.15	7.20-8.10	7.25-8.20	8.1-9.15	8.1-9.15	8.1-9.15
Radish	5.1-7.15	5.1-8.1	6.1-8.15	7.1-9.1	7.15-9.15	8.15-10.15	9.1-11.15	9.1-12.31	do	10.1-12.31
Rhubarb[1]	9.1-10.1	9.15-10.15	9.15-11.1	10.1-11.1	10.15-11.15	11.1-12.1				
Rutabaga	5.15-6.15	5.1-6.15	6.1-7.1	6.1-7.1	6.15-7.15	7.15-8.1	7.15-8.15	9.1-11.15	10.1-11.15	10.15-11.15
Salsify	5.15-6.1	5.10-6.10	5.20-6.20	6.1-20	6.1-7.1	6.1-7.10	6.15-7.20	8.15-9.30	8.15-10.15	
Shallot	(2)	(2)	(2)	(2)	(2)	(2)	8.1-10.1	8.15-10.15	9.15-11.1	9.15-11.1
Sorrel	5.15-6.15	5.1-6.15	6.1-7.1	6.1-7.15	7.1-8.1	8.1-9.15	8.15-10.1	9.1-11.15	9.1-12.15	9.1-12.31
Soybean				5.25-6.10	6.1-25	6.1-7.15	6.1-7.25	6.1-7.30	6.1-7.30	6.1-7.30
Spinach	5.15-7.1	6.1-7.15	6.1-8.1	7.1-8.15	8.1-9.1	9.1-10.1	9.15-11.1	10.1-12.31	10.1-12.31	10.1-12.31
Spinach, New Zealand				5.15-7.1	6.1-7.15	6.1-8.1	6.1-8.15			
Squash, summer	6.10-20	6.1-20	5.15-7.1	6.1-7.1	do	do	6.1-8.10	6.1-9.1	6.1-9.15	6.1-10.1
Squash, winter			5.20-6.10	6.1-15	6.1-7.1	6.10-7.10	6.20-7.20	7.15-8.15	8.1-9.1	8.1-9.1
Sweetpotato					5.20-6.10	6.1-15	6.1-7.1	6.1-7.1	6.1-7.1	6.1-7.1
Tomato	6.20-30	6.10-20	6.1-20	6.1-20	6.1-20	6.1-7.1	6.1-7.15	8.1-9.1	8.15-10.1	9.1-11.1
Turnip	5.15-6.15	6.1-7.1	6.1-7.15	6.1-8.1	7.1-8.1	8.1-9.15	9.1-10.15	9.1-11.15	10.1-12.1	10.1-12.31
Watermelon			5.1-6.15	5.15-6.1	6.1-6.15	7.1-7.15	7.15-7.30			

1. Plants
(2) Generally spring planted
NB: 5.15-6.15 means May 15-June 15.

160 by 270 feet. The short dimension is on the road to keep down the road frontage chargeable to the plot and to producing a good ratio between width and length. Climatic conditions are assumed to be the same as in the New York metropolitan region. The major ground areas are obviously interrelated and located so that one will be convenient to the other and to the buildings. Fruit trees are shown in rows along the whole northwest side of the plot, so as not to shade the vegetable garden and to offer some protection to it. They are dwarf varieties. The two large trees next to the main road might be nut trees. The space beyond a narrow lawn space at the rear of the house is devoted to flowers, berries and grapes.

The 15 x 60 foot plot, divided in two for convenient rotation of crops. A good orderly size for a beginner.

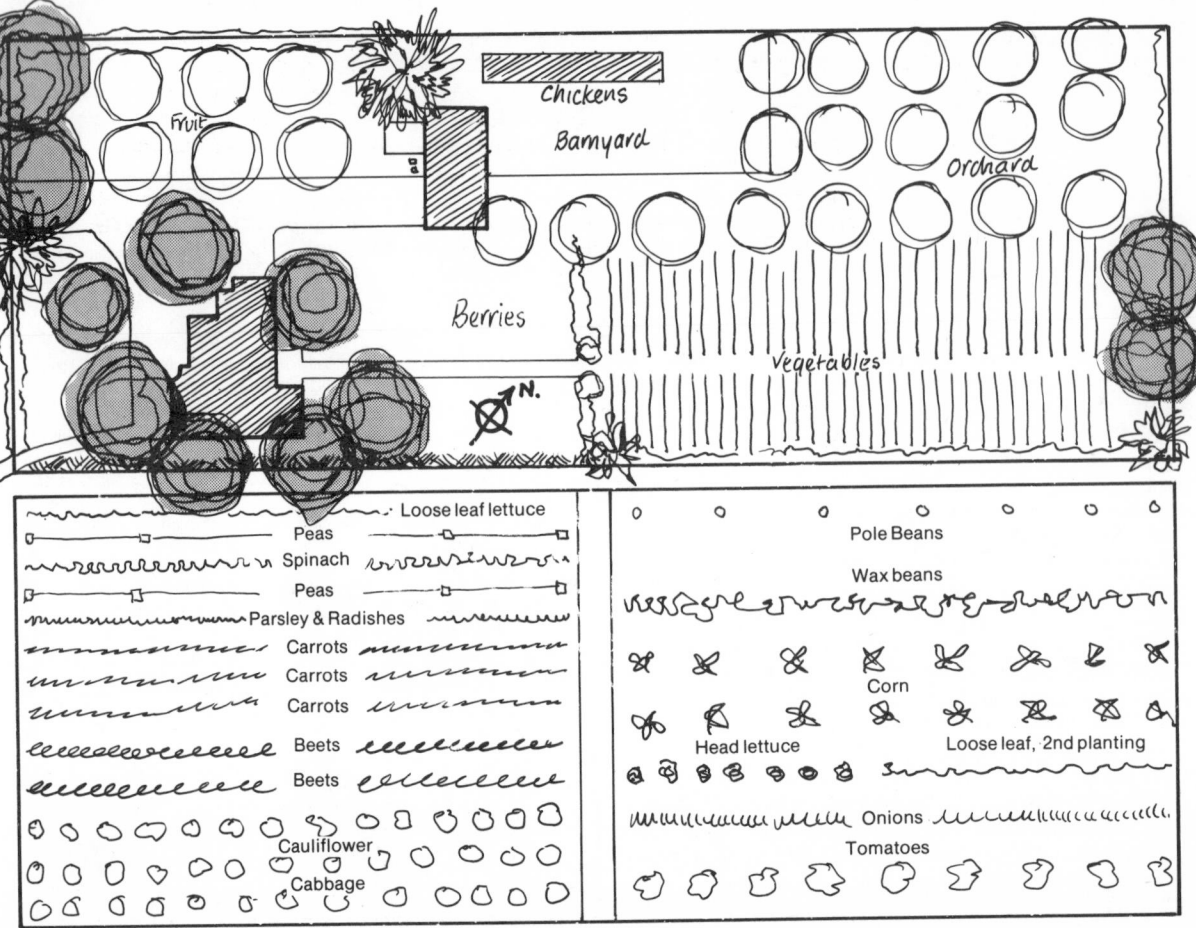

Fruit

Chickens

Barnyard

Orchard

Berries

Vegetables

N.

Loose leaf lettuce
Peas
Spinach
Peas
Parsley & Radishes
Carrots
Carrots
Carrots
Beets
Beets
Cauliflower
Cabbage

Pole Beans
Wax beans
Corn
Head lettuce
Loose leaf, 2nd planting
Onions
Tomatoes

112   *First Time Farmer's Guide*

To simplify the discussion of garden size, we have chosen the arbitrary dimension of 15 x 60 feet. Here is the suggested layout for this basic garden. Obviously you may choose to grow a larger first-time garden or one smaller. However, this size will give you plenty of food for a family of four, along with plenty of experience. The amount of food that you grow from this 1,000 square foot garden, and how you and your family like the various vegetables produced, will determine the size and varieties for the following year.

Choosing a suitable location for your first garden attempts depends on several variables. Here are the important ones:

It should be convenient to your farm house. Many of your vegetables will be picked on a daily basis. This is particularly true of salad vegetables such as lettuce, romaine, tomatoes, etc. There's no question that vegetables taste best when they are freshly picked. Therefore, there is good reason to place your home garden supply within a short distance of your kitchen. Even if the soil in this location is not the best, you can improve it with compost.

There is a truism about vegetables: as soon as they stop growing, they lose much of their goodness. That's why sunlight is such a vital factor. Avoid planting under or near large trees, shrubs or near your house or other farm buildings where there is the possibility that they will shade any part of your vegetable garden.

Equally as important is the handiness of an adequate water supply.

Your garden should be planted on level or slightly sloping ground. Make sure that it is not planted in a depression where water might accumulate after a heavy rain.

If your new farmstead is in primitive country, plan on protecting the plants from eating attacks by hungry rabbits, groundhogs, deer and other vegetable-loving animals. If you live in a region where there are more people than porcupines, make some provision to protect your garden from neighbors, children, chickens or dogs. A simple wire fence can serve in both cases. If animals continue to be a problem, try trapping them. A firm called Havahart, Box 551, Ossining, NY 10562 sells traps that will catch the animal unhurt. What you do with them from then on is a matter of your own conscience.

If all of the requirements for a vegetable garden are met, with the exception of the soil, don't be too concerned. First of all, no matter what kind of soil you have, it can be improved by adding compost. Secondly, if you feel the soil is truly hopeless—impenetrable clay, for example—then consider the method of growing vegetables with prepared soil in raised beds.

With these traps it is now possible for the first-time farmer to eliminate pests from his property without harming pets. He can simply transport the animals to a place where they can do no harm, and does not have to kill them.

As food prices soar and your patience diminishes, remember the dollar values at the bottom of this table

*1973: Inflation *did* go wild so just double (at least) the prices shown in the table. . . . All the more reason to grow your own goodies.

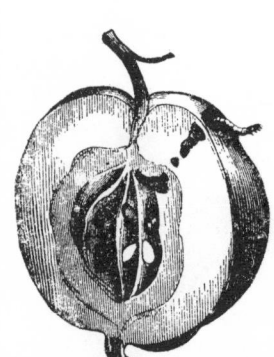

Estimated Value of 1 Acre Vegetable Garden*					
Vegetable	No. of 100 ft. rows	Yield per 1/ 100-ft. row	Total Yields	Unit 2/ Price	Wholesale Value
Asparagus	8	50#	400#	.20	$ 80.00
Beets	4	50#	280#	.09	25.20
Broccoli	4	50#	200#	.17	34.00
Cabbage	8	135#	1,080#	.04	43.20
Cauliflower	4	120#	480#	.12	57.60
Collards	4	75#	300#	.05	15.00
Sweet Corn	12	85#	1,020#	.10	102.00
Cucumber	4	180#	720#	.05	36.00
Green Pea (pods)	8	20#	160#	.14	22.40
Kale	4	75#	300#	.07	21.00
Lettuce	4	50(hds)	200(hds)	.10	20.00
Lima Beans	8	25#	200#	.12	24.00
Muskmelon	4	150#	600#	.11	66.00
Onions	8	75#	600#	.08	48.00
Pepper	4	70#	280#	.13	36.40
Potatoes	12	150#	1,800#	.04	72.00
Pumpkin	4	300#	1,200#	.03	36.00
Radish	4	45(bun)	180(bun)	.05	9.00
Snap Bean	8	30#	240#	.13	31.20
Spinach	4	40#	160#	.05	8.00
Squash	4	160#	640#	.04	25.60
Sweetpotato	8	100#	800#	.09	72.00
Tomato (staked)	8	160#	1,280#	.10	128.00
Turnip	4	65#	260#	.06	15.60
Watermelon	4	200#	800#	.04	32.00
TOTALS	148				1,060.30
Retail Value					1,378.26

The following table will give you some idea of the value of a one-acre vegetable garden in terms of dollars and cents as we got to press. If inflation goes wild, *you can adjust accordingly, but this will give you a starting point from which you can calculate the value of your efforts. The second table shows the value of some of the more expensive vegetables and small fruits. Note that on both tables tomatoes, asparagus and sweet corn yield a very high dollar value for time and garden space invested. Of course, as a first-time farmer, the dollar value of things will become secondary to your preferences in vegetables. However, if you are a lover of expensive vegetables and small fruits, these tables prove conclusively that you'll be very happy with your own garden.

Planting Procedures — Irrigation, Mulching & Harvesting

Preparing the soil for your vegetable garden has already been covered in a fundamental way in the chapters on soil and tilling. However, there are some pointers to make your vegetable garden both productive and neat in appearance.

Irrigate the soil to be planted until it is well watered without being muddy.

Cut a piece of string 50 feet long and tie each end to a stake. This simple device allows you to not only measure rows in units of 50 feet but plant in straight lines. Place the stakes so that the string is taut and then create a seed furrow or drill as it is called, with your hoe. Now you're ready to sow the seed or transplant seedlings. Cover with soil to the depth indicated in the handy garden chart. Use the back of your hoe or your foot to firm the soil over the seed. This will insure that the soil will stay moist since if you left it loose, water would evaporate and germination of the seed would be hindered.

First Time Farmer's Guide

If the weather is warm while you are planting, use pre-soaked seed. This will ensure that the seed has a good start towards germination.

Another step that you can take to prevent moisture loss is to cover the freshly planted area with a light mulch of straw, leaves or even strips of paper. Push the mulch aside as the seedlings appear.

Irrigation

Keeping your garden watered is a matter of judgment which will come from experience. If you water too much, plant roots won't get air and they will drown. If you don't water enough, your crops will wilt. Somewhere between the two extremes is the happy medium that you should try to achieve. The existing school of thought on irrigation is that a gardener should water regularly and deeply, soaking soil to a depth of two or three feet. In the average soil this means that about one inch of water provided with a sprinkler would be delivered to the soil. This can be checked by placing an open container under the sprinkler and measuring the depth of water with a ruler. But like the fallacy of plowing, the conventional method of watering could be less than optimum!

Quite recently it was reported in the magazine 'Vegetable Crop Management' that watering *a small amount, frequently* was far more desirable than heavy watering at relatively long intervals. Dr. E.D. de Remer is an independent irrigation consultant. The article in which he discusses Drip Irrigation appeared in the November, 1970, issue of 'Vegetable Crop Management', 251 Kearny Street, San Francisco, California 94108. Here's the theory in a nutshell.

Dr. de Remer states that with conventional watering the soil moisture level goes from too wet, in which the soil is saturated and roots can't get enough oxygen, to 'just right', to too dry—in the latter condition the plant can't grow because it doesn't have enough water. The good doctor points out that with this system, ground conditions are poor for about 50% of the time. With the system of drip irrigation where plants are watered daily, twice daily or even continuously, a constant soil moisture level is maintained (75 to 90% of filled capacity). This gives the plant the proper balance of soil moisture and soil aeration. We suggest that you try both methods in your home garden and check results. Perhaps you could water one row deeply at one week intervals, and apply water slowly and continuously with a soaker hose to an adjacent row. Then there would be *no question* which method would be correct for your garden. It's appropriate to report here that in the Negev Desert in Israel, drip irrigation methods produced the following increases in yields:

Tomatoes: 176%
Melons: 180%
Peppers: 100%
Sweet Corn: 233%

In Southern California experiments with strawberries produced a better fruit size for the latepicked, an increase of 144% in yield plus a savings of 50% in the amount of water used. An additional benefit was that the salt content on the top of the soil decreased by 400%. It's obvious from reading about this experiment that it pays to keep up with agricultural developments . . . they seem to be coming on as fast and strong as the improvements in other fields.

Mulching

One of the time-honored tasks associated with a vegetable garden is weeding. This onerous chore is typically

Be sure and read Ruth Stout's great book on mulching, her methods work exactly as she predicts

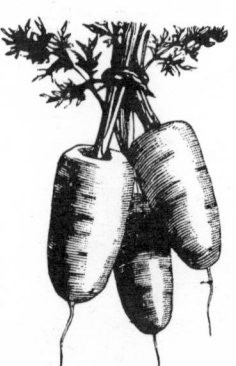

done by a sweating gardener or farmer on his hands and knees or by pushing a manual or powered cultivator. How would you like to be able to eliminate this unnecessary task? Since there is no question that you would, you owe a vote of thanks to Ruth Stout, a warm, wonderful, resolute, do-it-herself gardener. Here's how it all started. For years she had had indifferent success in growing her own vegetables. Then one spring, as her hired plowman prepared to till her garden, the tractor broke down. Although she was anxious to plant seeds, she felt that she would have to wait until the garden was plowed, according to age-old tradition. But suddenly she realized that her asparagus, a long-lived perennial, didn't have to be plowed, and a thought struck her. One never plows asparagus and yet it grows fine, so, except for new ground, why plow at all? Thus, she said to herself, 'I am not going to plow; *I am going to plant!*' From then on she

formed the habit of leaving all of the vegetable waste in her garden, adding straw to it to make a thick layer of mulch. The earth stayed so soft and moist beneath this layer that it was an easy thing to drill a hole with her finger to plant seeds.

If it works for Ruth, it will no doubt work for you. Forget cultivating and weeding and spading your garden. Simply keep it well mulched and there is no question that your vegetables and garden fruits will be as lush and delicious as Ruth Stout's. We strongly recommend that you read her book *How to Have a Green Thumb Without an Aching Back, A New Method of Mulch Gardening,* Exposition Press, NY. It's available at most libraries and well worth the time it takes to read. In fact, it can make your gardening efforts so effortless and successful that you'll wonder why the legend of hard-work farming ever materialized.

Harvesting

Harvesting vegetables is a matter of personal preference. Many people love to walk through their garden and pick themselves a stand-up salad. Grab a young carrot or beet, or pick a pea pod that's just an inch or two long . . . you've never tasted anything so delicious as a plant that's still far from maturity. So harvesting is a matter of what you like to do. Instructions for vegetables like onions and melons are presented in detail in the section on how to grow them. Storage and suggested use of your vegetables is provided later in the book.

WITHOUT MULCH   WITH 3″ MULCH

108° ROOT KILLING TEMPS.   98°

100°   90°

97°   87°

1″
2″
3″
4″
5″
6″
7″
8″

Vegetables & Herbs

'If you would be happy for a week
take a wife
If you would be happy for a month
kill a pig
But if you would be happy all your life
plant a garden.'

There are several major elements to be considered when you select your vegetables. First of all, grow what your family prefers to eat. If a wide selection is produced, there will be no problem in keeping everyone happy. Grow what grows best in your area. Strawberries do fine in the southern climes all year but trying to produce them in northern Montana from October on would be impossible, outside of a greenhouse. Consider what you grow from an over-all nutritional standpoint. Carrots, for example, have more vitamin A than most other vegetables. Where farm space is limited, growing the most food value per square foot is a vital consideration. For example, if your first-time farm is quite small, try to produce as many calories per foot of row as you can. The 'Grower's Guide' shows that lima beans rank the highest in calories per pound with corn and peas running a close second and third. Moreover, lima beans produce 64 quarts per 100 foot row, while peas produce about 32. Corn has a good calorie count but for the amount of space used, the output in calories is less than beans or peas. Of course, there's always the factor of personal preference. You'll have a lot easier time getting your children to eat fresh corn off the cob than lima beans . . . it's just a matter of intrinsic botanical appeal. In addition, check the nutritional content of each vegetable before you make your final garden plan. It's interesting to note that lima beans have twice the protein of corn and outrun peas.

The Grower's Guide

To provide you with information in a compact, easily understood form, we have prepared a 'Grower's Guide' which lists all of the pertinent data in tabular form. With this guide you can quickly determine the amount of seed you'll need for a 100 foot row (simply multiply for larger plantings); the cost of seeds to grow an entire acre; the yield per 100 feet or per acre (8 tons of squash can be grown on one acre); how deep to plant; how to space them; calories per pound; how long it takes to grow; how many feet of row to plant to feed a family of four generously; plus complete nutritional information. Use the 'Grower's Guide' to make up a plan that will give you the most nutrition from your favorites.

Following this Guide are some pointers on the various vegetables — how to insure a continuous crop, special instructions, varieties of each vegetable, as well as pest and disease control.

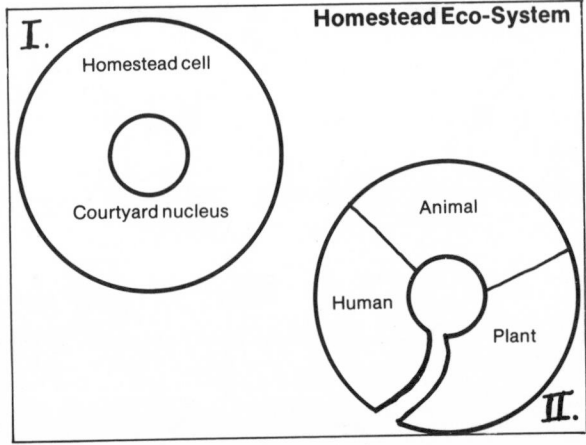

Vegetables

On the following pages appear directions for growing some of the most popular and worthwhile vegetables. They've all been specially selected to meet these qualifications:

They are all reasonably easy to grow in any part of the country.

They will all prosper in any good garden soil and will grow luxuriantly if you use the compost-based soil suggested in the chapter on soil.

They all have good nutritional values.

Most people enjoy eating all or nearly all of this selection.

Food
Animal
Stock feed
Nutrients
Manure
Wastes
Milk, meat, eggs
Compost
Greenhouse
Vegetables
Plant garden
Manure
Garbage
Human
Vegetables

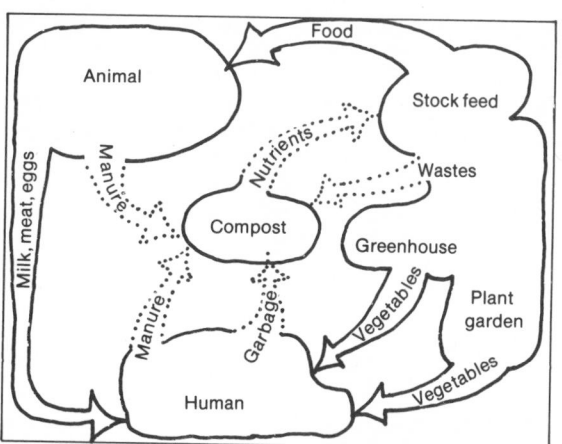

Some sketches to help you plan your *First-Time Farm*

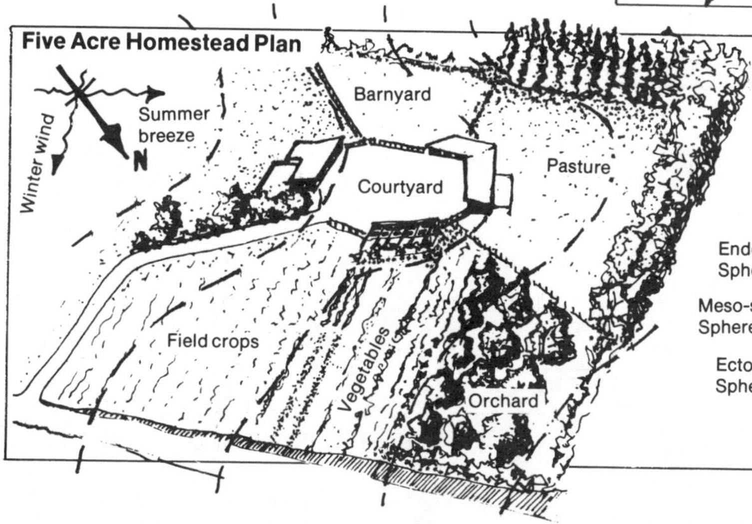

Five Acre Homestead Plan
Summer breeze
Winter wind
N
Barnyard
Courtyard
Pasture
Woodlot & Windbreak
Field crops
Vegetables
Orchard

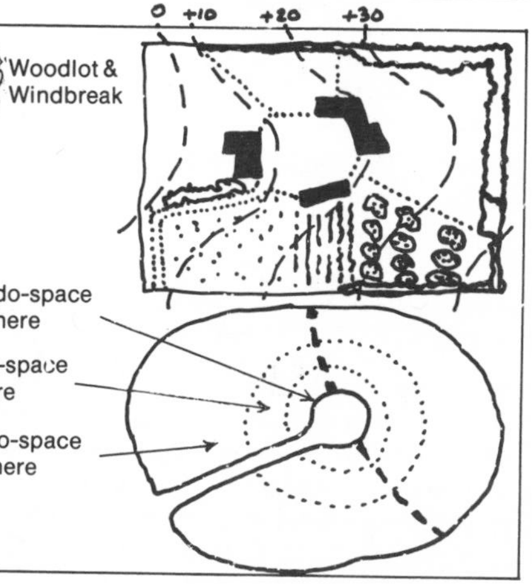

0
+10
+20
+30
Endo-space Sphere
Meso-space Sphere
Ecto-space Sphere

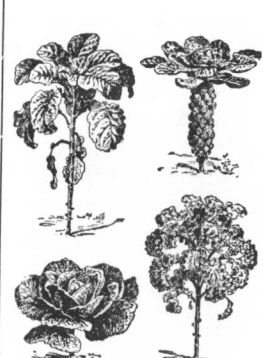

Growers Guide, Part One

	Beans, Lima	Beans, Snap	Beets	Cabbage	Carrots	Chard	Corn
Seed per 100' of row	1 lb.	1 lb.	1 oz.	Packet	½ oz.	Packet	4 oz.
Seed cost per 100' of row, approx.	$1.50	$1.50	95¢	50¢	60¢	35¢	50¢
Yield per 100' of row	2 bushels*	2 bushels	1½ bushels	45 heads	2 bushels	50 plants	48 ears
Seed per acre	75 lb.	75 lb.	5 lb.	4 oz.	3 lb.	8 lb.	12 lb.
Seed cost per acre, approx.	$30.00	$30.00	$10.00	$2 to $8	$7.50	$10-$15	$10.00
Yield per acre	95 bushels	100 bushels	400 bushels	300 bushels	400 bushels	4,500 stalks	6,000 ears
Distance between rows, hand cultivation	30 in.	30 in.	16 in.	30 in.	12 in.	30 in.	30 in.
Horse or tiller cultivation	36 in.	36 in.	24 in.	36 in.	12-18 in.	30 in.	36 in.
Depth to plant seed	1 in.	½ in.	½ in.	½ in.	½ in.	¼ in.	1 in.
Thin or plant to this distance apart	8 in.	2-4 in.	2-4 in.	18-24 in.	2 in.	12 in.	15 in.
Time in days to maturity, approx.	85	60	60	60 (early) 120 (late)	75	50	80
Calories per pound	595	190	205	130	205	150	490
Generous planting for family of four, feet of rows	100 ft.	100 ft.	100 ft.	100 ft.	100 ft.	50 ft.	100 ft. in 4 rc
Seed or plant best for start	Seed	Seed	Seed	Plant	Seed	Seed	Seed
Warm or cool season crop	Warm	Warm	Cool	Cool	Cool	Cool	Warm

1973 Note: Although you may have to double most of the seed costs

Lettuce	Melons	Onions	Peas	Peppers	Radishes	Squash	Tomatoes	Spinach
Packet	½ oz.	½ oz.	1 lb.	Packet	½ oz.	½ oz.	45 seeds	½ oz.
35¢	50¢	80¢	$1.25	45¢	25¢	45¢	45¢	35¢
80 heads	50 melons	1-½ bushels	1 bushel	4 bushels	100 bunches	25 squashes	4 bushels	3 bushels
4 oz. (plants)	3 lb.	4 lb.	90 lb.	4 oz. (plants)	10 lb.	3 lb.	3 oz.	10 lb.
$4.00	$10.00	$20 to $36	$35.00	$3.75	$10.00	$9.00	$9.00	$8.00
14,000 heads	4,000 melons	500 bushels	100 bushels	600 bushels	40,000 bunches	8 tons!	7 tons	600 bushels
16 in.	60 in.	12-18 in.	36 in.	36 in.	5 in.	7 ft.	48 in.	14 in.
24-30 in.	60 in.	24 in.	36 in.	42 in.	5 in.		48 in.	14 in.
¼ in.	½ in.	½ in.	1 in.	½ in.	½ in.	½ in.	½ in.	½ in.
14-16 in.	14 in.	2 in.	1 in.	20 in.	Touching	7 ft.	48 in.	1 in.
45-80	80	100-120	65	115	30	95	70	50-70
85	125	220	460	155	100	200	105	110
150 ft.	100 ft.	100 ft.	100 ft.	100 ft.	25 ft.	50 ft.	100 ft.	100 ft.
Seed	Seed	Sets	Seed	Plant	Seed	Seed	Plant	Seed
Warm	Warm	Cool	Cool	Warm	Warm	Warm	Warm	Cool

in this chart, you will benefit times two (at least) at harvest time.

Growers Guide, Part Two

Nutritional analysis, %

	Beans, Lima	Beans, Snap	Beets	Cabbage	Carrots	Chard	Corn
Water	66.5	88.9	87.6	92.4	88.2	95.2	73.9
Protein	7.5	2.4	1.6	1.4	1.2	1.0	3.7
Fat	.8	.2	.1	.2	.3	.1	1.2
Ash	1.71	.77	1.11	.75	1.02	.8	.66
Calcium	.031	.065	.026	.045	.042	-	.009
Total carbohydrates	23.5	7.7	9.6	5.3	9.3	2.9	20.5
Fiber	1.5	1.4	.9	1.0	1.1	.4	.8
Sugar	-	.4	-	3.5	7.5	1.1	4.3
Starch	-	2.2	-	-	-	.7	14.6
Iron	.0023	.0011	.0009	.004	.0007	-	.0005
Vitamins A	++	++	+	+	+++	+++	++
B^1	+++	++	++	++	++	-	++
B^2	+++	+	+	++	+	++	++
C	++	++	-	+++	+	++	+

*1 bushel = 32 quarts

First Time Farmer's Guide

Lettuce	Melons	Onions	Peas	Peppers	Radishes	Squash	Tomatoes	Spinach
94.8	92.7	87.5	74.3	91.5	93.6	88.6	94.1	92.7
1.2	.6	1.4	6.7	1.4	1.2	1.5	1.0	2.3
.2	.2	.2	.4	.4	.1	.3	.3	.3
.91	.6	.58	.92	.53	.95	.83	.57	1.5
.054	.017	.032	.022	.011	.037	.019	.011	.083
2.9	5.9	10.3	17.7	6.2	4.2	8.8	4.0	3.2
.6	.5	.8	2.2	1.6	.7	1.4	.6	.6
1.6	5.4	6.7	3.2	2.1	3.4	3.9	3.4	.3
–	–	.5	8.2	4.2	–	1.0	–	–
.0011	.0004	.0005	.0019	.0004	.001	.0006	.0006	.0034
+++	–	–	++	+++	–	+++	++	+++
++	–	–	+++	–	+	–	++	++
–	–	++	++	++	–	–	–	++
++	++	++	++	+++	++	–	++	+++

Lima Beans

A prominent and popular member of the bean family, which in turn is considered a most cosmopolitan vegetable. Beans are easy to grow and have a long history of providing good food to people from the earliest times. A big bowl of lima bean soup with ham chunks in it makes for 'stick to the ribs' fare that will relate most appropriately to life down on the farm.

With lima beans you get a choice, pole or bush. For pole limas, hammer an eight or ten foot, rough-surfaced sapling at the appropriate intervals in the center of your rows. Then place two or three seeds around each pole. Bush beans are even simpler and the yield from each is about the same. To avoid shading other plants, pole beans should be placed at the north end of the garden. Another good spot for them is against a fence or trellis. A great idea is to plant corn, sunflowers or other tall vegetables a month or so ahead of the pole beans. In that way the lima beans can climb up a living pole. How's that for compatibility in the garden? Harvest your lima beans as they mature. If you grow too many, don't worry . . . just let them dry on the vine and pick later. Alternatively, you can pull up the vines and place them in piles to dry. Place the vines over a piece of canvas and thresh out the dried beans with a stick.

Beans have been grown for so many centuries that an amazing number of varieties are now available. Here is just a small sampling from a current seed catalog:
Burpee's Fordhook (bush); the standard of the world.
Henderson Bush Lima; old standby of baby lima.
Prizetake (pole); produces the biggest beans you've seen!
King of the Garden (pole); an old favorite of home gardeners.

Snap Beans

Often called string beans. They are also known as bush beans because the plants grow about a foot to a foot and a half tall. Whatever you call them, they come in two varieties, green and yellow. Both colors may produce either a flat or a round pod. The color and shape of the pod are strictly a matter of personal preference . . . they are all tasty and full of good nutrition. The culture of snap beans is identical to that of pole beans—simply omit the poles.

Here are some of the varieties that are currently available:

Green Variety:
Kentucky Wonder; the famous one, long, tender, and meaty.
Lika Lake; a new bean variety with a delicious flavor.
Burpee's Tenderpod; most tender and best flavored the

seed people say.

Burpee's Richgreen; stays bright green when cooked for eye appeal.

King Horticultural; grown both as snap and green shelled bean.

Yellow Variety:

Resistant Cherokee; professionals choose this variety for market.

Kinghorn Wax; a pure, white bean that's great for canning.

Burpee's Brittle Wax; hardy plants, heavy yielding and *stringless!*

Surecrop Stringless Wax; long, wide and thick—flat the catalog says.

Pencil Pod Wax; wonderful flavor and a good old standby bean.

Beets

They've been cultivated for at least 300 years before the Christian era. It's a useful plant since both the red root and the lush dark green tops can be eaten. Another useful aspect of beet culture is that they will indicate soil acidity. If your beets flourish, you can be sure that the soil is not too acid for your other vegetables. Therefore, whether you want to eat beets or not, plant some for a reliable soil test. Incidentally, germination will be more certain if you soak the seed for 24 hours before planting.

If you like large beets, thin the young plants. Incidentally, the small ones you remove can be used in salads. Also, since beets are easily transplanted, you can use the ones you removed as seedlings in a different part of your garden. Transplanted beets will take about ten days more to develop than those you leave in the original row. Beets are relatively free of diseases and insect infestation. Thus,

Beets are relatively disease free. As with most root crops, they can be grown in cold weather.

Steam beet tops like spinach and serve with plenty of butter. Delicious.

Cabbage keeps a
long time, so if you
live in Alaska, plant
plenty

it's a good crop for first-time farmers. They are a great crop for succession planting. By sowing the seed every two or three weeks, you'll assure yourself of a fresh crop throughout the growing season. Furthermore, you can grow beets practically into winter. By sowing seed two months before the first killing frost, you will give the plants time to develop their roots. Then you can enjoy the beet greens just before the first frost kills them, and dig the roots at your pleasure.

Of the varieties available two are recommended for your small farm garden:

The Detroit Dark Red

The Crosby Early Egyptian.

Cabbage

It's one of the most important vegetables that you can grow in your garden. It is easy to grow, easy to store, can be eaten in dozens of different ways and contains lots of healthful food elements. In addition, it's a very hardy crop that is able to withstand temperature extremes. Cabbage will grow quite well even in poor soils and under adverse conditions. It keeps well either in solid head form or as sauerkraut.

To get an early start with cabbage, sow the seed in your cold frame or hotbed; then when they are well developed, plant per the Grower's Guide. Both humans and insects enjoy eating cabbage leaves. One of the best defenses is to plant plenty so there'll be a feast for both 'looper' and your family. The diseases of cabbage can best be conquered by growing healthy plants in your own organic soil mix and starting with varieties that are resistant.

Although the white varieties of cabbage are most popular, you might want to try a few red heads. Then

there is a Savoy variety that produces an abundance of wrinkled green leaves which are sweeter than either the white or the red.

White Cabbage:

Golden Acre; Marion Market; Globe Bugner; Danish Ballhead; Flat Dutch.

Red Cabbage:

Mammoth Red Rock; a Savoy variety.   The Drumhead; produces a large, loose-leafed head.

Carrots

Would you believe that a carrot could be three or four inches in diameter and a foot long? Well, you'd better, because that's the way many professionals grow them. Although growing big carrots would be lots of fun, carrots of any size are a must for your farm garden. Easy to plant and raise, virtually invulnerable to insects or dis-

eases, and full of top-level nourishment, carrots just have to be one of your first choices. In fact, if you only grew one root crop, we'd suggest them.

Don't throw away the carrots that you thin from the row—eat them on the spot or toss them in the next dinner salad. Incidentally, carrots that are two or three inches long are a real delicacy.

Since carrots can be used all year long, plant them every few weeks until about two months before your first severe frost. In the warmer parts of the country many farmers grow them all year around.

Here is a selection of carrot varieties:

Chantenay; fine-grained, tender sweet . . . everything a carrot should be.

Nantes; orange-scarlet and practically coreless.

Imperator; popular in home gardens and they grow big . . . 8 to 9 inches.

Danvers; produces heavy crops of tender, sweet roots.

Chard

Is most often known as Swiss chard. Records show that people have been cultivating it for more than forty centuries. Many years ago it was known as a spinach or leaf beet. It's been steadily improved and the Swiss chard that you will grow will produce broad, flat-ribbed, crisp, juicy leaves. Many people grow chard who don't grow any other vegetable. This is because it's ridiculously easy, can supply fresh greens seven days a week and can even be kept alive through the winter by a thick straw mulch. It's a fast-growing vegetable too—less than two months from seed to your salad bowl or soup pot. An unusual advantage of chard is that you may remove the mature outer leaves to eat and leave the balance of the plant to continue to grow. It's almost as though you had

Growing chard or spinach is incredibly easy

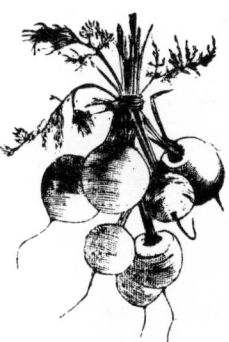

Vegetables and Herbs

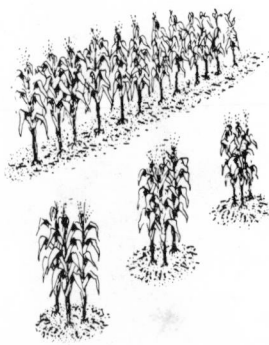

yourself a self-replenishing produce counter.

For first-time farmers, chard is a must. You can start it early in spring and grow your seedlings in your cold frame or hotbed. Then transplant to the spacing shown in the Grower's Guide. As chard grows, you can combine thinning with harvesting . . . eating a sufficient number of plants to allow ample space for the remaining plants to develop to good size (some grow to two feet or more). The same worms that eat cabbage will eat your chard. Pick them off and feed them to your chickens or if you are the big-hearted type, let the loopers have a few plants of their own. Another good insect control method is to run a few geese or ducks through the chard patch after carefully instructing them not to eat the chard.

Varieties available include:

The mild and popular Lucullus (the thick white stalks are great in a cream sauce).

Fordhook Chard; which will provide you with tender greens and pearl white stalks that can be prepared like asparagus.

Rhubarb Chard; with crimson stalks and a sweet flavor.

Spanish Beet; which has a well-developed leaf and delicate midrib.

Corn

No other vegetable that you can grow will put on such a fine display as a big stand of tall, green, wavy-leafed corn. Corn stands like a living signal, virtually shouting the news that you have a thriving, productive farm garden. In addition to its physical preeminence, corn yields one of the highest calorie counts per pound. From the dawn of history to the present time, corn has been an important crop of almost every race of people. The Indians of the Western Hemisphere created a corn

culture that maintained them in vigorous health throughout their lives. Today many tribal communities' and communes' fortunes rise and fall with the corn crop. Not only is corn one of the most delicious vegetables to eat fresh from the stalk, it can be easily preserved by drying, a process which will occur without any help from you. In its dried state it can be stored for many years and then prepared in many ways.

Just about the only drawback to corn is that it yields less food per foot of row than many other vegetables. However, it makes up for this by offering its stalk as cattle food and by its high calorie count per pound. Besides, it is an easy crop to grow, will look great with a scattering of golden pumpkins about Thanksgiving time and makes a festive indoor decoration for barn dances and harvest celebrations.

In addition to the sweet corn or eating varieties, you

First Time Farmer's Guide

might want to grow popcorn and ornamental corn. Popcorn's easy to grow and when dried will keep practically forever. It's a great cold winter night snack when eaten hot with lots of melted (homemade) butter. The ornamental corn can be dried and used to decorate your farmhouse. The rich color tones of deep red, bright yellow, flaming orange and mystical blue appear in endless kaleidoscopic combinations. A pound of ornamental seed only costs about $1.50 and will grow bushels of this highly picturesque corn. Always plant corn in adjacent rows. That is, if you want 100 feet of corn, place it in four side-by-side 25 foot rows. This assures proper pollination. Also consider planting corn rows approximately one week apart all through the spring and early summer. Then you will be able to harvest fresh corn on a continuous basis. For a thrill which you could never have enjoyed in the smoggy city, put on a pot of water, let it boil and then slip in a few ears of sweet corn fresh from the stalk. Whoooeee! as they say in the boondocks.

You'll have lots of fun perusing seed catalogs because they list so many varieties. Here's what we mean:

Spring Gold; an early variety (67 days) and perfect for stands.

Earliking; twelve rows of kernels in a 7-inch ear.

Northern Belle; a Harris hybrid that has up to 18 rows of kernels.

Gold Winner; rugged plants that grow under adverse conditions.

Seneca Chief; small ears of extra-fine quality.

Burpee Honeycross; the husks are so tight, the worms can't get in!

Burbank Hybrid; sweet, delicious with up to 20 rows of kernels.

Early Golden Giant Hybrid; only 63 days from seed to

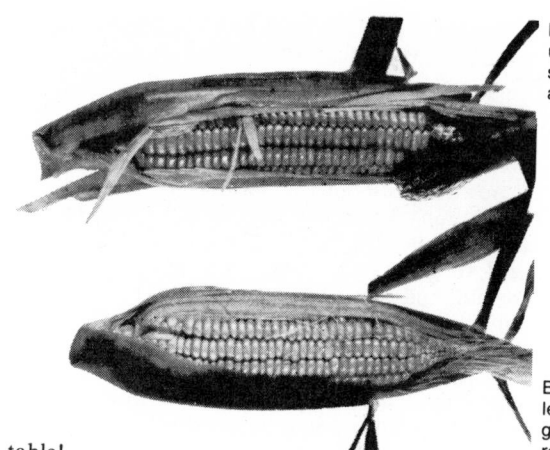

Plant corn all year . . . use young shoots for corn salad. Mmmm, good, and cheap too.

Basic for every salad, lettuce is so easy to grow you can stop reading this book right now

table!

Ioana; resists drought so the corn will grow if you're short of water.

Marcross; has large, cream-yellow kernels and freezes well.

Burpee's Golden Bantam; a famous name and a corn that you've probably eaten many times. Now grow it yourself.

Lettuce

A salad bowl is naked if it isn't dressed with lettuce. Simple to grow, full of vitamins and other good things, it was enjoyed by Persian kings about 500 B.C. according to Herodotus.

Start lettuce in your cold frame or hotbed about a month before you intend to transplant it outdoors. As with any vegetable that you intend to use constantly, keep a crop going. Once the ground warms up, you can

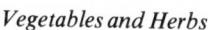

Vegetables and Herbs

Melons provide a fine
crop for roadside
stands . . . plant lots

sow seeds in the rows from which you harvested the previous crop. If you like, you can pull off the outer leaves of the looseleaf variety, and let the plant continue to grow for later use. Lettuce is so shallow-rooted that it can easily be grown in those raised beds that we told you about earlier. In fact, lettuce is so easy to grow that there's no excuse for you not to enjoy it all season long. If you don't believe it's easy, listen to this. The author's four-year-old daughter once scattered a single packet of seed all around the house—no tilling, no plowing, no thinning and only random watering—and yet this careless agricultural technique produced more lettuce than the family could eat!

The most famous variety of lettuce is the Iceberg type which is further subdivided into the following categories (and this is only a partial list):

Empire; makes fine, firm heads.

Fulton; uniform, solid, compact heads that resist disease.

Great Lakes; heavy, glistening, crackling-crisp heads.

Ithaca; performs well transplanted or direct seeded.

Mesa; a premium strain grown from coast to coast with success.

Minetto; small, fine, sweet heads with short cores; from Australia.

Oswego; these firm heads stand hot weather well.

Pennlake; mosaic, resistant and ideal for your roadside market.

If you prefer the less solid heads, then consider the loose-leaf Boston or 'Butter' varieties of which the following are characteristic:

Bibb; an old favorite of home gardeners that is famous for flavor.

Black Seeded Simpson; widely grown, loose-leaf with broad leaves.

Buttercrunch; thick clusters of tender, delicious leaves.

Dark Green Boston; rich green color with thick, tender leaves.

Grand Rapids; grows well outdoors or in your greenhouse.

Parris Island; this one's noted for vigor, color and dependability.

Slobolt; used for outdoor gardens and produces thick curly leaves.

Salad Bowl; notched and curled leaves for a fine rosette.

While we're on the subject of salad greens, there is a fast-growing lettuce-like plant called Salad Cress, which you can start eating just ten days after you plant it. The leaves are dark green, curly and parsley-like. Best of all, this green can be grown indoors all winter long in pots or shallow trays. The Burpee Company has its own plant called Curlycress.

Melons

Muskmelons or cantaloupes, as they are often called, can be thought of as a vegetable or fruit . . . either way they are bound to be a most popular product of your farm garden plot. The Egyptians dug melons as established by the Eleventh Chapter of Numbers in the Good Book:

'We remember the . . . melons which we did eat in Egypt freely.'

There is no question that melons you grow yourself will be far superior to those you have purchased in your supermarket. You see, melons sold in stores are picked green, whereas you'll be able to wait until the optimum moment of ripeness. Here's how to tell: Examine the stem end of the melon . . . it should not be picked unless it will separate easily with a slight touch of the

thumb. Melons need lots of room, so it's suggested that you plant them in your corn field where the space between the stalks would otherwise go unused. If you are a melon fan, then don't forget to grow such other wonderfully-flavored varieties as the Casaba, Honeydew and Cranshaw. While you're at it, drop a few watermelon seeds into the melon patch for a great companion crop.

There are a great variety of melons listed in seed catalogs. Here is a sampling:

Delicious; this is *the* standard early melon with sweet, juicy flesh.

Gold Star; these vines bear heavily over a considerable period.

Harper Hybrid; many people consider this the finest melon of all.

Harvest Queen; fine for your roadside stand . . . they are flavorful even a week after picking.

Iroquois; large melons with thick, flavorful flesh.

Saticoy; every one you grow will be a delight to eat . . . wonderfully sweet and tender.

As you check the available varieties, note that catalogs rate them from the standpoint of regional variations and adaptability to shipping and storage.

Onions

A remarkable vegetable . . . they are one of the oldest known to man with references in ancient Sanskrit and Hebrew literature. Apparently the people who first cultivated onions knew intuitively that they were an extremely healthful addition to one's diet. Recent research has substantiated this and it's clear now that large quantities of onions will keep most of your inner plumbing in top shape.

Onions are easy to grow and you have a choice of

While they are often cheaper to buy than grow, a large crop of onions are an excellent vegetable that last all winter

Vegetables and Herbs

Granma's Garden was
not complete without
a row or two of pea
vines

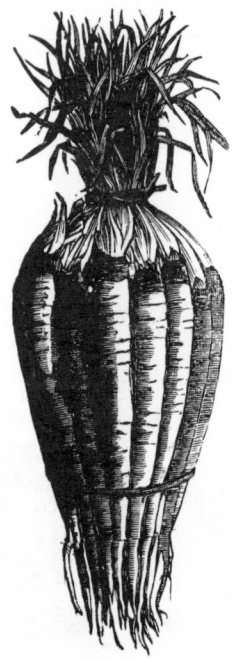

three methods; seeds, sets or transplanting of young plants. The instructions in the Grower's Guide apply no matter which method you use. Seeds are the simplest and cheapest and you can sow them quite thickly. An onion set is a small onion about the size of a dime. You can buy them through any seed catalog for about a dollar and a quarter a pound. One pound of seeds will plant 50 feet. Space them about three inches apart and cover them with about one inch of soil. They'll soon begin growing and will mature into large onions. The third method, young plants, involves the purchase of a batch from Southern onion growers. Just about every farm magazine has an ad going in the early spring. As soon as the postman delivers them, transplant them into rows four inches apart. Keep them well-watered and they'll reward you with good-sized onions in about three months.

When onions are finished growing, the tops fall over. You can leave them in the ground for some time after this, but eventually dig them up and allow them to dry and cure. They can be used right away in your farm kitchen or stored in a cool, dark cellar. For pest control, see Chapter 16. In addition to the guidelines presented there, keep your onion plants healthy and vigorous to discourage onion-eating insects or onion diseases.

There's a large selection of varieties from which to choose: round, flat, mild or strong with white, yellow or red skins, although the flesh is always white. Here's just a small selection from a single seed catalog:

Sweet Spanish—Yellow Utah; very large, exceptionally mild and sweet.

White Sweet Spanish; solid, crisp, pearl white . . . grow big.

Ebenezer; the onion with the old-fashioned name will keep over winter . . . so grow some.

Crystal White Wax; this is a Bermuda-type onion with sweet flavor.

Early Yellow Globe; these seeds produce bumper crops.

Yellow Bermuda; extremely mild, juicy white flesh. Matures early.

Yellow Globe Danvers; a famous name that will keep well in your cellar.

White Portugal; large, flat, white onion with firm, fine-grained flesh.

Peas

Visualize yourself shelling a potful of peas that you've just picked from your own vines. Add a little water and cook them quickly until they are *al dente* (just a little crisp). Now add a generous chunk of home-churned butter, a bit of salt and pepper, if you dig these, and dive in. We guarantee from thenceforth you will hurl canned

and frozen peas into the next county. Peas are typical of a vegetable that is a gourmet treat when fresh, but one that quickly loses its appeal when more than a few days old.

Peas should be started during cool weather so they'll be well-developed by the time summer heats up your garden. Sow them in the early spring according to the specifications in the Grower's Guide. To insure a continuous crop of peas for your table, sow at 10-day intervals, right through late summer. Your last planting will give you a late fall or early winter crop. If you plant a lot of them then you can freeze them, can them, or dry them for later use. Most organic gardeners are fighting the root rot disease by keeping the soil well-drained and rich with natural fertilizer. You can confound most insects by simply winning the harvest race, i.e., picking them young and tender before the insects know they are there.

As with beans, you can choose dwarf varieties or others that will grow five and six feet high. Here's a sample of pea varieties with emphasis on the sweet type:

Little Marvel; vigorous, sturdy, dwarf vines producing good crops.

Freezonian; a popular early pea with well-filled pods.

Nott's Excelsior; plump, straight pods thickly filled.

Progress No. 9; an early type with long pods filled with 7 to 9 peas.

Thomas Laxton; a heavy cropper that matures early.

Wando; this tolerates heat so you can grow it through the summer.

Alderman; unsurpassed flavor which stays green in the pot.

While we're discussing types, please consider the one known variously as Snow Peas, Chinese Peas or Sugar Peas. Whatever name is used, they have edible pods. Picked while still growing, totally stringless and succulent, the entire pea, pod and contents may be eaten raw or cooked. You've undoubtedly had some as part of a Chinese restaurant dinner. They are listed in many seed catalogs.

Peppers

There are many varieties of peppers . . . the hot ones, such as small red chili and long red cayenne, the cherry group which are far milder, and the pimento type, which include the giant and the Spanish. Then there is the pepper that most people think of—the big, succulent, crisp, green type that is so important for adding interest to casseroles, salads and stuffing with ground meat. Pepper plants are started in a hotbed and allowed to develop for 8 to 10 weeks. At this time, plants will be large enough to transplant to your garden, but be sure when

Peppers rank as prime favorites throughout the world. Boil slightly, then stuff with a seasoned rice mixture. Bake in a "good vibes" tomato sauce.

Radishes burst into
being with alacrity.
Keep them growing
all season

you do that all frost danger is past. Pepper plants are so handsome that you may want to grow several in pots or tubs and scatter them about your patio. Not only do peppers have ornamental value, they are full of health-giving elements. They have still another advantage—they are usually not bothered too much by insects or diseases. Just keep an eye out for cutworms immediately after you have set the plants out and send in your favorite chicken for a quick snack.

Here's a selection of pepper varieties that will provide you with plenty of big, thick-meated, dark green peppers:

Burpee's Fordhook; tender, sweet, crisp flesh and just right for stuffing.

Burpee's Tasty Hybrid; so sweet you can eat it like an apple.

Calwonder, Early; if you love stuffed peppers, grow this one.

Canape; when ripe, this delicious pepper turns brilliant red!

Cheese-Pak; thick meated with bright red coloring makes salads live.

Emerald Giant; smooth, well-shaped, this is a heavy producer.

Bell Boy Hybrid; medium long and blocky, an all purpose pepper.

You'll find many more listed in your favorite seed catalog.

Radishes

This is a true, nothing-to-it type crop. Many free-wheeling gardeners just take radish seeds and give them a toss. Radishes will grow between and under and around everything else you're growing. You might wonder why

we even include them in our list of basic vegetables and if so, here's why. Every gardener needs something that will defy the elements, poor horticultural care, insects and disease. So if nothing else in your garden grows, you'll still have a fine big crop of crisp, juicy, snappy morsels that go well in salads and as an hors d'oeuvres.

We suggest that you show your botanical *savoir faire* by investing in a couple of packets, seeding them according to the Grower's Guide and then enjoying the results in a little over three weeks. Incidentally, the best way to thin these plants is to go down the row and gobble them up as you perform the thinning operation.

For such a small vegetable, there's a variety from which to choose:

White Strassburg; crisp, tender and pungent; can take summer heat.

First Time Farmer's Guide

Long Black Spanish; black skin, white inside . . . 60 days.
White Chinese or Celestial; pure white roots, 6 to 8 inches long.
All Seasons White Radish; keeps well and has an ice-like texture.
Icicle Short Top; considered the best white radish going.
Scarlet Knight; quick growing, uniform and attractive.
Cherry Belle; an excellent variety for home use or to sell.
Red Boy; has a sparkling red color, short tops and round roots.

Squash

How would you like to grow a vegetable that produces 16,000 pounds of nutritious food per acre? At the same time, this vegetable practically stores itself. And coupled with these advantages, this outstanding candidate for your farm garden will be so easy to grow and give you so much pride of accomplishment that it will surely become one of your farm favorites. Of course, we're referring to the old traditional Hubbard Squash. Hubbard's are perfect for baking, boiling or using in many unusual ways. Of all the many squash varieties, the Hubbard will be the best one with which to start because of its rough hard shell, which makes it easy to keep all through even a long cold winter.

Squash seeds are planted in hills with plenty of space between them as you see by the notation in the Grower's Guide. Squash, like pumpkin, which can be grown in a similar fashion, can be interspersed with corn, sunflowers or other tall plants that will permit the squash the amount of room it needs to spread out its roving vines and widespreading leaves.

It's an interesting sidelight on squash that they can be eaten at any stage of development. Banana squash

Stays fresh for months . . . a vital food for backwoods farmers who seldom see a store

Keep squash forever . . . Boil, mash, dry in thin sheets. Write notes if you have too much.

will be just as delicious as Early White Bush picked while it's still some weeks from maturity. So play around with squashes . . . they are willing to grow for you with practically no effort on your part. Squash makes good use of land that you may not want to use for other purposes. You only have to provide your organic soil for the hills in which the seeds are planted. The squash then needs only room in which to extend its fantastic and verdant leaf system.

Once you become familiar with squash culture, you'll want to try some of the many others. Here's a partial list from a popular seed catalog:

Summer Squash:

Zucchini Elite; handsome, dark glossy green. Bears heavily.
Apollo; similar to Elite, but plants are even stronger.
Harris Hybrid Cocozelle; a productive, vigorous hybrid.

Vegetables and Herbs

Seneca Prolific; an early and heavy producer.
Early White Bush; flesh is milk white and delicious.

Winter Squash:

Butternut; this is one of the best you can grow. Keeps well.

Blue Hubbard; fine-grained, dry and sweet. Lasts all winter.

Table Queen; also known as acorn. Extremely productive.

Delicious; grows almost anywhere and an excellent market type.

Sweet Meat; this one improves its flavor for as long as six months.

Tomatoes

Have you ever thought about the many wonderful ways that tomatoes can be used . . . in spaghetti sauce, Spanish rice, salad and those super delicious sandwiches —bacon and tomato? No question that you have, and no question that tomatoes should figure prominently in your farm garden plans.

While tomatoes are subject to attack by many insects (bugs love tomatoes too) they are really not too difficult to grow. They can be started as seedlings in your cold frame, hotbed, hothouse or indoor flat. Using that good organic soil, cover the seed with about ¼ inch of fine soil or sand and keep the soil moist but not too wet. When the seedlings are two inches tall, transplant them to stand four inches apart each way, pot them in three inch pots, or use the new Jiffy 7 pellets or their equivalents. When all danger of frost is behind, transplant the seedlings in rows as specified in the Grower's Guide.

Tomatoes can be staked or unstaked as you wish. If unstaked, it's a good idea to use lots of mulch to keep the

tomatoes clean and dry. As your tomato plants grow (and they'll take about two months from seed to fruit) keep a sharp eye on them. There's an ugly monster called the tomato horn worm that will gobble up your plants faster than a two-headed cat can polish off a dish of cream. Bring your favorite chicken with you when you go horn worm hunting; the chicken will love them and may even spot a few of his own.

Tomatoes can be planted on a succession basis, especially if you live in a region of mild climate. Just start a plant or two every week right through late summer. If your area is really tropical or you have a greenhouse, consider tomato crops on an all-year basis.

If you would like to grow tomatoes with a minimum of hassle, applying a method where human error is eliminated, consider this. The Burpee Company plus other suppliers sell a cube pre-planted with two hybrid tomato seeds. The cube provides the nutrients. A clear film is shrunk around the unit making it a miniature greenhouse with perfect climate control. All you do is water them and place in a 65- to 75-degree area—nature does the rest. In quantity, these pre-planted, miniature greenhouses sell for less than a dime. That's about half what a developed seedling will cost in a nursery. An added convenience is that you can buy them by mail any time.

There is a variety from which to choose, ranging from the little cherry tomatoes (known as Small Fry to the Harris people) to the giant beefsteak (some weigh more than two pounds!), and on over to the unique Roma, which is plum or pear-shaped, very firm and used to make tomato paste and ketchup. Here is a rundown on some of the names that you'll encounter when you are in the tomato seed-buying mood:

Burpee's Big Boy Giant Hybrid; some of these giants

Tomatoes were once called love apples.

weigh two pounds! Imagine them in a sandwich.

Burpee's Pixie Tomato Hybrid; grow this novel tomato indoors in a pot!

Supersonic; just the plant for home and small farm gardens. Large fruit, heavy yields and disease resistant.

Moreton Hybrid; the leading tomato in many areas. Stake or ground.

Cardinal Hybrid; big fruit, smooth and firm. Great for roadside sales.

Jet Star; a Harris Company seed that has been enthusiastically received.

Springset; an extra-early tomato with medium-sized fruits.

Coronet; disease resistant with extra firmness. Keeps well.

Small Fry; a new hybrid that produces many 1-inch diameter fruits. You know them as 'cherry' tomatoes.

Spinach

Although there has been some attempt to discredit Popeye's favorite vegetable, there's no question that spinach contains lots of vitamins and plenty of iron. Even if that were of no concern, remember that spinach grows quickly (maturing in 40 days after you sow the seed), and it is also a plant of great hardiness and vigor. Just think of a vegetable that can be eaten in salads as well as hot and may be grown right through the winter in the Southern part of the United States! And if that weren't enough of an incentive, we'll provide you with a recipe for a spinach salad that you're sure to like.

Spinach is sown early and, as with other leafy garden crops, can be seeded every week or two to assure a virtually year-long crop.

Diseases are not much of a problem with spinach. The only one is the Yellow disease, which appears in the fall. It is best overcome by simply planting the resistant variety. Plant lice (aphids) are the only pest of any consequence and these may be blasted off by a high pressure stream of water. Once they are on the ground, run your chickens, ducks or geese through for an aphid feast.

There is a variety called New Zealand that has a special feature. You can leave the plant to continue its growth while you cut three or four inches of its leafy tips off for your kitchen. Cutting back the tips doesn't hurt the plant—in fact, it forces new shoots and will make the plant leafy. There are several other varieties from which to choose:

Bloomsdale Long-Standing; a heavy yielder of glossy, dark-green leaves.

New Zealand; strong, heat resistant leaves that can be planted late and picked all summer long.

Malabar Spinach; a vine spinach variety that grows bright glossy leaves. Can be trained to a fence.

Virginia Blight Resistant Savoy; leaves are extremely crisp and tender.

Winter Bloomsdale; this one resists cold weather and can live through the winter. Salads in January!

Wilted Spinach Salad

Saute until crisp: 4 or 5 slices of bacon.
Remove from pan, drain on paper towel and crumble.
Then heat: 2 tablespoons melted butter, bacon drippings or oil.
Add: ¼ cup mild vinegar, 1 teaspoon chopped fresh herbs.
Add the crumbled bacon and 1 teaspoon grated onion and a teaspoon of sugar or honey.

Pour this dressing while hot over fresh young spinach leaves which have been torn into bite-sized pieces. Serve at once onto warm plates. May be garnished with sliced hardboiled eggs. This recipe will serve four.

Two other staples—Potatoes and eggplants. Try the combination sautéed in olive oil, butter and some of our favorite herbs.

Herb gardening used
to be an essential
culinary art, you can
never cease being
amazed how many
there are and the
extent of their power

Herbs

Would spaghetti be spaghetti without a sprinkle of oregano in the sauce? Would chili con carne have its characteristic vigor without ground cumin seed? And how could you possibly make pickles without dill? Throughout history, men have balked at eating the same old spaghetti, beans and rice without some variation in their flavor. Thus, the herb and spice industry is one that is solidly based in the fundamental desires of all people. In the old days when ships made the long voyage from Europe to the Spice Islands, herbs and spices were extremely expensive, pepper being worth its weight in gold in many markets. Today, however, vegetative flavorings are far less costly. Furthermore, most of them can be grown in your own garden or gathered free from the countryside.

The use of herbs is quite well-known and reference to any good cookbook will teach you how to use even the most obscure varieties. But what we'd like to tell you here is how easy it is to create your own seasonings. First of all, here's a review of some of the most popular herbs.

Garlic

If you are fond of Italian food or French cooking, you must have a bed of garlic on your first-time farm. It is a perennial that can be started from seeds or you can buy bulbs and plant them base down about an inch and a half deep. When the tops begin to dry and turn yellow, it's time to harvest.

There is a variety of giant garlic that you can grow for your own use or possible sale. It's quite a novelty and will intrigue your farm visitors. For complete informa-

tion on giant garlic, write to Nichols Garden Nursery, Park North, Albany, Oregon 97321.

Chives

This dark-green perennial that does so much for cottage cheese, eggs and soups is one of the easiest fresh herbs to grow. You can start from seeds or divide bulb clumps. Both are available from large seed and stock suppliers. Chives grow best where there is lots of moisture and perhaps a little shade. A bed would probably do well near your faucet where the water that spills from a leaky hose could be put to good use.

Keep the lavender flowers picked off to keep fresh leaves growing. It's fun to experiment with chopped chives in addition to the usual ways, try to sprinkle on a hamburger or some over a big steaming bowl of chili. With its mild but unique onion flavor, it has to do good things for foods.

Dill

Traditional to farms, both today's and yesterday's, is the pickle barrel. Usually stored in the cellar, green pickles swim in a cool brine flavored with bunches of dill, the herb that was designed by nature to bring out the best in a pickled cucumber.

This annual can be planted every spring by sprinkling seeds and thinning the seedlings to 18 inches apart. It becomes a tall, vigorous plant closely resembling anise or fennel. When using it to make your own pickles, toss in the tops—leaves, flower heads, seeds and all. Dill seed makes a nice herb flavor by itself, so when plants are dry, shake them out on a piece of paper and preserve them in a nice old, clean pickle jar.

Tarragon

In gourmet grocery stores you'll find bottles of vinegar 'flavored' with tarragon. If you look closely, you'll see the herb itself suspended in the light brown liquid. Now you'll be able to make your own tarragon flavored vinegar. It's grown from divisions or cuttings, but not from seeds. You may buy these from any of the larger mail order nurseries or companies specializing in herbs. Like the other herbs, tarragon is usually grown with little care except enough water to keep it from wilting and protection from weeds and insects.

Chives, showing root system, an easy herb to propagate

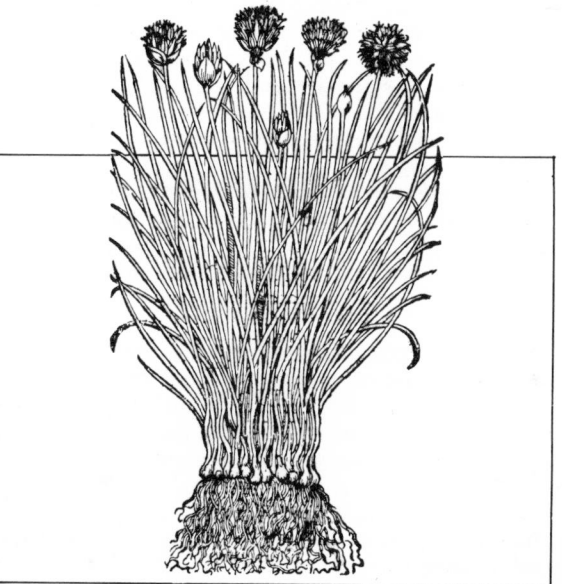

Caraway seeds add
something wonderful
to homemade cheese.
See Chapter 17 for
recipe.

Caraway

You've eaten lots of caraway in that good Jewish rye bread. Caraway seeds can also be used for flavoring meat dishes or added to boiled new potatoes.

To grow caraway, sprinkle as much seed as you wish into rich, well-drained soil. It's a perennial plant with carrot-like leaves and white flowers. Look for it to flower early the second spring and produce the first mature seeds by summer. Gather them when dry by shaking into a clean flour sack or paper bag.

Marjoram

No good cook will function well without this very popular herb. Most people like it in meat dishes, big green salads or cheesy casseroles.

Marjoram is a perennial so one planting will keep you for many years. Very cold areas will freeze it to death, so you'll have to plant it every spring if you live near Duluth or other places resembling the South Pole. Marjoram is very easily grown from seed, cuttings or root division. You'll recognize it when it comes up by its grayish green leaves and small clusters of white blossoms.

Mint

If you're planning your first-time farm for a Southern location, you're probably thinking of those big, tall, icy mint juleps that you will sip on the veranda on a lazy August afternoon. Providing the mint will be the easiest thing you've ever done because mint is one of the plants that will grow not because of the care you give it but in spite of it. If you put a few cuttings or roots near that leaky pump or faucet, you'll soon have a huge bed of lush, cool green mint.

Aside from using its fresh green leaves in drinks

Marjoram

and as a garnish, try drying a couple of big bunches, mix it with some dried alfalfa and you'll have a treat known as alfalfa mint tea. Prepare and drink this just like you would conventional tea.

Basil

This is one of the really favorite herbs and, lucky for you, it will grow easily from a packet of seeds. Just broadcast some where there's lots of sun and water them frequently. Basil grows so fast that you'll find yourself using a great deal of it, fresh or dried, in savory meat loaves, spaghetti sauce, sprinkled on scrambled eggs and minced in crisp green salads.

Parsley

This is the herb that made Simon and Garfunkle famous along with the three others that we'll discuss presently. It's a perennial with the familiar lush, dark green leaf structure that you've seen as a garnish on so many steak plates in the big city.

To help it germinate, soak the seeds for a day or so. Then sow wherever you would like to have a good decorative border for your other herbs or vegetables. To keep it producing the tasty and highly nutritious leaves, pinch off any blooms. For real convenience, grow some in a kitchen windowbox so that the cook can snip off leaves just before she serves that veal parmigiana.

Sage

If you live in a desert area or travel through one on occasion, you won't even need to grow this perennial. Just look for a shrub with silver gray leaves and violet flowers. You can pick enough to last you for years for nothing. But if you'd like to grow it yourself, start from

Sage

Sage grows wild in many western regions. Just transplant some Perennial parsley is hard to kill and always welcome

Two more of the priority herbs, Rosemary and Thyme (below)

seeds obtained from any seed supplier and sow it in well-drained soil. Don't give it too much water. A few plants should provide you with enough seasoning for all the pork sausage and turkey stuffing that you could possibly make.

Rosemary

This herb with the beautiful girl's name has leaves like pine needles and light blue blossoms. It's best grown from seedlings you can buy from most nurseries. A seed packet costs about a quarter, but you'll find it slow to get started. It's not only a great seasoning for all kinds of meats, it's a beautiful plant that will be an asset to your herb or flower garden.

Thyme

The root of many kitchen-oriented puns and gags, this decorative perennial can easily be grown from seed to maturity in about three months. It's a favorite herb for borders, or simply to cover bare spots in your garden. Water it occasionally and when it reaches its maturity (about a foot high) pick the leaves. Dry and store them in a handsome china crock. Thyme goes great with many kinds of meats as well as in casseroles, soups and sauces.

Aside from the value of herbs as a seasoning for your foods, many herbs have medicinal properties. An acquaintance with some of the better-known medicinal botanicals can be obtained by buying a copy of *The Herbalist* ($3.95). You'll find it in most health food stores and head shops. Otherwise the constantly reprinted *Culpeper's Complete Herbal* of the 1600's is the real turn-on ($5.95).

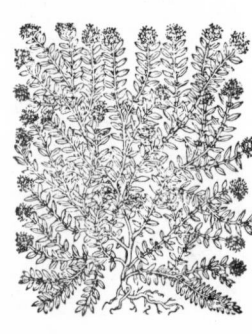

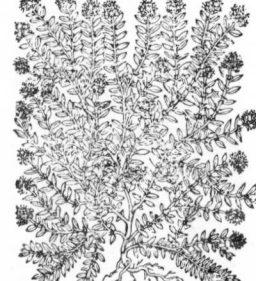

Wormwood and Mugwort, not commonly used, though both grow profusely wild, are very aromatic. Wormwood grows 3 ft high!

Small Fruits, Big Fruits, Nuts & Seeds

'Forward in the name of God: Plant, graft and nourish up trees in your ground; the labor is small, the cost is nothing, the commodity is great; yourselves shall have plenty, the poor shall have somewhat in time of want, and God shall reward your good merits and diligence.' — *Anonymous*

Fruit trees have lots
of advantages; for ex-
ample, snails can't
stand the rough bark

Every homemaker knows that if there's company for dinner, the food that takes longest to cook must be started first. There are two good reasons for beginning your fruit orchard first, for the sooner they are planted, the sooner they will bear and even if you find a better farm and sell the one on which you planted the trees, it will be worth a lot more money just because of the infant orchard.

Most of us are familiar with conventional fruit trees—big, spreading apples, peach, plum and cherry. These trees grow throughout the United States, some surviving under adverse conditions. Regardless of where they grow, they have one thing in common, they are big. Being big causes a number of problems, as they take lots of room and care. If spraying or dusting is needed, the necessary equipment is large and expensive. It takes from four to five years . . . sometimes longer, for a large

fruit tree to bear, and because of their height they are difficult to prune and to pick. With these thoughts in mind, horticultural experts proceeded to develop what should be considered as a botanical miracle (fanfare)—the dwarf fruit tree. Here's a comparison in size between a standard and a dwarf tree. Incidentally, more recently a few varieties of apple trees have been reduced in size to double dwarf trees.

Dwarf And Double Dwarf Trees

Although dwarf and double dwarf trees are small in size, the fruit they bear is big or even bigger than that from full size trees. Only the tree is small . . . everything else—blossoms, leaves, and fruit—are big. Dwarf fruit trees are ideal for a small farmstead for many reasons. They take far less space and can be sprayed or dusted (if needed) with the same equipment that one would use for shrubs or plants. The need for high pressure equipment and long wands is totally eliminated. Dwarf trees frequently begin bearing two years after planting and produce big crops within three or four years. They can be pruned with ordinary pruning equipment. Again, expensive, infrequently used, long-reach pruning shears or saws are unnecessary. Dwarf trees grow large fruit. Because of a dwarf tree's convenient size, it is a simple matter to thin small fruits to produce larger fruit for harvest. You can plant more trees in a smaller space, you can obtain greater fruit variety even if your farmstead is an acre or less. Cultivation and irrigation (particularly where pipes must be laid) are less costly in labor and equipment since the total space involved is so much smaller. Dwarf trees can be harvested quickly and safely because the danger of climbing a shaky ladder or break-

First Time Farmer's Guide

ing branches while climbing around in the tree is eliminated. Children have no problem harvesting the fruit crop. Even dwarves can load up on fruit from this kind of orchard! These trees produce less damaged fruit since any fruit that drops to the ground has a shorter distance to fall, and the fruit from dwarf trees often tastes better than from standard trees because it is easier to give dwarf trees the care that a fruit tree needs.

About the only disadvantages to dwarf trees are that the initial cost is greater and they have a shorter life span — 20 to 30 years of useful life compared to 35 to 50 years for a standard tree. There are a number of dwarf tree suppliers in the United States. We suggest that you obtain their catalogs and compare varieties, sizes and prices. Suppliers of fruit trees, like almost everyone else in the seed and stock business, give off good vibes. They almost invariably guarantee what they sell to be exactly as represented or better.

Here are a several dwarf fruit tree suppliers:

Stark Bros, Louisiana, Missouri 63353

Henry Field, Shenandoah, Iowa 51601

Gurneys, Jankton, South Dakota 57078

Planting dwarf fruit trees is so simple and straightforward a husky ten-year-old could do it. Just read him the following: keep the roots covered with wet burlap or keep trees in their package until ready for planting. Do not expose roots to sun or wind. Dig a large, deep hole to hold the roots without crowding or bending. Under most conditions, it is advisable to plant dwarf apple trees 1 to 2 inches deeper than they stood in the nursery row. Dwarf peach, dwarf pear and dwarf cherry on the other hand, should be planted shallower than other fruit trees. The offset at the base of the dwarf trunk should be at or just above ground level after the hole is filled. Stake dwarf pear, peach and cherry trees. Fill the hole 2/3 full with pulverized soil and tamp firmly around roots. When soil is firmly tamped, pour in one bucket of water and let soak. We recommend that no chemicals, insecticides or fertilizers be placed in the hole with the roots. Fill the hole to surface level. Spread a mulch around tree about June 1st. Soak the soil frequently and deeply throughout first season. Prune back as indicated by supplier.

Oranges in Your Orchard

How would you like a tree that bears fresh fruit and fragrant blossoms at the same time . . . a tree that stays green all year long, a tree that requires very little care and returns bountiful crops of sweet vitamin and mineral rich fruits? It's an orange tree, of course, a tree which you will need on your farmstead to make breakfast time complete. Orange trees as well as other citrus (grapefruit, lemons, tangerines, mandarins, tangelos and tangors) require a climate reasonably free from frost. However, with protection it is possible to grow citrus successfully in northern latitudes . . . in fact, far north of where they are commonly grown. It may be just a legend but there is supposed to be an area in British Columbia . . . a notably chilly region . . . that actually has an extensive orange culture. If you would like to take a chance to see whether oranges could be successful on your farm, why not start out small with a couple of trees and see what happens. In this way you won't be out much in time or money if they do freeze or fail to prosper. On the other hand, if they grow successfully, you could plant a large number and enjoy fresh sliced oranges or delicious juice almost the year around.

Starting right is important. Purchase trees from an

Orange trees are one of the few plants that permit you to store your crop without picking it. Furthermore, you *need* orange marmalade on that homemade bread

experienced, reliable nursery man. Here's how to tell a good tree. Well-grown, one-year-old citrus trees should be about ½ to ¾ of an inch in diameter. Two-year-old trees should be ¾ to 1 inch in diameter. All measurements should be taken about an inch above the union of the bud and root stock. Trees are usually sold with their roots surrounded by an earth ball and wrapped in heavy burlap. Don't buy a tree on which the soil has been broken away from the roots by careless handling. Here's what a healthy young orange tree should look like. It's far better to buy this one than the more mature tree shown here. Faster growth will occur when a young tree is planted and allowed to expand its root system without restriction.

Citrus trees do best on well-drained loam or sandy loam soils. With good care, though, they can be made to produce on almost any well-drained soil that does not contain injurious amounts of alkali.

Planting can be done any time after the danger of frost has passed. Early planting is especially desirable in the interior areas where sudden hot spells are likely to damage trees that are not well established. In most regions, April or May is a good time to plant.

In commercial orchards, the trees are commonly planted 22 or 24 feet apart; in home grounds much closer planting is often desirable or necessary.

Holes for planting the trees need be only deep enough to accommodate the ball and wide enough to permit easy filling. If holes are unnecessarily deep, there will be excessive settling after planting. In poor soil dig large holes and fill back with good top soil, then allow the new soil to settle 2 or 3 months before planting.

The balled trees are placed in the holes without removing the sacking. Plant them so that they will finally

First Time Farmer's Guide

be a little higher than in the nursery, with 2 or 3 inches allowed for settling. Try to have the uppermost roots branch out at about ground level after the trees have settled. These precautions are important because trees set too deep are likely to be killed by brown rot gummosis, which frequently develops where the soil comes into contact with the bark.

When a tree is properly placed, fill the hole three-fourths full of soil, and tamp it firmly around the ball. Next release the sacking which covers the ball, fold it back so as to expose the top of the ball, and complete filling the hole. Throw up a small basin around the tree and irrigate thoroughly. The bottom of the basin should slope toward the tree trunk so that most of the water goes into the ball.

To protect trees from sunburn during the first year, wrap the trunks in several thicknesses of newspaper.

It is sometimes recommended that fertilizers be placed in the hole when the trees are planted. This practice has frequently resulted in severe damage to the trees. Fertilizers can be more safely applied to the surface of the soil after the trees have been planted.

Young citrus trees will grow more rapidly if they receive lots of nitrogen. As with the rest of your organically grown garden, use your compost and spread it around the tree but keep it from direct contact with the tree trunk. Use of nitrogen-rich rabbit manure in compost prepared for orange trees would be especially beneficial.

With the exception of the Clementine mandarin, Minneola tangelo and Orlando tangelo, citrus trees do not need cross pollination and can be grown as single trees.

The most important point in caring for the young

Great care is necessary in planting out young trees

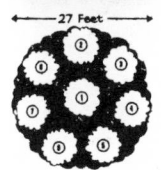

Small Fruits, Big Fruits, Nuts and Seeds

153

Opposite: when considering your environment, and in your planning, just remember that the wilder and more naturally you allow things to grow, the better the results. Beware the false propaganda that promotes 'factory farming' type cleanliness and neatness. Natural balance is the *only* way

citrus trees is to see that they get plenty of water. Under most conditions, water every week or 10 days during the first year, and about every two weeks for the next two or three years. After the third year, trees will require irrigation every two to six weeks, according to soil and locality. On sandy soil or in hot weather, irrigation must be more frequent than on clay soils and in cool weather.

For the first year, the best way to apply water is in basins of about two feet in diameter around the trunks of the trees and deep enough to hold three or four inches of water. When the trees are established, water may be applied in furrows or basins or by sprinklers. After the first year, enlarge the basin and keep water away from the trunk of the trees as much as possible to avoid gum disease. This can be achieved with an inner circular ridge of soil around the trunk, and one to two feet from it.

Cultivation is necessary only to maintain irrigation furrows or basins and to control weeds and grass, which compete with the trees for water and fertility. It is not beneficial of itself and should be kept to a minimum.

Avoid pruning young trees as much as possible. The removal of green leaves retards growth and increases the time required for the trees to come into bearing. For the sake of appearance, rub off growth on the tree trunk while it is young and succulent, but leave the tops unpruned until the trees are in bearing.

Young citrus trees are likely to be damaged by frost and in most regions must be given protection for the first two or three winters. The most common method is to wrap the trunk and ain branches in some material such as cornstalks. The wrapping should be 3 or 4 inches thick and snug enough to prevent free access of cold air to the trunk. Cover only the trunk and main limbs and be sure the wrapping makes good contact with the soil.

Trees are fed by materials produced in green leaves in the presence of light. Therefore, if the leaves are covered or shaded, the tree is starved and becomes more liable to cold damage. It is better to risk injury to the leaves by frost than to cover them and starve the tree. Examine the wrapping occasionally to see that it remains in place. When there are only a few trees, a cover can be thrown over them at night and removed during the day. On very cold nights, a lighted lantern or electric light placed under the cover will give excellent protection.

If your orange trees are maintained in a healthy condition, it is unlikely that they will be troubled by insects. Young trees might be affected by aphids but these can be eliminated by spraying with an organic material, nicotine sulphate, in the proportion of one teaspoon to one gallon of soapy water. All other insects— thrips, red spiders, mites and others can be easily controlled by turning loose your friendly ladybugs. See the chapter on Pest Control for more information.

Growing Evergreens

Did you know that you can buy *1,000* American Red Pine trees for about $50 or $60? Of course, these trees will only be about six inches tall, but they will grow fast, look like Christmas trees all their lives and eventually produce valuable wood. Although evergreen trees produce little in the way of food for your first-time garden (pine nuts), they do provide several valuable benefits. They will beautify your farm. Planted in rocky areas, they will hold what soil there is, will act as windbreaks, and if you plant them thickly, will be an almost impenetrable fence. When mature, evergreens can be cut for lumber or logs for your fireplace, and certain varieties produce useful saps and resins (turpentine comes from a variety

Small Fruits, Big Fruits, Nuts and Seeds

Six popular pine trees (excluding the important lumber producing Ponderosa pine which grows at about the same rate as the Jeffrey pine), all shown here at ten years old.

of pine).

While there are many types of evergreen trees such as spruce, hemlock, cedar and fir, we've chosen pine as being best for your first-time farm. Pines will grow in almost any type of soil and many of them will grow very rapidly.

Here is a selection of pines and their characteristics:

American Red Pine; deep green all year. Excess trees could be sold at Christmas.

Scotch Pine; grows well even in very poor soil. Has thick foliage and is very hardy.

White Pine; has soft, beautiful, bluegreen needles. Grows into a fine large tree.

Bristlecone Pine; noted as the oldest living thing on earth. Outdates the oldest sequoia by *fifteen* centuries. Withstands temperatures of 50 degrees below zero to 100 above. Plant this one for your great-

great-great-ad infinitum-grandchildren.

Corsican Pine; tall and narrow with rich green foliage. Much beloved in Italy and possibly inspired Respighi's *Pines of Rome.*

Most anyone can grow evergreen trees if a few simple rules are followed. First, select a well-drained area. If soil is hard, spade in some of your compost. Plant the seeds to a depth of three times their diameter. Roll lightly and then protect the seedbed with a lath shade twelve inches above the ground. Water when necessary but do not overwater. Be patient, some seeds will germinate quickly but others may take up to a year or two. If you would rather, you can buy all types of evergreens in seedling form. Both seeds and seedlings are available from suppliers listed in farm magazines. A nursery that specializes in many types of evergreens is Girard Nurseries, Geneva, Ohio 44041. Your local Forestry Service

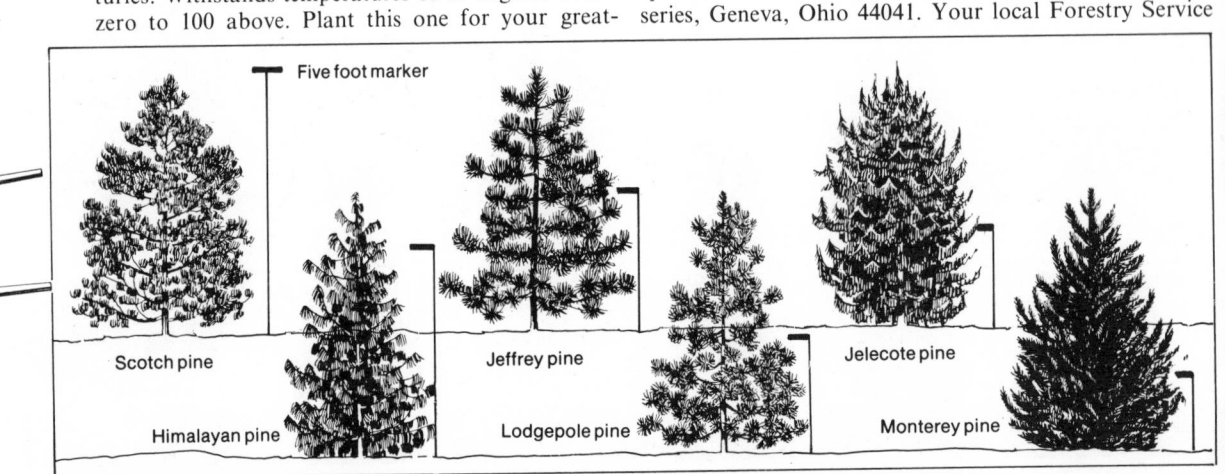

Five foot marker

Scotch pine

Himalayan pine

Jeffrey pine

Lodgepole pine

Jelecote pine

Monterey pine

First Time Farmer's Guide

will give you seedlings if you ask.

Orchard Irrigation

Soil structure is a key property of the soil. It has a primary influence on the rate at which water and air can enter and move through the soil. Soil structure also affects the nutrient-supplying power of the soil and penetration of roots. Each of these affects plant growth. Fortunately, if you prepare your soil using the instructions in Chapter 3 as a guide, your irrigation problems will be minimized. This is because good soil has the capability of holding water and making it easily available to plant roots.

To obtain minimum growth, keep the soil wet throughout the root zone. Here's a chart that shows how deep you need to water to accommodate various plants. To make an accurate check on how deep water is pen-

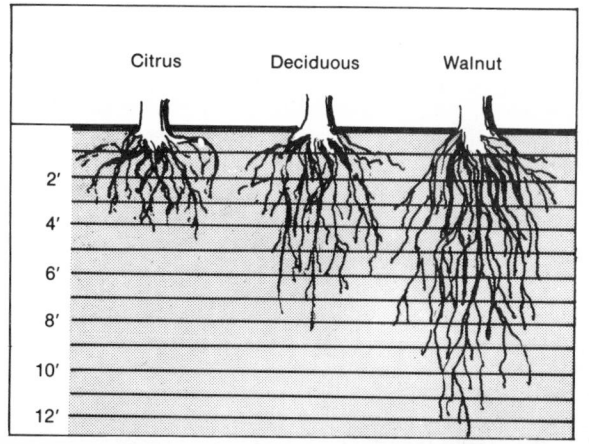

Planting trees—especially evergreens in places where there will be a good grass cover for a few years—creates ideal 'odd area' habitats for cottontail rabbits and other kinds of wildlife. Plantings of pines in 'odd areas' such as fence corners, rocky spots, land isolated by ditches, gullies, hedgerows, etc, are particularly valuable for wildlife since the trees harvested before they are large enough to shade out all the grass cover. Then, where necessary, trees, shrubs, and other plants that provide wildlife food and cover can be added. (Trees are being planted at the rate of 910,000 acres a year, and 'odd areas' account for 10 million acres.)

Small Fruits, Big Fruits, Nuts and Seeds

157

Contour planting

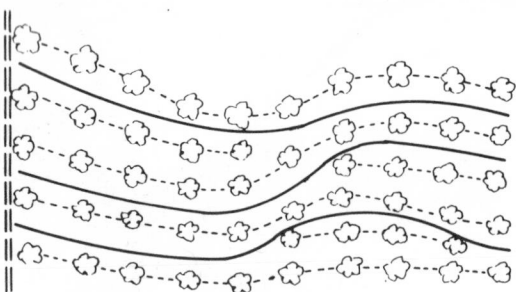

A half-acre fruit and nut garden in northern districts: Row A—1 to 3, pecans. B—1 to 4, apples; 5 to 6, pears. C—1 to 3, plums; 4 to 8, peaches. D—trailing blackberries. E—raspberries (half row); erect blackberries. F—strawberries (two varieties). G—muscadine grapes on a trellis. Fruit and nut trees should be placed on the north side.

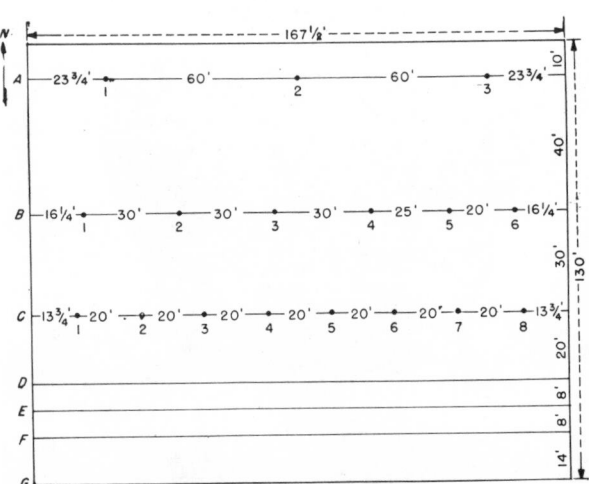

First Time Farmer's Guide

etrating in your garden, you can use an auger as shown here. If you don't want to invest in an auger, you can drive a metal pipe or tube into the ground and examine the condition of the earth at the bottom of the tube at different levels. Barring these devices, an ordinary trowel will let you examine your soil and moisture content by simply digging a small hole adjacent to the trees.

Strawberries, Blueberries, Grapes and the Bramble Family

Great news! Strawberries want you to grow them, otherwise why would there be so many varieties . . . so many that you can have strawberry plants producing berries the entire year. By simply planting a number of different strawberries, you can be picking them from January through December. With the aid of a hothouse, even the less hardy types will produce continuously. Here are a number of strawberry varieties arranged according to their degree of hardiness. If your farm has very cold winters and is located in the higher altitudes, these varieties are best: Gem, Rockhill and 20th Century. For areas with cold winters but a lower elevation, you can try Northwest and Dorsett plus the ones mentioned above. If you live where there is fairly mild winter weather and reasonably cool summers, you are fortunate because this is a great climate for strawberry culture. Plant any of the following with great expectations: Marshall, Brightmore, Corvallis, Narcissa, Red Heart, Shasta, Lassen, Donner, Red Rich, Utah and Everbearer.

Strawberry plants produce best in light textured, well-drained soil. A 50-50 mixture of the best top soil in your garden plus the compost you make yourself should prove satisfactory. Strawberries are usually planted in

Strawberries are just one of the small fruits that make farming, first or last time, fun!

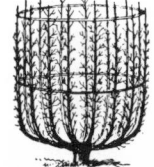

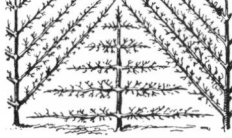

early spring and should be placed with the crowns just above the surface of the soil. To insure having a permanent bed of strawberries, make three rows of plants spaced six inches apart. Each plant should be placed one foot from its neighbor. Strawberries propagate by sending out runners . . . new shoots that creep along the ground and take root. By eliminating all runners except two, one up and one down each row, you will insure enough new plants to replace those that become too old to furnish fruit. With this system you never have to buy new strawberry plants. For best results, remove the blossoms from first year plants. To keep the strawberries clean, mulch with fresh straw.

A major seed company offers to supply strawberry plants that will produce throughout the season. The plants range from extra early to everbearing, for a total of five different varieties. 50 each cost less than $20. 250 plants would provide three times the amount the average family can use. If you'd like to start with a smaller amount, you could purchase 125 plants (25 of each variety) for about $12. For more information, write Burpee Company, Riverside, California 92502; Philadelphia, Pennsylvania 19132, or Clinton, Iowa 52732.

Blueberries

A small restaurant in a seaport town has survived through wars and depressions, good times and bad, because of one thing . . . they make the most delicious, super-yummy blueberry pie that you've ever tasted! These blueberry pies are not the usual store-bought variety with pasteboard crust and a gelatinous mush, colored pale blue. Instead, these pies have a crust that's so full of butter and other good things, it crumbles under the lightest touch of your eager fork. The pies are stuffed to the bursting point with big round juicy blueberries, lightly captured by a delicate sweet-tart blueberry sauce. Topped with whipped cream, the combination produces a culinary euphoria that demands frequent repeat performances.

Blueberries for these pies are grown by a little old farmer who has improved on the wild blueberries which are native to the Atlantic coast. His entire output goes to the successful restaurant in both fresh, frozen and canned form, depending on the season. It is likely that if you devote part of your farm to blueberries, you too could establish yourself as a permanent supplier for an equally successful restaurant. Furthermore, bakeries, gourmet food stores and similar outlets would be most receptive to a steady supply of high-class blueberries. You can produce berries continuously through the growing season by using an early, mid-season and late variety. Here are the names of three varieties that fulfill these requirements: Early Blue (early), Rancocas (mid-season), and Jersey (late).

Blueberries require cross pollination so that you must plant at least two of each variety. To grow blueberries you'll need an acid soil and a climate with moderately cool summers. It's much easier to make your soil acid than it is to cool down your summers. Just add a generous supply of leaf mold . . . at least a bushel full for each plant. When you are digging the hole for the blueberry plant, mix a bushel full of top soil with the bushel of leaf mold and use this mixture to surround the plant, placing about six inches of the mixture beneath it. Then add a mulch of two or three inches. To keep the soil acid, don't put any alkaline materials such as lime or wood ashes near them.

Plant about four or five feet apart in rows six to eight feet apart. However, if you'd like a blueberry hedge for decorative or fencing purposes, they may be planted three feet apart. Blueberries begin to bear in their third year, working up to maximum production in eight to ten years. To insure vigorous growth and development, prune blueberries in the early spring. Cut out bushy branches and any weak shoots. Your goal should be to develop an uncrowded plant so that it can receive as much sun and air as possible.

Since commercial blueberry plants are still close relatives of the wild varieties the Pilgrims found, you'll find them a hardy plant. If you will keep them mulched and the soil moist, they will produce for you year after year. You can expect about five quarts of blueberries per plant. One hundred plants in rows 25 feet long would comprise a blueberry patch of about 2500 square feet. Thus, at full production you could realize about 500 quarts. This would be enough to make 1,000 delectable blueberry pies. If you just want blueberries for the home, plant a hundred foot row, which will give you all the berries you and your family can eat (125 quarts). But if you'd like to have extras to sell, grow yourself a bigger patch . . . they'll do practically all of the hard work for you.

The Noble Grape

Grapes are easier to grow than you think

Have you ever thought of how many thousands of acres and hectares are devoted to vineyards? All over the world—along the Rhine in Germany, clinging to rocky hillsides in Italy, ranging for miles and miles along rivers in France whose names evoke ancient battle stories, in cool, unpopulated upstate New York and rolling over hill and dale in the wine country of Northern California—are found the gnarled and picturesque trunks of venerable grapevines. Cloaked with artistically-shaped green leaves in summer, they tantalize grape lovers by half concealing bunches of grapes that appear to be ready to burst their skins with delicious juice at any moment. Even in winter when leaves and grapes have gone, the twisted canes wrapped about their supports or clinging to a trellis or arbor possess a robust charm and bring to mind visions of biblical events. Greeks bearing gifts, and a restatement of faith in the continuity of growing things.

Why shouldn't grapes be popular? What other plant is so beautiful and produces fresh clusters of flavorful grapes with as many new taste sensations as there are varieties; deep purple grape juice, richly colored jelly, sweet raisins that put the sun to work for you, and the drink that inspires so much poetry—wine, with its limitless colors and flavors. For all their versatile productivity, you will find that grapes are easily grown, are extremely hardy, comparatively free from pests and will probably live to provide your children's children with the bounty of a vigorous and mature vineyard.

Here are but a few of the many varieties of grapes from which you can choose:
Catawba; these dark copper-colored grapes can be kept in cold storage longer than any other variety.

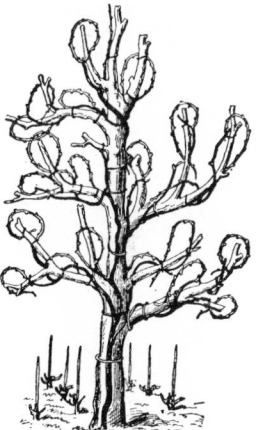

Small Fruits, Big Fruits, Nuts and Seeds

No question, the flavor of grapes is one of Nature's greatest gifts to man

Concord; favorite sweet grape that convinces many people that this is truly the best of all possible worlds.

Niagara; pale green clusters that fade to white and posses a rich aroma. Pick the heavy bunches in mid-fall.

Golden Muscat; these huge grapes are almost too sweet. Eaten warm from the vine, they can make you swoon with delight.

Other varieties from which to choose include Fredonia, Seneca, Ontario, Diamond, Pearl of Casaba, Black Monukka, Cardinal, Malaga, Thompson, Delight and Pearlette.

A basic requirement for all grapes is that they have a full measure of sunshine. Soil that is adequate for vegetables will be fine for grapes. Many highly productive vineyards have been planted in sandy soil. Mulch the vines with hay or grass clippings and add compost, working it into the soil every year. When you receive your vines from the supplier or a friend, bury the entire root and stem except for the top inch or two. A hole about 16 inches deep should be adequate. Tamp the soil firmly and cover the stem with loose soil. Water sufficiently to keep the soil moist. After the first year of growth, grape vines should be pruned and trained to supporting wires or a trellis. Here is a pictorial guide to pruning. However, pruning really depends upon the shape of the supporting structure. For example, if you are creating a decorative grape arbor, canes would be pruned to conform to the arbor shape. Fortunately grapes are relatively untroubled by pests and may be protected from birds by placing a paper bag over each cluster as the grapes ripen.

The Bramble Family

Even if you don't have a green thumb . . . even if every weed, sprout and leaf you touch promptly dies . . . even if you've never successfully grown anything, take heart!! There's one growing thing that even the most hapless, first-time farmer cannot kill, and that is blackberries!

Here are two instances that prove this contention. In the posh suburb of Santa Barbara called Montecito, there are a few empty lots. In keeping with the general tidiness of the area, these lots are regularly plowed to eliminate weeds and clutter. On one of the lots is a vigorous stand of blackberry vines. Every year harrow blades slash and tear the vines, cutting some, burying others, chewing up leaves and roots alike. But every year new growth comes forth from the husky, hardy, never-say-die root systems. And each year a wonderful crop of sweet

All vines and brambles need extensive pruning

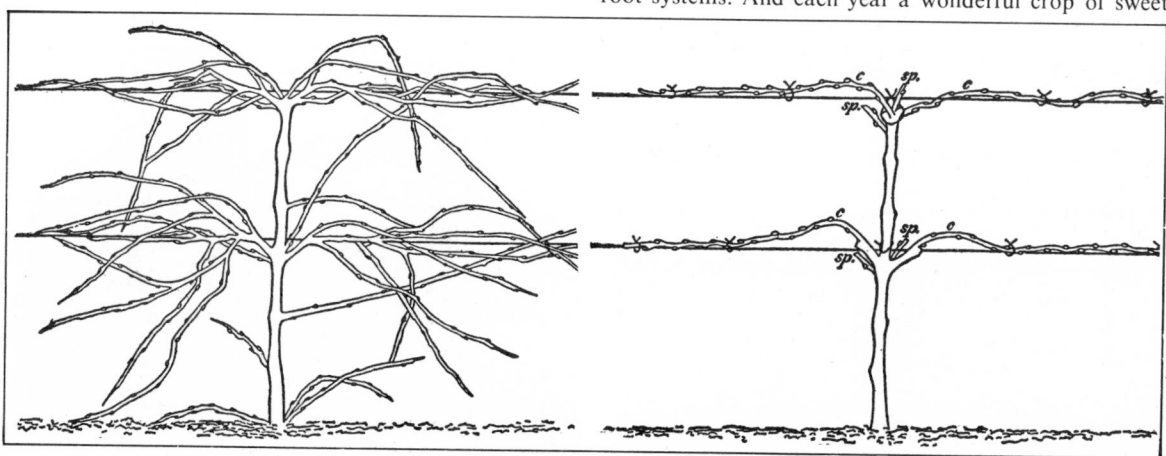

The popular four-arm training and pruning system for American bunch grapes.

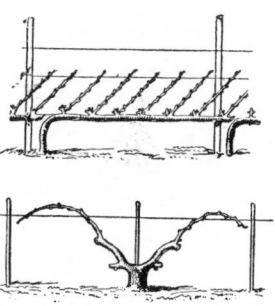

and luscious blackberries springs forth . . . without care,
concern, irrigation or fertilizer.

Pioneers who braved Indian attacks, short rations
and the dire predictions of their stay-at-home neighbors
in Indiana, plodded into Oregon and Washington carry-
ing blackberry canes. When planted these canes put forth
such lush growth that their owners were forced to cut
back and haul away huge quantities of excess growth.
In dumping these unwanted vines in out-of-the-way creek
beds, they unwittingly began the volunteer culture of
blackberries throughout the Pacific Northwest. Gigantic
thickets of blackberry vines now range for miles along
clear streams. In Hood River, Oregon, rampaging blackberries, displaying nearly explosive growth, festoon pear
and apple trees of abandoned orchards. There one can
enjoy buckets of juicy blackberries and bushels of absolutely free ripe pears simultaneously. In both cases

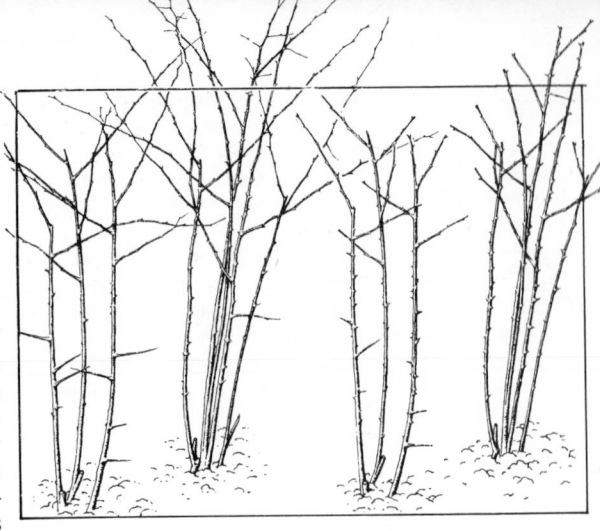

Train trailing black-
berries to a two-wire
trellis and erect plants
to a one-wire trellis.

Raspberry vines in
the spring.

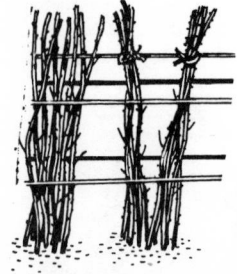

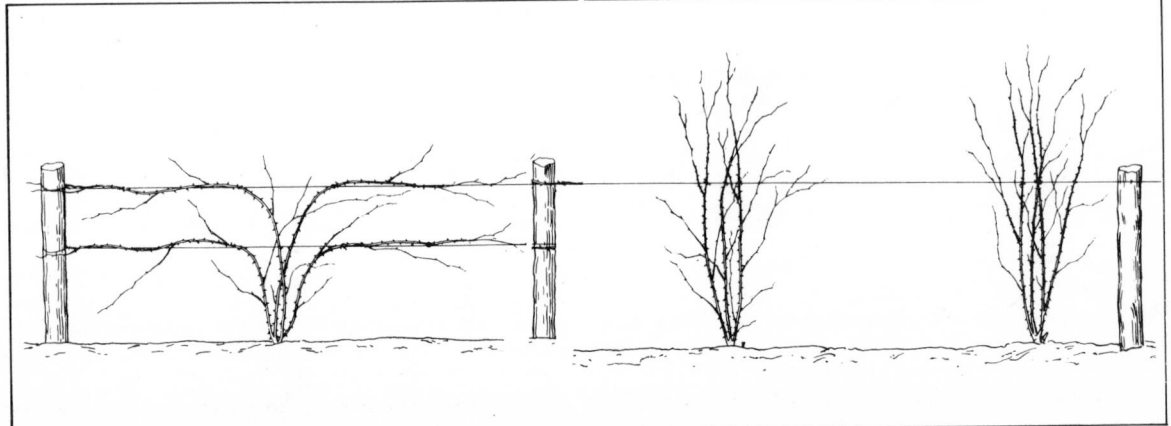

164

First: Time Farmer's Guide

blackberries have not only survived but flourished magnificently—not only without care, but in spite of total abandonment and in some cases rigorous efforts to eliminate them. All of this should tell you something. If you buy a young rooted blackberry vine or two from a good nursery, dig a hole in the ground and toss them in, kick a little dirt over them and dash them with a bucket or two of water occasionally, you'll have more blackberries than you know what to do with!

Since blackberries really do go out of control, here's one of the best ways to keep them from conquering your homestead. By training them to grow along wires or fences and walls, they'll provide a decorative background, be handy to pick and prune and (hopefully) stay in their own territory. If you find blackberry seedlings sprouting all over your farmstead a year or two after your own blackberries have borne fruit, attribute it to birds. They eat the berries but spread the indigestible seeds in their droppings. Again, blackberry seeds need no human help to start their botanical rampage. It must be now apparent that blackberries will grow in almost any type of soil. Of course, they'll do best where they get plenty of nutrients and as much water as they can hold. This is why they grow so well near irrigation ditches, streams and lakesides. The blackberry vines that crowd the shores of Mercer Island in Lake Washington, Seattle, produce giant berries that are totally irresistible.

For fastest results, purchase what is known as one-year-old bedded plants. Place them in holes deep enough to cover the root system, spaced about 8 to 12 feet apart. About three plants will provide enough for the average family's needs. As mentioned previously, control of this mad vine is most efficiently accomplished by training to grow on wire or wood trellises or against a fence or wall to which wires have been nailed.

When the blackberry has finished fruiting, cut back all of the old canes except two or three of the strongest. New growth will emerge from the root system. In the early spring the canes from the previous year can be pruned back two or three feet, which will produce strong lateral growth. Whatever you do, be sure to prune them each fall. This will keep them from growing rank and making threats to take over the garden. Furthermore, new growth provides the bearing stock. One final note, blackberries as a class have many sub-varieties. You may find these names when you browse through a catalog or a nursery: boysenberry, loganberry, youngberry, nectarberry, Cory thornless, Cascade, Olallie and thornless. Incidentally, the latter is a great boon since it allows you to pick your fresh blackberries without being torn by thorns. Planting and growing instructions apply uniformly to all blackberry types.

The Nut Trees

The meat industry has done a good job of selling meat as one of the best sources of protein. However, as many of us have come to understand, animal protein is not without its drawbacks. Thus, a source of high quality protein from a vegetable origin would be a most welcome addition to your farm. Walnuts, almonds, pecans and other common nuts have high protein content and can be grown easily in practically every part of the country. In fact, a common wild tree in America, the black walnut, thrives amidst hostile environments with little or no care. Here are some facts about the nutritional content of English walnuts. The data is typical of the food values that can be expected from your nut crops and should convince you that half a dozen nut trees would be

Small Fruits, Big Fruits, Nuts and Seeds

a beneficial and bountiful addition to your small farm.

Nutritive Values of English Walnuts

Two important essentials with nut trees are that they must have well-drained soil to survive and must have plenty of room to grow. Plant almonds about 15 feet apart; chestnuts 30 feet and all others 40 to 50 feet for best results. Plant nut trees the same as fruit trees except in the case of tap-rooted trees such as walnuts. With such trees dig a U or V-shaped hole and fill in the soil carefully all the way up over the tap and side roots. Stake nut trees securely so that they won't whip about in the wind and keep them well-watered, especially during dry periods. Nut trees should be protected from rodent damage as with fruit trees. It is also a good idea to protect these trees from sun-scald the first winter with tree-wrap paper. Nut trees are usually very slow to leaf out

after they are planted so be patient. A few varieties of nut trees either will not bear at all, or will not bear consistently good crops unless they are pollinated with another variety. It is best to purchase two or more varieties of Chinese chestnut, almond and English walnut to ensure fruiting.

Nutritive Values of English Walnuts	
Water	4%
Calories	650
Protein	15 grams
Fat	64 grams
Carbohydrates	16 grams
Calcium	99 mgms
Iron	3.1 mgms
Vitamin A	30 int. units
Thiamin	.33 mgms
Riboflavin	.13 mgms
Niacin	.9 mgms
Ascorbic Acid	3 mgms
1 cup = 100 grams	

First Time Farmer's Guide

Seeds for Health

'If ye have the faith of a mustard seed then ye can move mountains.'

The Incas thought so much of one kind of seed that they made beautiful models in pure gold of the flower from which it came. Parrots, who live longer than any other bird, thrive almost exclusively on a diet of this seed. The plant itself is heliotropic . . . every morning the flower faces the East and then slowly turns to follow the sun's transit until it sets. It then turns back at night to start a new day. You've probably eaten these seeds as a snack and then again you may not have. Or you may have classified them as just another 'bird seed'. If you haven't guessed what we're talking about by now, it's sunflowers and their seeds.

Sunflower Seeds

Provide an excellent example to describe just what a seed is. A seed may be described as a small package (there are about 90,000 celery seeds in an ounce—is that small enough?) that contains all of the instructions that are needed for the seed to grow into a complete plant of its variety. Botanical scientists are fond of telling people how many thousands of books the size of an encyclopedia it would take to relate the same instructions that are contained within one carrot seed. Bible scholars are delighted to point out that men could move mountains if they possessed the same faith as a mustard seed. In addition to all of the wonderful facts, fantasy and lore concerning seeds is the often neglected fact that many seeds provide an excellent source of nutrition in themselves.

The value of sunflower seeds as a food has been known for many centuries by canny peasants. In Russia,

12½ million acres are being cultivated exclusively in sunflowers. In short, more and more people throughout the world are becoming aware of the tremendous value of sunflower seeds as a really good food. Fortunately, sunflowers are as easy to grow as a weed. They are hardy plants that will do well almost anywhere. Plant them as an entire field and have the fun of watching their big, round, yellow moon faces swinging in unison from East to West. Plant them as a border around your flower garden or vegetable plot. Plant them as a living bean pole by putting a seed or two next to every climbing bean. The sunflower will beat the bean into the air and the bean can intertwine itself around the strong sunflower stalk. Sunflowers are great to plant along the front of your farm as an attention-getter. Those huge 20 to 30 inch diameter heads will stop lots of customers for your roadside stand.

If erosion is a problem on your farm, try a nice thick stand of sunflowers at the eroded point. When you harvest, just chop the stalks a little above ground level and leave the roots in to hold the earth.

Sunflowers are such a tough plant that you'll hardly need concern yourself with respect to soil conditions and irrigation. The seed is cheap, so why not scatter it in many places on your farm and see where it does best. About the only thing you'll have to look out for is birds that will follow your seeding. If that's the case, cover each seed with a small amount of earth as you sow. As the sunflower stalk rises above your farmstead, you begin to wonder just how tall they will grow. Heights of six, eight and ten feet are not uncommon for the giant sunflower. As the huge heads mature, birds will begin to take an interest. If so, just throw a piece of old net curtain or other loosely woven material over the heads and tie them around the stalk. In that way the heads will

Small Fruits, Big Fruits, Nuts and Seeds

Pumpkins . . . the no work crop with the giant return . . . Pumpkin can be preserved just like squash— cooked, dried in the sun and stored in a cool dry place.

fully mature and dry on the stalk. Harvesting and using sunflower seeds is almost as much fun as growing them. As soon as they are dry, cut the heads off and rub the seeds into a basket. This is a great fun-task for the children. The seeds with their hulls on make a perfect food for your pet parrot, your chickens or any other type of bird. If you really have a lot of them, feed some to your pigs as a health-building bonus. For your own use, it's best to hull the seeds. Set your old-fashioned meat grinder to its coarsest cut. Then run the sunflowers through the grinder once. This will crack the outer hulls and release the tasty sunflower seed tidbit inside. At this point you can air separate them. Toss them into the air when a light breeze is blowing, which causes the seeds to fall back into your basket and the hulls to blow away. Or water-separate them; dump the coarsely ground seeds into a clean pail of water and voila! there are your nutritious sunflower seeds ready for drying and storage.

Keep a number of jars of seeds handy; they can be used in many ways. Try grinding them up as sunflower meal and adding them to all kinds of baked goods. Sprinkle them on cookies before baking as a delectable topping. Add a handful to whatever breakfast cereal you are eating that day. And scattered on fruit, fresh or canned, they provide a delicate and crunchy flavor boost. One thing is certain . . . your enjoyment of sunflower seeds and the improved health of your entire family will turn you into a sunflower farmer for sure. Incidentally, wild sunflowers grow in many parts of the United States. While the heads are much smaller than domestic varieties, they can still be gathered, dried, hulled and used just like the ones you grow. Just be sure you leave enough of them in the fields to insure next year's crop. After all, the birds like them too.

Pumpkin

When you grow pumpkins as a companion crop to your corn, be sure to scoop out the seeds and put them in a bucket. Fill the bucket with water, and let it stand for several days, stirring occasionally. The connecting membrane will atrophy and the seeds will eventually drop to the bottom of the bucket. Remove them and dry them carefully in the sun, but be sure to protect them from those hungry birds. Pumpkin seeds are big enough to permit you to crack them with your teeth and enjoy the fresh kernel. Otherwise they can be cracked with a grinder or a stick and separated in the same manner as sunflower seeds.

Peanuts

Peanuts are officially a legume but since they are closer to our current topic of seeds rather than nuts, we'll

First Time Farmer's Guide

discuss them here. After they are harvested by digging them from the ground, they can be dried in the sun. Shelled at this point, they may be eaten as raw peanuts . . . in this form they possess their greatest healthfulness. If you prefer them roasted, place them in a slow oven (150° for several hours). The degree of roastedness can be determined by experiment.

Sesame Seeds

You have undoubtedly enjoyed sesame seeds for many years as a topping for hamburger buns and rolls. As with many other seeds, the nutritional benefits are great. Sesame is easily grown and a small crop will provide plenty for your entire family.

Among the many other seeds that you might consider as foods are safflower, squash, alfalfa, poppy and acorn. Don't forget, any seed can be sprouted quickly and easily, which adds to its nutritional value as well as its bulk.

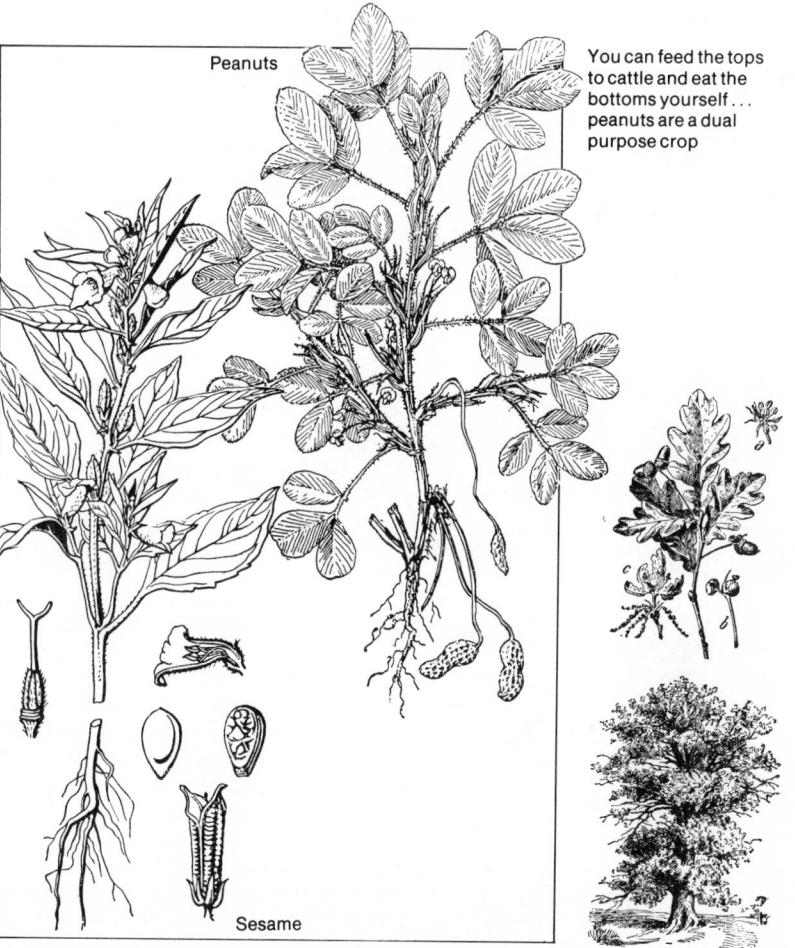

Peanuts

You can feed the tops to cattle and eat the bottoms yourself . . . peanuts are a dual purpose crop

Sesame

Grasses and Grains

'And I will send grass in thy fields for thy cattle that thou mayest eat and be full.'
Deuteronomy, Chapter 11:15

Why it's uneconomic
to grow your own
grains — but smart to
know how if you
have to

Did you know that the basis for all food in the world is grass? The grass family (gramineae) includes the great food crops wheat, rice, corn, millet, barley, rye and oats. The grass family also includes those members that provide pasture for all kinds of farm animals — clover, alfalfa, timothy, fescue and rye. Grasses are important to farmers for many reasons. They provide easily-grown food, and can be fed to farm animals for conversion into high protein meat. Grass can be grown simply to provide nutritive values to the soil. Moreover, many kinds of grass produce erosion control. Grass is highly ornamental, giving the green verdant look that we all like to see in the country.

The word grass or pasture appears often in the bible and in poetry . . . 'He maketh me to lie down in green pastures' . . . Whitman's *Leaves of Grass* . . . Sandburg's 'I am the grass, let me work.' As a farmer, first-time or otherwise, you will be close to grass. You will see green grass become meat and milk. You will see it become wheat and rice. Then, much more than in our saying so, you will realize the importance of such a simple plant. We'll consider grass from two standpoints: grass such as wheat, corn, barley, oats and rice for human and/or animal food, and grass used exclusively for animals.

Cultivated Grains

With the exception of corn, the growing of which we discussed in the Vegetable Chapter, it is unlikely that you will be growing many of the foods grains on your first-time farm. The reason is this. Throughout the world there are vast reaches of level plains and gently rolling hills. The soil and climate are perfect for growing the food grains. Producers of wheat, barley and oats use this land very efficiently. They plow and seed with

Wholesale Prices of Basic Grains, 100 pounds

September, 1973

Wheat: $4.50   Rice: $16.50   Oats: $4.20
Corn: $3.50   Barley: $4.00

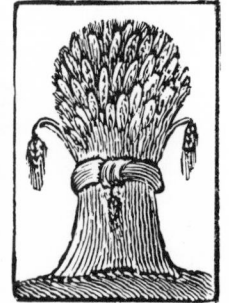

heavy machinery. They count on natural rainfall for irrigation. After the waving fields of grain change slowly from verdant green to a warm beige, enormous harvesting machines known as combines move across the ripening fields and take in the crop automatically. Combines cut the stalk, thresh out the grain, discard the chaff and load the bulging sacks of wheat, barley or oats directly onto a truck which follows the combine. As an ex-city person, you are aware that when any operation becomes very large, the cost per unit or per pound drops very low. Thus, grain farmers who talk in terms of tens of thousands of acres think nothing of producing 100 pounds of wheat for two or three dollars. As a first-time farmer, it would be difficult for you to buy the seed and plant enough for 100 pounds for three dollars. Your time is worth something per hour and even a minimal amount of equipment such as a seed broadcaster would be more than the total price of the 100 pound sack. Furthermore, you haven't begun to consider the time and expense of harvesting, threshing and sacking your grain crop.

Here's a table showing current wholesale food grain prices per 100 pounds as this book goes to press.

By no stretch of imagination could you produce this much usable food for the prices shown. Even if you had to pay double or triple these prices, which you probably would in a retail food store, they would still be far cheaper than growing them yourself.

Table B lists retail commodities from a large supplier on the West Coast. Of course, it is altogether reasonable to assume that if the social and economic fabric of our society begins to rip and tear, you may have to grow your own food grains, simply because Andy's Feed Store doesn't stock them anymore.

Growing and Storing

...and here's how

The method for growing any of the food grains, such as wheat, oats, barley, millet and rye is essentially the same. If your land is loose, merely broadcast handfuls of the desired grain seeds as evenly as possible where you want it to grow. Cover with a rake. The best time for sowing the seed is just before the spring rains. This will ensure proper germination. Most grains are produced by 'dry farming'. This means that the farmer plans on having Mother Nature do all of his irrigation by natural rainfall. Dry farming is, of course, a gamble. If sufficient rain does not fall, the dry farmer goes bankrupt that year. If your grain field is fairly small, you could irrigate it with a hose and sprinkler. Many astute grain farmers 'plant some for the crow and some to grow;' thus seeding extra grain will ensure that the birds don't rip off your entire seed bed.

Grow It or Buy It?	1/2#	1#	2#	5#	10#	25#	Each
Alfalfa Seed		1.26	2.43	5.79		24.20	
Barley, Hulled (Whole)		.29	.43	.84	1.49	3.19	
Corn, White (Whole)						3.70	
Corn Meal, Yellow Coarse A		.34	.58	1.22	2.20	4.72	
Rolled Oats		.32	.51	1.05	1.89	4.28	
Pumpkin Seed, Hulled	.89	1.69				35.95	
Rice, Brown, Long Grain		.43	.76	1.59	2.90	6.60	
Rye (Whole)			.49	.99		3.53	
Soy Beans (whole) Cook's Best		.39	.65	1.24	2.29	5.40	
Soya Meal			.65			5.85	
Sunflower Seed, Hulled	.49	.89	1.59	3.99	7.39	16.90	
Wheat Hard Red (Whole)		.29	.49	.95	1.59	3.19	
Whole Wheat Flour			.59	1.19	1.95	4.17	
Wheat Germ		.45	.69	1.49	2.79	6.59	

Once you have planted, there is very little else to do but worry a bit. So worry about whether it's going to rain or not and whether you'll survive the next series of floods, earthquakes, elections and other holocausts. Meantime your grain will do its thing . . . push up bright green leaves, grow two to three feet tall, 'head-out' or produce the green clusters. When the grain has become hard and dry, it is time to harvest. This is lots of fun— striding through the fields of ripe wheat or oats chopping the stalks with a sickle or scythe, the ancient tools that look like this.

First Time Farmer's Guide

Bring the ripened grain back to your farm house or shed and spread it out on a clean floor—wood or cement. Now simply walk on it or whack it with a stick. The grains will then pop out of the heads. Sweep everything up, grains and stalks, and carry them outside where the wind is blowing. Spread a clean canvas on the ground. Now toss the grains and stalks into the air. While doing this you'll look like a painting of some primitive culture specimen engaged in a harvest ritual. The wind will blow the stalks and chaff away, while the ripened golden grain will fall onto the cloth. After you've done this operation a few times, you'll have a better understanding of why we say you can spend your time more profitably growing strawberries, rhubarb or tomatoes. Nevertheless, grain growing know-how may some day be the most valuable information you've obtained from this book.

Storing your grain is simple . . . just put it in a container, such as a big metal trash can, and slam on the lid. This will keep the rats away. There's a unique way of preventing weevils from developing in your grain. Just get a piece of carbide from your hardware store or mail order house, drop a small chunk in a tin can full of water, and place the bubbling result inside the grain container. The acetylene gas produced will kill the insects but won't hurt either the grain or you. The left-over straw can be fed to cows, horses or rabbits or used as a mulch in your vegetable fields. Thus, you'll be making complete use of the plant, since the roots left in the ground will decay and provide nutrients for your soil. This process will work for any of the popular grains with only minor variations which you will discover as you try simple grain plantings.

Wild Grasses

Here's a mind-boggling fact: there are thousands of

The noble grass . . . ripe wheat in the early autumn sun

Wild foxtail millet
The value of grass,
grain and legume

varieties of wild grasses that grow on this planet. Practically all of them are considered very tasty by herbivorous animals. Examples of just a few of these wild and domestic grasses are:

Wild rye	Red Top	Buffalo grass
Texas bluegrass	Smooth broome	Silver beard grass
Crested wheatgrass	Foxtail millet	Lovegrass
Blue panic	Sorghum	
Kentucky bluegrass	Meadow fescue	

Some of the names may be familiar to you. You are probably also familiar with the closely related grass-like plants which are called the legumes. Legumous plants include such popular varieties as alfalfa and peanuts. We bet you didn't think of peanut hay as cattle feed. Not only that, while the cattle eat the top, you can enjoy fresh home-roasted peanuts. Growing grass and legumes for your livestock is an even easier process than growing food grains. This is because you will probably only seed the pasture once. From then on it will re-seed itself. The animals will do all of your harvesting for you—eating the grass as they wish. And they will drop their manure exactly where it will do the most good . . . right in the pasture. Without any effort on your part, those green pastures will stay green from the bountiful soil nutrients supplied by the decomposed animal manure. Meadow fescue, rye foxtail, millet and sorghum are some of the varieties of pasture grass that have proven themselves as high quality food for your livestock.

Grass, grains and legumes should play an important part in the drama of your first-time farm. In addition to their value as food for you, your family and your livestock, these easily grown and beautiful plants have many benefits and advantages.

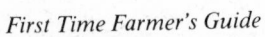

First Time Farmer's Guide

They will provide much beauty to your farmstead. Little in the world is more beautiful than fields of lush green grass interspersed with red, blue and yellow wildflowers, gently undulating in the wind of a bright June day.

More prosaic but equally important is the ability of grass to prevent erosion on your land. You may recall that one of the first tasks that follows a forest fire is to re-seed the burned off area with a tough, fast-growing grass like wild rye. We guarantee that if you will spread lots of grass seed all over your farm lands, the soil will stay where it belongs.

Even if you don't eat your grains and even if you don't pasture animals, the culture of the grass family will steadily raise the nutritive level of your farm lands. It is a common practice to plant some alfalfa, fescue or sorghum and then harrow it under to give the soil better tilth (a looser, more workable structure).

If you live in an area where winters are severe and the fields are covered with snow, you will have to make some effort to store and preserve fodder (grasses and legumes) for your livestock. The method most common and certainly the simplest is to cut the hay by hand or with a rented mower and stack it in a big haystack. Covered with a piece of waterproof canvas, it should stay dry and ready for your animals to eat all winter long. Alternatively, you could put the hay in the loft of your barn. This creates a great place for the children to play, besides furnishing your livestock with feed. Many barns have an opening above so that the hay can be tossed down to the cows, horses or goats below. In the unlikely event that you have an extensive grass growing operation, you may consider renting a haybaler. This noisy device takes huge volumes of hay and turns it into heavy, unwieldy but highly practical bales. The machine that does this is very expensive and you should have this work done for you on contract rather than making such a large capital investment. Still another way to store fodder is to cut it up with a machine designed for this purpose called a chopper, and blow the particles into a silo. Silos are those tall, cylindrical, round-roofed buildings that are as characteristic of a farmstead as a windmill. However, it's more than likely that as a first-time farmer, you will be able to store what you need for a few animals in a haystack, barn or shed.

To help you identify the grasses that you will use on your first-time farm, here is a pictorial guide to the most popular.

Smooth brome   Meadow fescue   Italian ryegrass   Tall catgrass

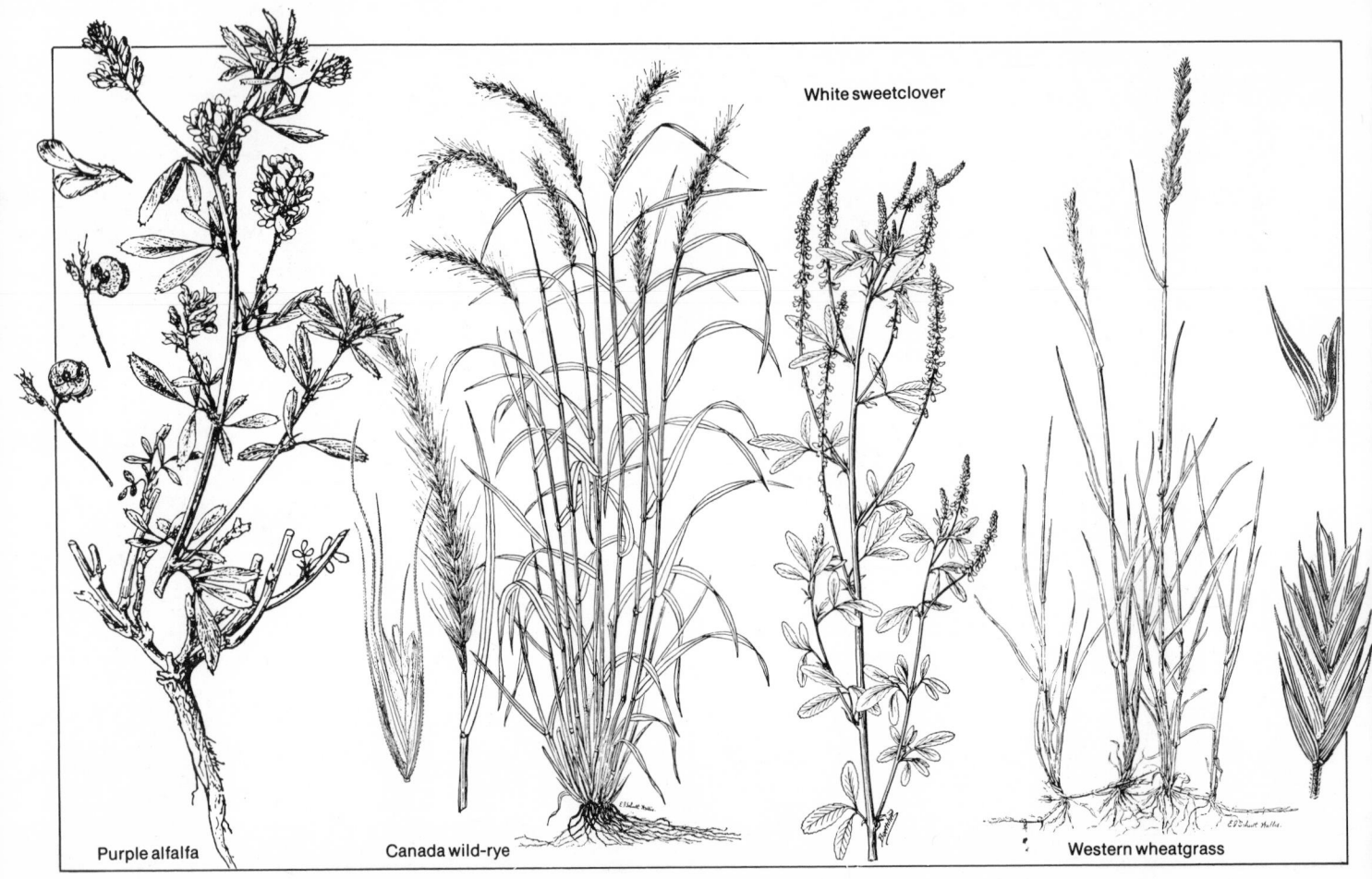

Purple alfalfa

Canada wild-rye

White sweetclover

Western wheatgrass

First Time Farmer's Guide

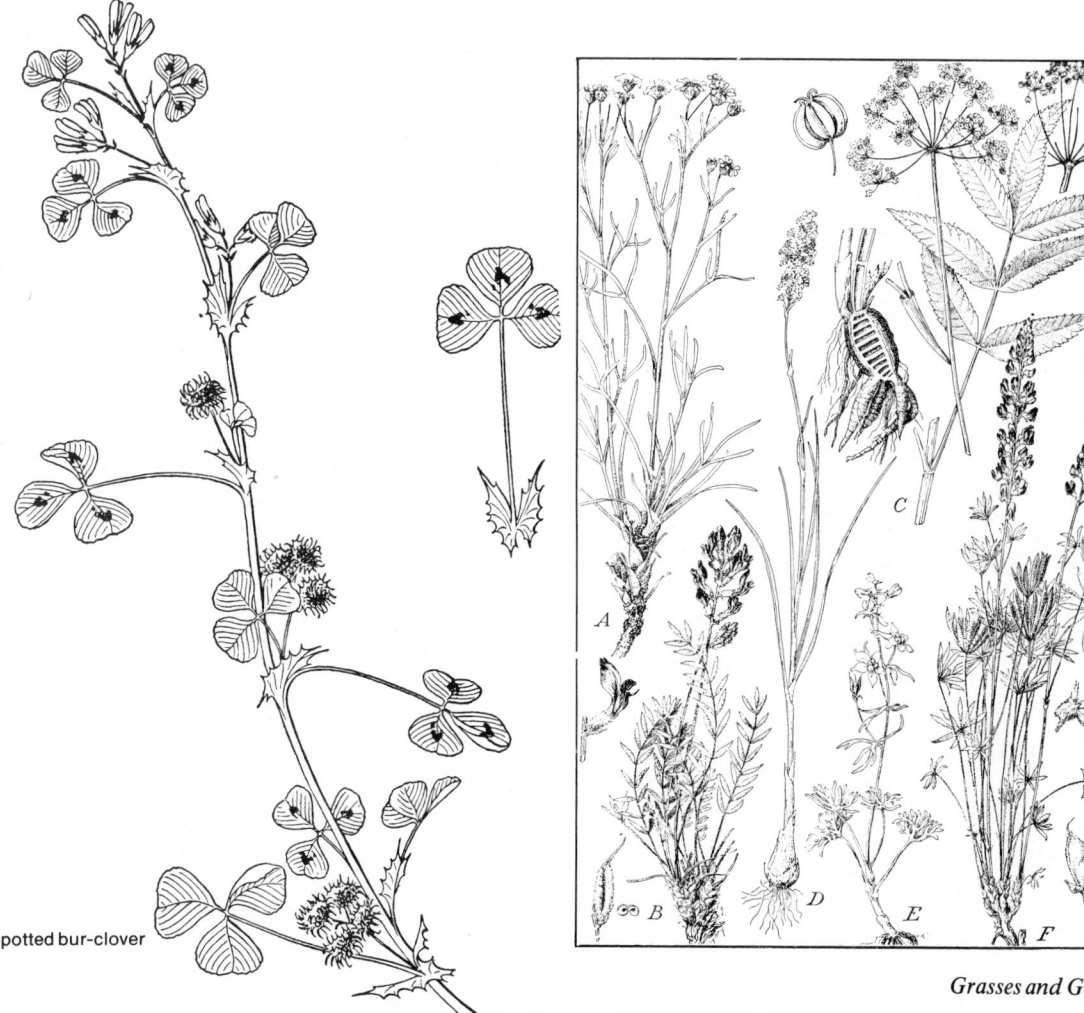

Spotted bur-clover

Some common range stock-poisoning plants: *A*, Pingue; *B*, crazyweed; *C*, Douglas waterhemlock; *D*, grassy deathcamas; *E*, Menzies larkspur; *F*, tailcup lupine. Root them out, harrow them under, move your animals, but *don't* use 2-4D.

Grasses and Grains

Livestock

'Welcome the animals of the field to your farm. Let them live amongst you as brethren and sister. Be kindly unto them.'
— *Better World News*

Everyone who has been heavy on farming from the un-named prehistoric farmer who prodded saber-toothed tigers out of his catnip patch to the oracles of organic farming, Rodale and Associates, generally agrees that animals, or at least animal fertilizers, are a must for a successful farm. Here are some of the benefits of keeping one or more different kinds of animals on your first-time farm:

They will provide manure with which you can establish that beautiful balance between nature's four-legged creations and the wonderful things that grow out of the ground.

Although not absolutely necessary for a good diet, animal proteins are complete and can add to the well-being of a first-time farmer's family.

Animals give a farm *life*. Although vegetable gardens look great, they really can't compare with the warm rapport you'll have with the farm workhorse or the newest lamb. Entertainment of a most unusually rewarding kind plus traditional aesthetic value are bonus benefits. For example, a green pasture without a meandering cow to graze and complete the picture just doesn't have it.

Among the many miscellaneous benefits, the first-time farmer should be aware that his bees will pollinate, the cow will provide the raw material for butter and cheese, the meat and eggs will be wholesome as nature intended them to be and pigs will eliminate the need for a garbage disposal unit under the sink.

In one sentence we can sum up the importance of animals on your farm and here it is. Although your first-time farm can survive on vegetables alone, farm animals will give you the balance needed for permanent independence. Every farmer has had this problem and so will you: as philosophic Henry Tetlow pointed out, 'The nat-ural tendency of most people is to make pets of farm animals, so the problem involves overcoming one's dis-inclination to kill an animal for its meat'. Perhaps the viewpoint of the old Indian hunter best circumscribes this dilemma. Indians recognized that although they did eat an animal, its descendants would eventually eat the Indian, through the dust-to-dust and back-to-life through green-plants cycle.

Should You Keep A Cow?

'If you see a poor, rundown farm . . . you need not look in the barn to know there are no cows in it.
— *Henry Tetlow*

A good cow will be the cornerstone of your farm. Here are reasons why:

A good certified milk cow will give between 2500 and 3500 quarts of rich healthful raw milk a year, which

Plants nourish your
animals; animals ferti-
lize your plants . . .
beautiful symbiosis!

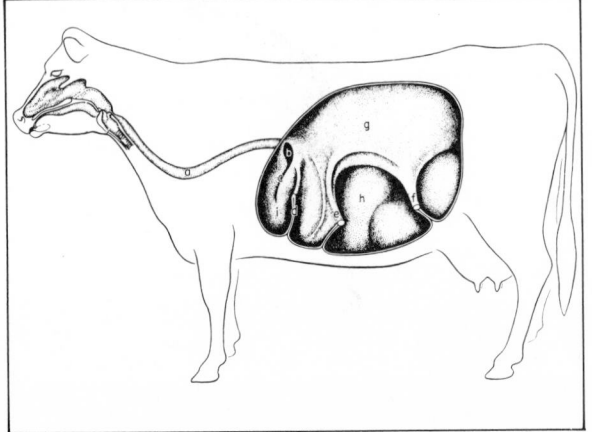

is about two gallons a day. This is enough to supply all of the milk and butter needs for at least five people for about ten months of the year. (A cow will produce no milk for one and a half to two months a year.)

A cow will also produce about 30,000 pounds (15 tons) of high quality manure. This manure, spread on your land, will help you grow lush, organic, healthful crops of anything you want to grow.

These reasons are more than enough to warrant the initial expense, feed and labor required to maintain at least one cow. However, there are other benefits that will become apparent to you as you experience life with Bossy. Just imagine the thickness and richness of cream that you will get from your own cow. It will probably be thicker than those little cartons of 'whipping cream' that you've been buying in the supermarket. Spooned over fresh wild blackberries, you will enjoy a taste sensation

enjoyed only by farm families in America. With a churn, you can turn your surplus cream into the finest, freshest butter you've ever sampled. Free of any additives or coloring, your own butter will make everything you eat, from homemade pancakes to freshly steamed carrots **and string beans taste like gourmets would like foods to taste.** For as Tetlow said:

'There is no secret of good cooking; it is the intelligent use of the best materials and the greatest of these is butter. If you use the finest butter in sufficient quantities, the cooking can hardly go wrong.'

Imagine having so much butter that you can use it as the shortening for all of your home-baked goodies. Just visualize cutting a slice off your own butter-crust bread and spreading it with a thick layer of freshly churned sweet butter. There are many places to use the milk and cream that you will receive daily from your own

This system prevents waste of natural liquids and nutrients, and the usual 50% loss of animal fertilizer. It can pay for itself in one to three years.

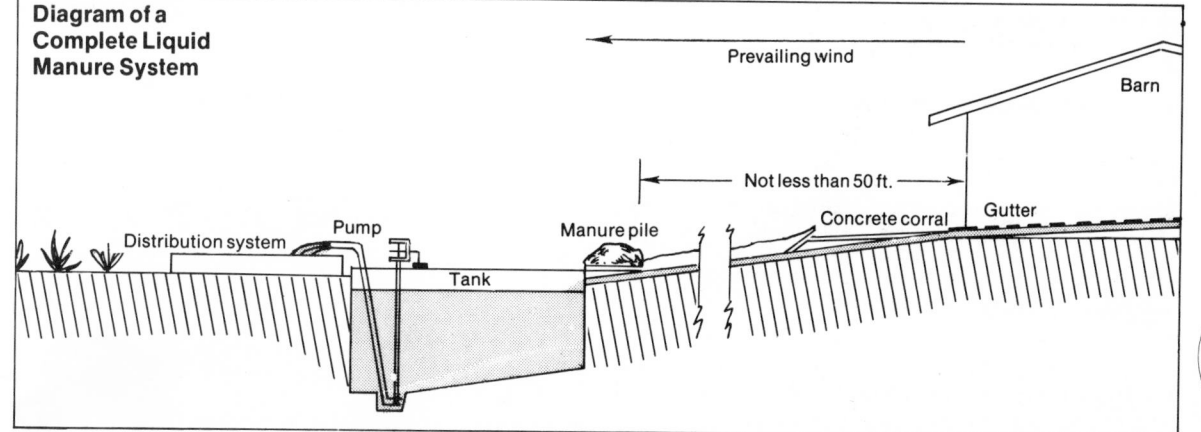

Diagram of a Complete Liquid Manure System

Prevailing wind

Barn

Not less than 50 ft.

Distribution system

Pump

Manure pile

Concrete corral

Gutter

Tank

Below: Simple cow or
cattle feeding barn,
feed trough and pail
with nipple for
feeding calves

cow. With a cream separator, you can produce skim milk, which is a wonderful food for any of your other livestock, from chickens to pigs. You will be able to make your own cottage cheese, buttermilk and yoghurt, and if that isn't enough, think about preparing homemade cheeses. A cream separator is a unit that will almost instantly separate the cream from the milk. Of course, you can do this by just letting the milk stand and the cream will rise to the surface. However, this takes time and if you are handling many gallons of whole milk per week, a separator would be worthwhile to have.

It is no coincidence that countries where the living and health standards are really high are the same countries that produce and use large quantities of fresh certified raw milk. The pink cheeks and robust health of the Swiss, Swedes, Norwegians, Finns and Danes can be attributed largely to their use of these wholesome dairy

products.

The feed that you give your cow actually produces a double benefit. Not only do you enjoy all of the rich milk, cream, butter, cheese and various milk products, your cow will produce the nutrient-rich manure that is a must for organic gardening and farming. Experts agree that cow manure is, pound for pound, the best fertilizer that any type of soil needs. If your cow is kept close to your compost pile, only minimal labor will be required to put the manure to good use.

Aside from the initial labor expended in preparing the cow's quarters, which can be a barn as small as the one illustrated, it should not take more than thirty minutes a day to feed and milk your cow. Feeding involves placing hay, grain or other daily feed in the cow's feed trough or manger. Watering can be simplified and automated by installing a large tub equipped with a float

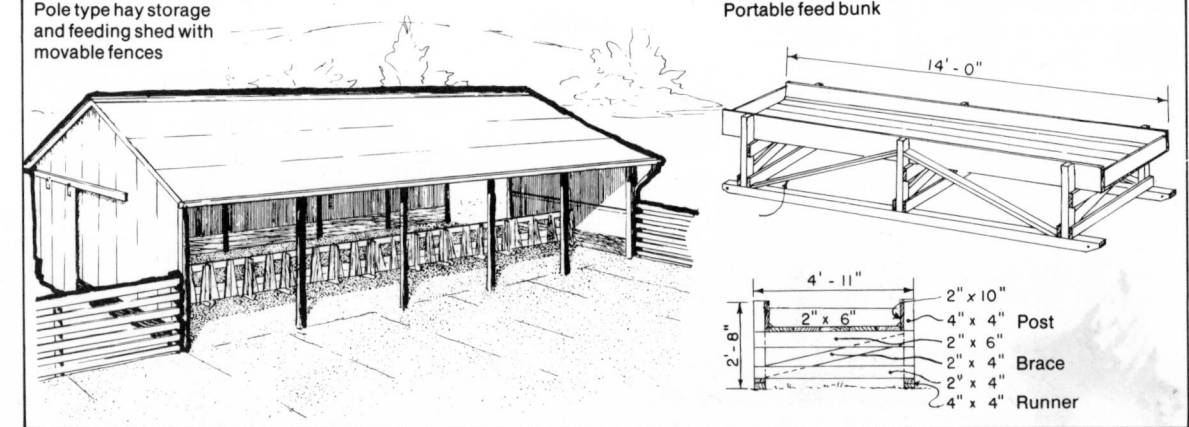

Pole type hay storage and feeding shed with movable fences

Portable feed bunk

14' - 0"

4' - 11"

2' - 8"

2" x 10"
2" x 6"
4" x 4" Post
2" x 6"
2" x 4" Brace
2" x 4"
4" x 4" Runner

First Time Farmer's Guide

valve similar to that used to keep the water level in a toilet tank. A float valve is a simple but effective unit that automatically shuts off water when it reaches a desired level. Shown here is a typical cow's feed trough and water tank. Incidentally, it's an old farm practice to keep a pair of goldfish in the tank to prevent algae from forming. In the winter you can keep the water from freezing by dropping in an electric heater. These heaters use electricity to create enough heat to warm a large amount of water sufficiently so that it will not freeze. They are inexpensive and long-lasting, and they will more than repay their cost by insuring that your cow has water to drink regardless of low temperatures.

Milking a cow is really not difficult and can be learned in a short time from the experts at the dairy closest to you. Milking machines have been highly perfected and are available at reasonable cost from a number of sources. However, for just one cow, it would probably be simpler to milk by hand.

The cost of feed for a cow would be about $80 to $100 for the two and a half tons of hay that she'll need annually and somewhat less than $100 for grain and purchased daily feed. However, if your farm is large enough to pasture the cow or you are able to grow some of the feed in the form of hay or corn, then these costs would be proportionately reduced.

The initial cost of your cow will vary depending on many factors. But here is a current price quote for a registered Holstein—$400-$500.

A small milk pasteurizer that will handle the output of one cow costs about $55 from one of the big mail order houses like Sears or Wards. These units raise the temperature of milk sufficiently to kill any bacteria. However, if your cow is certified and checked periodi-

Below: Concrete pipe section used as waterer, and demand type watering device

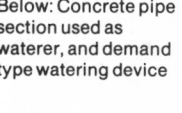

cally for tuberculosis or other transmittable diseases, fresh raw milk is far more nutritious and as safe to drink as pasteurized milk.

Illustrated here are some of the other items that you can acquire to make life with your cow easier and more pleasant.

For more information, send for these publications:
Magazines:

'The Dairyman', PO 819, Corona, California
'Dairyman's League News', 100 Park Avenue, New York 10017

Booklets:

'Feeding Diary Cattle', 'Dairy Cattle Breeds', 'Raising Dairy Calves and Heifers'. (These booklets can be had for free from USDA).

Beef Cattle and the Small Farm

If you keep a cow and breed her, once a year you'll receive a calf. The calf will either be female, in which case you will probably keep it and eventually own another producing cow, or it will be a male, in which case you will have a choice of raising a steer (castrated male calf) or a bull. Since there would be very little need for a bull on a small farm, the choice would lean heavily in the direction of making your male calves into easily handled steers. A local veterinarian can best handle this job.

Another method of obtaining beef cattle for a farm would be to purchase newborn calves from a nearby dairy. Prices vary with the current supply and demand fluctuations. However, buying a newborn calf and feeding it with surplus milk from your own cow until it is weaned would be less expensive than buying what is known as a feeder steer. Feeder steers can be purchased from cattle ranches or at auctions. However, the purchase price of a feeder steer added to the cost of fattening it on your farm, plus butchering costs and other miscellaneous expenses, would probably not be as wise an investment as raising your own calf or fattening some pigs or rabbits. Typical of suppliers of calves is Walter McFarland, Watertown, Wisconsin 53094. If you will send him a card, he will mail you a brochure and a price list. These describe respectively, the calves that he will ship to your first-time farm and the cost including delivery.

Big animals require large quantities of food and lots of water. A steer will eat between 20 and 30 pounds of hay, clover or alfalfa a day and drink about twelve gallons of water. To provide this much forage, you would need at least an acre or two of pasture per steer, plus two or more acres of hay. If your farm has sufficient, well-

watered pastureland, it would be practical to keep as many head as you would need for your own purposes. The time and trouble involved in marketing a few head of cattle would not be practical from a financial standpoint. However, if you do your own butchering, it may be possible to realize a profit by selling the meat locally.

A small scale cattleman who lives within an hour's drive of a large city, has been able to show a fairly good profit by letting his cattle graze on leased land. His own 40-acre spread lies adjacent to about 600 acres of grassy, hilly land unused by its owner. The cattleman leases this land on a percentage-of-the-profits basis. He gives the landowner a percentage of what he makes from the sale of 15 or 20 head of finished steers per year.

Another way of obtaining low cost cattle-grazing land is to apply to your local office of the Bureau of Land Management. It is possible that you will be able to lease unused government land for grazing purposes. See the list of land offices in the Chapter on 'Land'.

In addition to food, a fair amount of equipment and housing is needed for the home beef herd. This equipment need not be expensive, in fact, you can make most of it yourself from scrap lumber and salvaged materials. Here are some typical items that would be useful but not mandatory.

A long-lasting concrete tank would provide sanitary drinking water for your cattle. The tank could be made from a section of concrete or galvanized iron pipe placed on a circular paving.

Where temperatures are high in summer, a shade shelter would be much appreciated by your steers. Of course, if you have trees, this will be unnecessary. A simple shade shelter would suffice until the trees you plant grow big enough to do the job.

First Time Farmer's Guide

A fixed feeding shed would keep the hay and feeds clean and dry. A typical pole-type feeding shed (as shown in the cow section) can be used.

Unless you can let your steers roam freely over range land, they will need to be fenced. The most inexpensive and common fence is one made from 4 x 4 posts or poles and barbed wire. If you have lots of trees, then two or three-inch diameter sapling poles can be employed. A modern and highly effective fence is the charged wire type or electric fence. This consists of a single strand of wire through which a current of high voltage electricity pulses. Any animal touching the wire receives a shock and soon learns to stay well away from the fence. Despite initial costs this fence, because of its simplicity, may be the least expensive.

To avoid the nuisance of opening and shutting gates, you can build what is known as a cattle guard. Cattle will not step where they may have their hooves trapped. Thus, a series of parallel timbers, pipes or old railroad tracks four or five feet long and ten feet wide will keep the cattle in but let you and your pickup out.

Miscellaneous items that will help you operate more effectively are a portable scale to weigh your animals to see how fast or slowly they are gaining, a loading shoot to make it easy to transport them to market, and a chute. This latter is necessary to hold animals while they are being examined.

From this rather extensive review of what is needed, it is plain that the first-time farmer should take time to consider everything involved before including beef production as a part of farm activities. However, if you are fond of good beef raised organically, then it will undoubtedly be worth the effort.

There are a number of beef cattle associations that

Left: Portable cattle scale. Below: cattle guard... animals will not risk having their feet trapped by spaces between rails or pipes

will be happy to send you free literature. Here are several typical associations plus companies that sell equipment, supplies or feed for beef cattle.

American Angus Association
3201 Frederick Boulevard
St Joseph, Missouri 64501
(Information)

American Hereford Association
715 Hereford Drive
Kansas City, Missouri 64105
(Information)

American International Charolais Association
1610 Old Spanish Trail
Houston, Texas 77025
(Information)

Beef Industry Council
National Live Stock and Meat Board
36 South Wabash Avenue
Chicago, Illinois 60603
(Information)

Brauer Corporation
PO Box 7272
Ingleside, Texas 78362
(Equipment)

Hesston Corporation
Hesston, Kansas 67062
(Equipment)

Ralston Purina Company
Checkerboard Square
St Louis, Missouri 63199
(Cattle Feed) (This firm also has free animal care booklets).

Typical periodicals that can help you are:

American Cattle Producer
801 E 17th Avenue
Denver, Colorado 80218

California Cattleman
Mezzanine, Senator Hotel
12th & L Streets
Sacramento, California 95814

The Cattleman
410 E Weatherford Street
Ft Worth, Texas 76102

Livestock Breeder Journal
PO 4264, 1506 Hardeman Avenue
Macon, Georgia 31208

For just 25¢ for both you can obtain two booklets that will be helpful. There are 'Feedlot and Ranch Equipment' and 'The Farm Beef Herd' which are available from the USDA, Washington DC 20250.

Pigs

'We just love the pigs. They are regular pets already. They sure can put away a flake of green alfalfa in a hurry. Again, I want to say that we were more than pleased with the pigs. We didn't think they would be that big for their age.' — *John Kaufman, San Diego, California.*

'The Duroc gilt farrowed two weeks after arrival — a litter of nine, which she raised very well indeed. They look excellent and draw very favorable comments. We are quite pleased with the whole group.' — *L.J. Merek, Alberta, Canada.*

These are letters that people have written to a farm that supplies breeding stock for those who wish to grow their own pigs. This farm does business with all fifty of the United States as well as with Mexico, Japan, Cuba, Venezuela and many other countries. It is possible to begin your pig adventure with one of their package offers. For example, they will ship you two gilts and one unrelated boar for $210. You can have your choice of registered pure bred stock from many breeds — Landrace, English, Canadian or American, Yorkshire, Lacombe, Tamworth or Blue Spotted Hybrids. For a catalog and current prices, write Tweddle Farms, Fergus, Ontario, Canada.

There are many ways to look at the possibility of keeping a few pigs on your farm:

From a nutritional standpoint, pork and pork products have fallen into some disrepute. Although many people like to use a little crisp bacon as a condiment, the ingestion of many pounds of pork is less than desirable due to its high animal fat content. But suit yourself on this. If you're a pork lover and it seems to agree with you, then make it with the hogs.

Studies by various agricultural institutions have shown that you can buy a mature pig ready for butchering for about the same cost as raising one on purchased feeds. Of course, if you have lots of land, grow corn or other forage and most of your pigs' food is grown inhouse, then you'll be able to grow your own pork for less than the professionals. You'll also have the added advantage that your pork chops won't be full of weird, 'approved' chemicals.

While pigs being dirty by nature is a myth (they'll stay just as clean as you if you'll keep their quarters clean), their manure is pretty strong stuff. To keep a sweet-smelling farm, you should invest in a pig manure disposal system, such as described in this chapter, a liquid manure system. So with these considerations in mind, let's proceed to some plain talk about pigs.

The best way to start with pigs on your first-time farm is to buy a young pig or two in the spring. Be sure that the piglet is from good stock, innoculated against hog cholera, and has been wormed. It is a truism that the quality of pig that you buy will determine whether you will come out ahead or behind. Therefore, make certain that it's a bona fide healthy young pig. Pigs are one of the easiest animals to feed in that they will happily gobble up almost everything and anything. Save all your vegetable trimmings, scraps from the table and surplus garden produce. Your pig will enjoy this food in addition to any grain such as corn, wheat or barley and any type of hay or grass. Probably the best thing about a pig on your farm is that nothing edible will go to waste.

If your farm is in a mild climate, the only housing needed while you are raising the pig is some simple shade. Even a tree would be sufficient. These accommodations assume that you are keeping the pig outdoors. If you wish, you can build a concrete-floored hog pen which

'Pigs are more than just pigs... they're our friends!'

Pigs really put on the pounds in a hurry

will make for maximum sanitation. By hosing off the floor daily and flushing it into a liquid manure system, you will eliminate most of the problems usually associated with pig production.

The diagram on page 185 shows a liquid manure system that you can build. As shown, the barn and holding tank are placed so that the water-manure mixture may be flushed, using gravity flow. From the holding tank the liquid manure is then pumped to your fields or distributed by a tank truck. An alternative system for eliminating pig wastes efficiently is described in the Chapter on Power.

In addition to the housing, you will need a hog trough which is built of wood. Watering can be done automatically by using a drinking cup purchased from one of the mail order houses. It will surprise you how fast your first-time farm pig will grow. In about two months

he'll weigh nearly 100 pounds and in a little over four months he will probably tip the scales at about 200 pounds. After a pig reaches about 220 pounds, the ratio of weight gained to the amount of food he eats drops substantially. Thus, slaughtering and dressing a pig is best done at about 220 pounds.

It is best to have a professional help you with this task, at least the first time. Alternatively, the USDA has a booklet on slaughtering and preparing farm animals for consumption. Write to the USDA, Washington, DC 20250, and ask for MRR 755, 'Hog Slaughtering and Dressing Systems'. Another useful booklet is 'Slaughtering, Cutting and Processing Pork on the Farm', F 2138 (both are free). If a general guide on pigs proves successful for you, then subscribe to 'The National Hog Farmer', 1999 Sheperd Road, St Paul, Minnesota 55116. It contains much information and ads pertaining to pig produc-

Whether you're a "veg" or not, honey-cured bacon with buckwheat cakes *has* to be *the* farm breakfast!

First Time Farmer's Guide

tion, feeds and equipment

In the wild country of parts of the Los Padres National Forest, live bands of wild pigs . . . the descendants of domestic pigs that broke free from 19th century California homesteads. The author has seen these pigs roaming among the oak trees rooting acorns. They appear to be as happy and healthy as only wild animals can be. They are clean, sleek and plenty feisty, snorting at onlookers with dignified arrogance. This further documents the contention that wild animals, or domestic animals maintained in a nearly wild state, suffer from few diseases . . . nature's way is best.

Pigs can even become pets for your children. The author has a friend whose young daughter has been raising a boar and a sow. She calls them Pigmalion and Pigfemalion.

Goats

Here are some facts about goats obtained from magazines, books and contacts with goat owners.

Goats are extremely clean animals. They are selective about their food, eating only that which is clean and fresh. The legend that goats will eat an old tin can began when a starving goat was tethered in some alley and licked the adhesive that once held the label to a tin can.

Goats are hardy animals. If given clean quarters and healthful pasture, you should have no disease problems at all. Goats rarely get tuberculosis or other diseases characteristic of cows.

Goat owners all agree that goats have rare intelligence, interesting personalities and are productive of rich milk, butter, cheese, meat, furs and skins. It would be difficult to match this value in output for the input in time and labor. Try to think of a goat as the Volkswagen

The major problem with young goats is overfeeding . . . so beware accommodating their overwhelming appetites. If they do develop gas, just give them a terrific squeeze. It works!

'I guess you might call goats, the poor man's cow.'—*Anonymous*

of the dairy world . . . cheap to buy, cheap to operate and lots of good, trouble-free 'mileage'.

The simplest way to get started with goats is to purchase a doe that is producing milk, There are many breeds—Saanen, Toggenburg and Nubian, to mention three—but regardless of the breed, it is advisable to buy one that is registered and has a good milking record. If you'd like to review the goat scene, send for sample copies of some of the publications devoted to goats:

Dairy Goat Journal
PO 836
Columbia, Missouri 65201

Dairy Goat Guide
318 Waterloo Road
Marshall, Wisconsin 53559

You can expect to pay from about $125 up for a milking doe of good lineage. Acquiring your first goat at a time when spring has already sprung is desirable because you will be able to tether the goat on any grassy plot on your farm. This means that you won't have to invest in any housing until the following winter. If you have a fenced pasture that is goat-proof, you can eliminate the chain. Incidentally, if you keep sheep also, goats may be kept in with the sheep with no problems.

If you are just as enthusiastic about keeping a goat in the fall as you were in the spring, then you can make room for your goat in your barn or build a simple shelter.

Since the goat will be getting most of its food from the pasture, you will only have to add a pound or two of grain and perhaps kitchen scraps or surplus carrots, turnips and other vegetables. Clean water is the only other item necessary to this basic goat raising plan.

Milking a goat is exactly the same process as milking a cow. The only difference is that it will take less time since a goat gives about two to three quarts of milk per day. Goats may be milked in the pasture or you may

First Time Farmer's Guide

build a milking stand. This is an 18 inch high platform, long enough and wide enough to accommodate your goat. Two posts, one removable, keep the goat in place while you are milking. Goats are such affectionate, pet-like animals that you'll probably enjoy the milking process as much as she will. Because they are small and friendly, milking chores can be entrusted to women and children.

The care and use of goat's milk is identical to that of cows, with these exceptions. Goat's milk is naturally homogenized so that it does not separate as quickly as cow's milk. Due to this fact, it is more easily digested and frequently advised for people who are allergic to cow's milk.

When you have decided that you would like to expand your goat herd, here are several reference works that will provide the details of breeding, care and feeding of kids, care of bucks, dehorning and other treatment.

Aids to Goat Keeping by C.A. Leach, available from Dairy Goat, Box 836, Columbia, Missouri 65201.

The Goat Book by J.D. Belanger, available from Daily Goat Guide, Marshall, Wisconsin 53559.

Sheep

If you have ever seen a newborn lamb, we don't need to describe it. If you haven't, here is an attempt to communicate what they are like. First of all, they are much smaller than the frisky lambs you've seen in still or moving pictures. They look like toy, stuffed lambs come to life. They can walk as soon as they are born and stagger about somewhat awkwardly, uttering little cries and looking for the lunch counter.

Along with carrots and apples, you should grow a little pure joy on your farm. We guarantee that an occasional lamb delivered by your own ewe will more than fulfill this need. Sheep are easy to raise, particularly so if you have enough good pasture. An acre or two of lush grass plus as much grain as one sheep will eat in 10 or 15 minutes plus fresh water are all you need. As with any of the other suggested farm livestock projects, start small. A bred ewe or a ram and a ewe couple would be fine. If you can't buy these locally, write for sample copies of 'Sheep Breeder & Sheepman', P.O. 796, Columbia, Missouri 65201, or 'Sheep & Goat Raiser', 233 W. Twohig, San Angelo, Texas 76901.

Advertisers in these publications sell all kinds of sheep. Here's just some of the breeds available today: Hampshires, Cheviots, Rambouillets, Corriedales and Suffolk. These quiet animals produce nutritious meat, useful wool which you can spin yourself and warm sheepskins with lots of applications around the farm. Of course the real advantage is the joy of watching these woolly creatures quietly graze and their unbelievably beautiful offspring kick up their little heels over the grass. Probably the biggest problem you'll have is that your children will become so attached to your sheep and rams

One of the easiest animals to raise on your first time farm

that you will never have lamb chops that were grown on your own farm.

About the only other requirement for keeping sheep would be a small shelter. Here's one that is both modern in design and inexpensive to build.

Tips on Sheep Raising:

Buy the very best you can afford. Healthy sheep maintained naturally should give you no problems.

Ewes seldom require aid in giving birth. However, check the lambs for 'pinning' . . . their tails become plastered against their rear ends due to the richness of the mother's milk.

You can shear a ram any time except before winter when he needs his own coat. In Europe it has long been the custom to cut off wool in handfuls and spin it with a simple device like this hand spinner. To make yarn from raw wool, draw it out, attach it to the hook end of the spinner and then give the lower end a quick twist. The wool will then be drawn into tightly twisted yarn ready to knit. After knitting, it can be washed and dyed to suit.

Here are some tips on sheep raising gleaned from the relaxed and casual fan magazine for sheep called 'The Shepherd':

Sheep raising is unique among livestock enterprises. You don't have to hassle with federal, state, county and local health inspectors like, for example, dairymen.

There's no set size of operation. You can start with a small flock . . . even one, bred ewe. Then, if everything works out, develop a one- or two-ram flock.

Sheep can be started with an absolute minimum of capital. You won't have to owe money to a bank, equipment manufacturers or feed stores.

Sheep provide something of engaging interest to every member of the family, from the youngest to the oldest. Little Mary can have her lamb, son Bob and Dad can do the shearing, while Mom spins and weaves goodies for a roadside stand.

Rather than buy equipment, make a survey of what's on hand. Is there an old shed or barn that could be used as a sheep shelter? Perhaps a neighbor has one that may be had for taking it away. How about a local auction? Any used wood, all you need are hammer and saw, nails, a square, tape measure and pencil. Then you're ready to build fences and make pens and feeders. For bedding, use straw or shavings from a lumber mill.

Beginners and even professional sheep men pick up stale bread from bakeries and over-age greens from the green grocer. Where vegetable crops are grown, small or misshapen carrots, beets and potatoes can be had cheaply or free. Sheep love apples, wild or domestic, and if there's a cider mill nearby, try to arrange to haul away their pomace (the pulp left over after pressing out the apple juice). Just make sure that all the food that you pick for your sheep is free of harmful chemicals and pesticides.

Two booklets available free from the USDA, Washington, DC 20250 are 'Fencing, Feeding and Creep Panels for Sheep' and 'Slaughtering, Cutting and Processing Lamb on the farm'.

First Time Farmer's Guide

Horses

One of the easiest farm animals to care for is the horse. They are intelligent, friendly animals that have served man well for many thousands of years. There's really nothing to their care as long as you let them live as naturally as they once did when they roamed the world. You can keep a horse on as little as one-quarter acre. Of course with this amount of pasture, you will have to feed the horse hay and grain. However, if you have ten or twenty acres or more, your horse can forage for most of his own feed. Horses will eat almost any kind of grass, wild or domestic. They particularly like oat hay, alfalfa and similar domestic grasses. They will also nibble your rye grass, lawn or wildflower stalks and dote on hand-held carrots and apples. An occasional feeding of wheat or corn would be welcome. Unlimited fresh water plus a block of salt are all that is needed to complete your horse's nutritional needs.

Although it isn't mandatory, currying or brushing a horse will keep his hair clean and attractive. Be sure to take the brambles and thorns out of his tail because he uses that a lot to switch away pesky flies.

Wild horses don't need shoes because they wear down their hooves naturally. However, a pastured horse should have his hooves trimmed or trimmed and shod by a farrier regularly. Almost every farm community has a blacksmith, farrier or other professional who can do the job. The cost averages about ten to fifteen dollars.

The author once kept a horse for four years and other than the expense for hay, grain and shoeing, there was only a small bill for a vet when the horse developed watering eyes. It turned out to be only a temporary upset due to the horse's getting pollen in its eyes.

Livestock

Horses can be extremely useful around the farm. Harnessed to a wagon or sled, they can be used for much of the heavy pulling work that you would have to do by hand or with a tractor. If you have a large farm, your horse will make an excellent non-polluting transportation medium. And let's face it, the real reason you'll keep a horse is for your children. The fun they will have growing up with Pixie or old Tom will far exceed any expense or work. Just imagine your twins riding gentle Betsy down the road to the old schoolhouse on a fine June morning!

An added bonus of keeping a horse or two on your farm is the steady supply of manure which they will generate for your compost pile.

The minimum equipment that you'll need to ride your horse is a bridle, reins, a saddle blanket and a saddle. The latter is optional because for the relaxed, casual riding done around a farm, you can use a bareback pad. The bridle is placed over the horse's head and the reins attached to it. This gives you steering control. The saddle or bareback pad is placed on the horse's back and held tightly with a cinch which passes under the animal's stomach. If you intend to use your horse for power, check with your local veterinarian for a source of harness. It's no longer as freely available as several decades ago, but it can still be purchased. Much of this equipment can be purchased secondhand in a rural community. Even new the basic necessities aren't too prohibitive.

For more information, write to the following magazines: 'Horsemen's Journal, 20412 Center Ridge Road, Rocky River, Ohio 44116 and the 'Horse Lovers Magazine', PO 1432, Richmond, California 94802.

These low-cost booklets: 'Light Horses' and 'Saddle Horse Barn' can be obtained from the good old USDA, Washington 20250.

Chickens

Chickens are easy. Keeping chickens for eggs and Sunday dinner can be as simple as you wish. Here are several methods arranged in ascending order of time and money expenditures.

The Practically No-Work, No-Expense Egg Factory

Go to the nearest neighboring farm or ranch that has young laying hens. Buy three of them. The price will vary depending on the type of chicken, the season of the year and your bargaining powers. Put the chickens in a cardboard box, punch some holes in it and take them home. As soon as you let them out of the box, feed them some of the chicken feed that you purchased with the chickens. Be good to them, radiate love, give them a nice non-tipable dish of fresh cold water. Toss them an occasional treat like a few leaves of lettuce or cabbage. From then on, these chickens will be your friends and hang around you to see what kind of goodies you are going to give them next. Find an old wooden box and fill it half full of straw. Nail it to the inside wall of your barn or shed. The next time you feed the chickens, feed them near the box so that they will get the idea that this is where they should pay back your kindness. Since chickens are not intellectual giants, you might put one of your store-bought eggs or a china egg in the nest to acquaint them with its purpose. At night these chickens will probably roost in a nearby tree or on the rafters of your barn.

And that's really *all* there is to it! You feed them a little, they range around your farm yard eating stray insects, seeds and other chicken delights, while simultaneously fertilizing your whole farm. They'll cluck contentedly and enjoy the sunshine. This is the way chickens *want* to live and *should* live. Because they are living

They're stupid but lovable

a natural life and not cooped up in a little wire cage with three or four other inmates, they will probably produce groovy, nutritious, healthful eggs, never get any diseases and give your farmyard that traditional Currier and Ives calendar look.

The next step in your super simple chicken works is to buy a rooster of the same species. From then on most of the eggs will be fertile. Some people believe that fertile eggs are healthier—suit yourself. But one thing sure about fertile eggs is that if you'll leave half a dozen in a secluded nest instead of eating them, one of your hens will get the broody, maternal instinct and begin spending most of her time keeping those eggs warm. After a spell, little fluffy chicks will emerge from these eggs and you'll be on your way to a larger flock.

The above description is based on actual experience with chickens. It's the way that chickens are raised and tended all over the world. It's completely natural and is guaranteed to produce the *most* in eggs and fried chicken with the *least* effort.

A Slightly More Sophisticated Egg Business

If your farm needs more eggs and more chickens, then perhaps it would be wise to consider creating a permanent henhouse and yard. Plan on giving each hen about four square feet of inside living area. For a couple of dozen hens, a henhouse about 10′ x 10′ would be dandy. Here's a typical henhouse, showing the layout. They also need a fenced yard in which they can run and play and create good vibrations among themselves. You can let them run around the farm occasionally for a nice outing that will keep them clucking happily for weeks thereafter. Again, if you treat these often mistreated, not-too-bright little creatures of God with genuine affection,

First Time Farmer's Guide

they'll reward you with the best eggs you've ever eaten.

Two varieties of chickens that have been good egg producers are White Leghorns and Rhode Island Reds. Great for a start, you may want to get into other types latter on. To give you an idea of price, you can buy White Leghorn pullets (a pullet is a young chicken which will soon begin laying eggs) for thirty to forty dollars per hundred. An advantage of buying in these quantities by mail is that they'll come to you postpaid with guaranteed 100 per cent safe arrival. The mail order people do this by putting in enough extra chickens to make up for any that don't survive the trip. Two typical sources of chickens by mail is Gurney's, Yankton, South Dakota 57078 and Mrs. Berry's Farm, Box 142, Clarinda, Iowa.

What To Feed Them

Any feed store has a wide selection of both commer-

cial and natural feeds. The former are prepared mixes containing various chemicals, growth-hasteners ('chicken speed') and other unnatural substances. If you like eggs and chicken meat with lots of weird molecules roaming around in them, buy the commercial feed. If you lean more to the natural way of life, then buy some cracked corn and other grains like wheat, oats, barley and rye. A little mash, which is simply grains crushed to a fine powder, is a good idea. Your friendly feed store will also stock crushed oyster shells and similar sources of calcium, which is needed for strong shell development. Chickens also need grit . . . finely crushed rock . . . to enable them to digest their food. These items plus fresh water, kitchen scraps and the natural foods on your farm like insects, worms and scattered seeds and tidbits are all you'll need to keep your chickens healthy and happy.

Chicken-Raising Accessories

An incubator is a heated enclosure that is used to hatch fertile eggs. You can provide your own fertile eggs or buy them. When you place the eggs in the incubator and turn the heat on, the climate will simulate the furry, warm, underneath side of a brood hen. One wonderful day when you look in the incubator you will see fuzzy yellow baby chicks running around peeping their heads off. Others will be in the process of pecking their way through the shell. When they're all out, it's time to move them to the brooder.

A brooder is a heated cover that provides the warmth and protection that chicks need while they grow into pullets. Both incubators and brooders can be purchased through mail order supply houses like Wards and Sears. But if you'd rather, you can build your own. For example an incubator can be just a container in which

A simple hen house that you can build for under $50

Livestock

you place a light bulb and maintain a steady heat of about 90 to 100 degrees. A brooder can be nothing more than three or four heat lamps (infra red) placed over an area spread with sawdust. The chicks will gather under heat without any orders from you.

Things like feeders and waterers can be purchased or, for economy you can improvise them from pieces of scrap lumber, pet dishes and other odds and ends.

As we go into the home stretch of the Twentieth Century, we are all finding that it's getting more and more difficult to live a natural life . . . to enjoy natural foods. Thus, keeping a flock of chickens to provide you and your family with eggs and poultry is a very good idea. For the amount of time and money invested, few farm projects produce greater rewards in food and fun.

Here are two interesting poultry magazines. Check your rural library for samples or write to 'Poultry Digest', Garden State Building, Sea Island City, New Jersey 08243 or 'Everybody's Poultry Magazine', Hanover, Pennsylvania 17331.

These well-written booklets, 'Farm Poultry Management', 'The Home Chicken Flock', and 'Automatic Feeding Equipment for Poultry' are available from USDA, Washington, DC 20250.

Rabbits, a Definition

'Hey, George, kin I take care of the rabbits, kin I, George, huh, kin I, George?' — *Of Mice and Men, John Steinbeck*

An animal easily raised by anyone under any climatic conditions in all parts of the United States and Canada.

An animal that produces young 30 days after breeding, raising up to 8 young each time it litters—raising four to five litters a year safely.

An animal that must not be confused with ordinary 'pet rabbits'. Standard bred rabbits are larger, grow faster, produce meat quicker, have better fur, are more prolific, with health and vitality bred into them, and are therefore subject to few diseases.

An animal without peer as a meat, fur and wool producer. Multiplies fast and reaches marketing age quicker than any meat producing animal, 2 to 2½ pounds edible meat at 8 weeks. A commercial animal that now is playing, and will in the future, play a big part in the meat, fur and wool supply of the world.

A first-time farmer will enjoy the easy success that will be his in growing rabbits because no other meat supply is easier, less troublesome or cheaper to produce.

Here's a system that costs little more than your time. First make a collection of wooden boxes. You can find them behind grocery, hardware and many other stores. Size isn't too important because even the smaller ones can be used as nesting boxes. Next buy a couple of square yards of hardware mesh (½ inch squares) and a pair of brass hinges. A handful of galvanized staples and a few scraps of roofing paper or asbestos shingles plus a little scrap lumber from your farmstead will get you into the rabbit business. Just follow these directions to make the easiest and least expensive rabbit hutches in the world:

Take a saw and cut four rectangular openings in one large box. Cover two of these with wire mesh to make a window. Hinge one of the remaining pieces to make a door. Attach the bottom of a smaller box to the remaining opening. This will provide a secluded nest for the mother rabbit to have her young. Now staple wire mesh to the entire open bottom of the large box. Nail four two-by-twos, three feet long, to the four corners of the large box vertically. Voila . . . there's your first low-cost rabbit hutch. You can build others like this or make them in conventional form as shown here. Eventually you may want to make them like the professionals do . . . all wire mesh — top, sides and bottom. However, the box-type that we've described gives the rabbit some of the privacy that they

like and shelter in cold or windy weather. You can build in a feeding trough and fasten a coffee can to the bottom for water so it can't be tipped. Put a screen hook latch on the door and your first rabbit domicile is ready for occupancy.

The least expensive source of high-quality meat

There are a great many varieties of rabbits. Here are some popular types and their characteristics:

Chinchilla — a medium meat rabbit.

New Zealand White — a popular medium weight meat rabbit.

Flemish Giants — these grow to be rabbit monsters, so if your bag is big rabbits, try a pair.

If you are unable to buy a buck (boy rabbit) and two does (girl rabbits) locally, there are a number of companies that will sell you breeding stock by mail:

Strombergs	MAR-CEL Rabbit Farms
Fort Dodge	216 Canal Street
Iowa 50501	Brattleboro, Vermont 05301
American Rabbit Assoc	Pete Naylors Rabbitry
32 ARBA Building	2019 N. 13th Street
Pittsburgh, Penn 15217	Kansas City, Missouri 66104

A couple of does and a buck should yield about fifty young fryers per year. It's very likely that rabbit on your menu once a week would be often enough to consider it a treat. Incidentally, a rabbit can be eaten when it's about three months old.

It's difficult to believe but after you have built the hutch and put in the bred pair, (feeding and watering them, of course) you can just go on about your other business. From here on out you'll have a steady supply of wholesome, nutritious, chemical-free meat with less than five minutes' attention per day. Lots of people will be surprised that raising meat for the table could be so

Livestock

simple, but the author recalls growing a steady supply of rabbits from about the age of ten on, without any problems or concern.

The greatest thing about rabbits is that you don't really have to buy commercial rabbit pellets, barley or other fancy grasses and grains. Your rabbits will eat scraps from your table (they particularly love stale bread crusts), vegetable parings, tops from carrots, beets, turnips and other root vegetables, lawn trimmings and many kinds of weeds. If you have the room, you might put in a quarter or half acre of alfalfa, timothy or clover and grow your own hay. Peter will eat it fresh or dried. Because of this fact, rabbits are no problem to keep throughout the winter. A supply of fresh water is the only other requirement for their diet.

The manure from rabbits is an extremely valuable fertilizer. Mixed in with the earth that you'll use to raise corn, it will probably create the kind of corn that reaches above an elephant's eye. There's a way to prepare the manure without work . . . just add earthworms which you can buy by mail. Red earthworms will digest the manure, removing the parts that make it smell bad. Save a few worms from each batch of manure as you transfer it to your corn patch. In that way you can continue to breed useful earthworms. Earthworms may be obtained from Carter Earthworms, Plains, Georgia 31780; Charlie Morgan, 116 E., Bushnell, Florida 33513; Fains Hatchery, Edison, Georgia 31746.

Many city folk have never tasted rabbit, domestic or wild, but once you've eaten it, you're sure to become a rabbit meat lover. Try this recipe for a starter:

Fried Rabbit

Fry a quarter of a pound of bacon in a large cast iron

skillet. Add two large onions cut in chunks and continue frying. Roll pieces of young rabbit in a mixture of flour, salt and pepper. Brown in hot bacon fat on both sides. Place cover over skillet and turn down burner to lowest possible level and slowly braise until tender, 45 minutes to one hour.

This is so delicious it will make a permanent rabbit lover of you. Also, the recipe works for wild rabbits which you may catch on your farm.

One of the great advantages to rabbit growing is that you can start very small and make the operation as large as you wish with very little expense, trouble or labor. It's extremely likely that in the down/up years to come, a supply of healthful, organically-grown, chemical-free meat will be a most profitable enterprise for many small-scale farmers.

A good reference publication is the National Rabbit Raiser, 241 W. Snelling, Appleton, Minnesota 56208, while these inexpensive booklets can be obtained from the Government Printing Office, Washington, DC 20402: 'Raising Rabbits' and 'Commercial Rabbit Raising'.

First Time Farmer's Guide

Beekeeping

If you owned an apple orchard and in one year the crop increased from 18 to 1,000 bushels, you'd undoubtedly be very happy. If you were an alfalfa farmer and your seed crop went from a half bushel to more than 12 bushels per acre, there is no question of your elation. If in both cases you were able to harvest 75 pounds of pure fresh honey, you would be convinced that your cup really runneth over . . . especially when the time involved to achieve all this was less than an hour a month and the total start-up expense was about $35.

These statements are facts based on real experiences of farmers just like yourself. They range from the one-acre farm owner who has a single hive to provide both honey and pollination service for his apple orchard, to the commercial beekeeper in California who started with bees as a hobby and now has thousands of colonies and

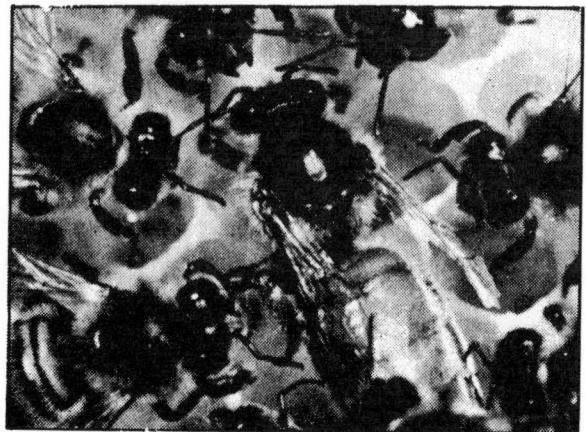

exports tons of honey to Germany. You can be somewhere in between if you wish, one of the tens of thousands of American beekeepers who enjoy delicious, practically free honey and the fascinating experience of watching the interesting and complex activity of bee society.

Like many farming activities, beekeeping requires the knowledge of a few essential facts. By starting with just one hive, you'll gain enough experience to enlarge the operation to suit your own objectives. Here's a list of the basic equipment needed for one colony of bees:

One 2-story 10-frame hive   One smoker
One 2- or 3-pound package of bees with queen
One queen excluder   One hive tool
One bee veil   One spur embedder
Four ounces of No. 28 wire (Used to attach wax sheets)

Getting Started

Hobby or part-time apiaries are best located reasonably close to home. It is essential that you locate the hives where the bees' flight will not disturb your neighbors, field workers, livestock or traffic. Provide a watering place, avoiding nearby watering places where your bees may go and make themselves nuisances. If a swimming pool or any watering place is located close to your colony, it is advisable to sweeten your colony's water with sugar to keep the bees from going to the other water. Add sufficient sugar to make a 5 per cent solution by weight or volume, or add enough salt to make the water slightly salty to your taste.

Provide shade for hives in summertime.

Protect hives from strong winds, and from ants and cattle.

Protect bottom boards of hives from wet ground.

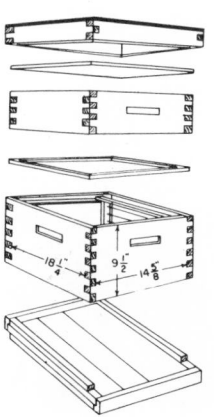

Locate hives away from flood or fire hazards; keep apiary free of dry weeds and grasses.

You can begin beekeeping at any time, but it is best to begin in the spring when nectar-and pollen-producing blossoms will supply ample bee food. Bees can be acquired by buying a colony in a hive from a beekeeper, by purchasing them in packages, or by hiving a swarm (when you have more experience).

Buying a colony in a hive from a beekeeper is the best way to get started, as the experienced beekeeper will usually be able to give you valuable help. A certificate of inspection from your County Agricultural Commissioner showing freedom from disease should be requested when you purchase bees or used beekeeping equipment. See your local Farm Advisor for the names of nearby beekeepers. Packaged bees can be purchased from the beekeeper or from a bee supply house if a colony in a hive is not readily available. You can install the bees in the hive you have purchased, or built for them yourself. Directions for placing bees in a hive are on the package.

It is important to place your order for bees early enough so that they arrive 6 to 8 weeks before the principal nectar-producing plants bloom in your neighborhood. This will give the bees time to build a colony sizable enough to take maximum advantage of nectar in the plants.

There are many variables in bee production . . . weather, availability of nectar to the bees, and bee health. However, most bee experts agree that you can remove five or ten pounds of honey after the first year. By the end of the second year, your bee population will have expanded three or fourfold and you should harvest from 50 to 100 pounds of honey. This would be plenty for

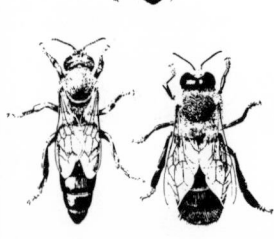

your own use with some for sale in your roadside stand. Here is a list of sources for bee equipment:

Sears and Montgomery Ward (through their mail order catalogs).

The American Honey Institute, 333 N. Michigan Avenue, Chicago, Illinois 60601, can supply you with much information on both supply sources and honey promotion. In addition, the following periodicals contain many ads for bee equipment as well as providing practical information on beekeeping:

'Bee Word', 678-80 Salisbury House, London Wall, London EC2, England

'American Bee Journal', Hamilton, Illinois

'Gleanings in Bee Culture', Median, Ohio

Reference books you should acquire:

First Lessons in Beekeeping by CP Dadant, $1.00.
The Hive and the Honey Bee by Roy Grout, $5.75
ABC and XYZ of Bee Culture by AI and ER Root, $5.50
The Honey Cookbook by Juliet Elkon, $5.95, to make good use of your crop.

Glossary

Hive — A man-made dwelling place for bees.
Apiary — Hives (or a hive) located in one place for beekeeping.
Colony — A group of worker bees, drones, and queen bee living together as one social unit. A colony may consist of from 10,000 to 90,000 bees, depending on time of year. A hive never holds more than one colony.
Nectar — A sweetish liquid produced by plants and found principally in flowers.

Propolis — A gummy material collected from tree buds used by bees as a glue.

Super — The section of the hive in which the honey is stored.

No-Cost Bee Culture

Scattered throughout the United States are many thousands of colonies of wild bees. In the event that you are too busy with your other farming activities to become an apiarist, then why not consider tracking down a wild bee hive? There's lots of excitement and some danger, as the author will attest. All you need to steal the honey is a bee veil, gloves and tight fitting clothing. The wild hive can be raided at night when the bees are sleepy and cold, or you can blow smoke in the hive which stupefies them and makes the 'liberation' of the wild honey an easy matter. Someone has even written a book on how to find wild bee trees. It's called *Bee Hunting* by John R. Lockhart (70¢). It, as well as the books mentioned above, is available from the 'American Bee Journal', Hamilton, Illinois 62341. All books are postpaid.

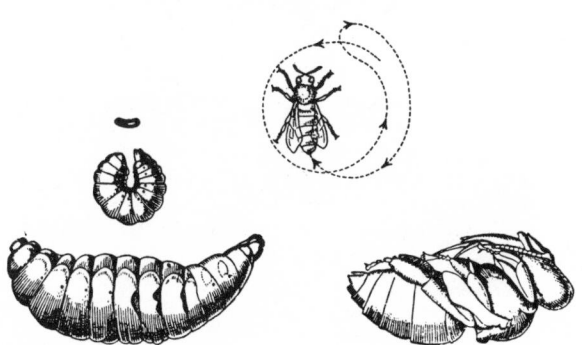

Wild Game Birds

How's this for ingenuity? A man who has a ranch with 30 acres of otherwise unusable canyons, raises game birds for his own use as well as for sale to avid customers. Here's how he does it. The birds (pheasants, quail, guinea hens and other wild varieties) are incubated in captivity and set free in this rugged canyon as soon as they are old enough to fly. They find much of their own feed but the rancher puts feed for them inside a large wire netting trap. During their entire lives they eat both wild fare and what the rancher provides for them. On the day that they have reached marketable size, the rancher springs the trap and there are his ready-to-eat or ready-to-market wild game birds.

This system could be adapted to almost anyone's farm. It eliminates the necessity for cages, permits the

Letting nature raise your birds . . .

Your birds will have to be protected from weasels, raccoons and other bird-loving animals
Right: Some of the many types of wild birds you can keep on your farm

Golden Pheasent, Button Quail, Red Grouse, Partridge and below, the Black Footed Ferret

birds a free life, reduces the amount of food needed and the birds are available whenever the owner desires them. As with any of the livestock ventures discussed, it's best to start small and gain experience as your flock grows.

Food for most game birds is a mixture of grains and seeds similar to chicken feed. Food and plenty of water are all that is needed to make a start in this fascinating field of game bird breeding. Actually, raising game birds is not much different than raising any other type of fowl. While there are differences which are related to climate, for the most part game birds can be an important part of your farm with no more trouble and effort than you would have with chickens.

Here's a selection of game bird varieties from which to choose:

Wild turkeys	Prairie chickens
Wild geese and ducks	Grouse
Quail	Partridges
Pheasants	Pea fowl

If you will send 50¢ to Stromberg's, PO 717, Ft. Dodge, Iowa 50501, they'll send you a well-illustrated catalog of just about every game bird you could possibly want to grow. And here are some books that you can buy directly from Stromberg's by mail or perhaps find in your local library:

Raising Game Birds in Captivity by David Greenberg, $8.50

Game Birds — Wild Turkeys, Chukars, Quail, $2.26

Commercial Game Bird Management, $2.50

A magazine is available on the subject also called 'Game Breeder's Gazette', $5 per year. Sample copy 65¢ from Stromberg's.

First Time Farmer's Guide

Keeping Farm Animals Healthy

'Improper foods cause disease; proper foods cure disease.'— *Henry Bieler, M.D.*

The author of *Food is Your Best Medicine* makes a good case for preserving health in man by encouraging right foods and living a natural life. Since a man is really only an advanced animal, it is logical to assume that if you treat your farm animals the same way, they too will enjoy robust and continuing health.

Another way of looking at the subject is that: if you think sick, it is likely that you will be sick. Therefore, if you go into animal husbandry with the idea that your cows, horses, pigs and chickens are going to be sick and need medication and care, in all probability that's exactly what will happen. Go back 150 years or so. The pioneers of early America didn't have the time to bother with their chickens. A pioneer's flock usually roamed the homestead at will. They picked up what natural foods they could — bugs, wild seeds and worms — and in the evening they were thrown a handful or two of cracked corn or other grain by the farmer's wife or children. After dinner, hens and roosters flew into nearby trees where they were reasonably safe from nighttime predators.

The farmer's pigs were held in a little more restraint. A corner of the farm was fenced off — perhaps an acre or two — and the pigs turned into it to root about happily in this natural pasture. They ate the wild grasses that grew and whatever kitchen garbage and corn the pioneer farmer could spare. The thought of giving these natural-living farm animals a 'shot' would have made the pioneer farmer double up and hold his sides to avoid having them split from raucous laughter.

In order to have a retinue of farm animals that are happy and healthy, simply emulate these elementary

Raising animals on the farm the *natural* way

Crested Roman Goose

Minimum care, mini-
mum housing, mini-
mum hassle

practices. After all, it will take a lot less work than if you tried to copy so-called 'modern' methods.

Until recently the author cared for two horses. The horses were pastured on a half acre of natural grass. With 20,000 square feet of space to wander about, canter or gallop or lie in the sun as their moods dictated, there was no problem in maintaining these horses in top shape. Their only food was oat and alfalfa hay plus a little grain and all the water they could drink from a well-scoured old bathtub. The horses were saddled and ridden quite often, but other than this they lived a placid, relaxed life, as natural as life can be for a domestic horse.

In our chapter on keeping livestock, you'll note that we've stressed minimum care, minimum housing, in short, minimum hassle. Just let your animals grow naturally and be themselves, enjoying their lives of at least relative freedom, just as you enjoy your own liberty. It is more than likely that if your livestock are selected from healthy, naturally raised breeds, they will give you little or no trouble. In most cases, many upsets that occur can be remedied by withholding or changing the animal's food.

Below, the Great Snipe

212

First Time Farmer's Guide

Fish Farming

°And God said, let the waters bring forth
abundantly—*Genesis, chapter 1:20*

Map: areas where trout farming is most likely to be successful.

Types of Trout:

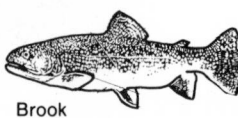

Rainbow

Brook

Cutthroat

Brown

A 'new' type of farming is gaining in popularity. It combines the best aspects of sound land use and economic opportunities with production of a delicious foodstuff. It also affords fine recreational and sporting experiences for cityfolk. This type of farming is called fish farming. It is 'new' only in the sense that many farmers and others are just beginning to get into the business. Actually, fish farming dates back to the dawn of history, with people 'managing' ponds to ensure their supply of finny food. However, it is a relatively new enterprise in the United States, with the most rapid development occurring since World War II.

While commercial, fresh-water fisheries in lakes and rivers have been declining during recent years, well-managed fishponds have been increasing. The state of Arkansas has been the national leader in this enterprise, particularly where several varieties of catfish are concerned. Other states with a significant amount of fish farming include Missouri, Kansas, Texas, Oklahoma, Mississippi, Alabama, Georgia and the Carolinas.

A special type of fish farming has been popular in states where there is a large population combined with several small natural places to fish. For example, in California, there are dozens of public fish ponds where anyone can catch all the fish they want for a fixed price per fish. Families with young children especially enjoy this type of fishing because it is convenient, all things considered, it is far less expensive per fish, and one is assured of a catch. Another advantage is that no license is required since fishing is done on private property.

Labor & Cost

Two major factors are helping to expand fish farming. The first is that the quality of fish grown can be higher than that of fish which may be suffering from the effects of water pollution. Secondly, the cash returns from fish farming can be *far greater* with *less work* than for many other types of conventional farming. In fact, some farms have made so much money from fish farming, they have abandoned all crop agriculture and are in the process of converting their entire farms to ponds and fish farm equipment!

Fish farming can be handled by very small amount of labor. In fact, the USDA reports that with the exception of temporary help needed at harvest time, one man can operate a 20-acre fish farm. (Twenty acres is considered by the USDA as the minimal size needed for a truly profitable operation). With an entire family assisting, the work of tending a fish farm would be very light. A certain amount of mechanization would eliminate heavy work. For example, mechanical seines or nets could help with fish harvesting. Automatic feeders to supply pelleted feed would eliminate physical handling of fish food. With power assists in the feeding and harvesting aspects, the balance of the work could be done by hand labor. Processing of the fish for food markets could be handled exactly as it is on a home basis. Cleaning and packaging fish could be adapted to a division-of-work program where each member of the family handles a job in which he or she becomes expert.

The USDA estimates that a typical twenty-acre enterprise would cost approximately $20,000. This amount would cover the land, the preparation of the pools and all necessary buildings and equipment, including a well, pump and motor, where natural water supplies were not available. Annual costs of the following items were calculated to average about $6,000 for a twenty-acre operation: amortization of equipment, feed, purchased labor,

216

First Time Farmer's Guide

MILES
0   100   200

Catfish

American chard

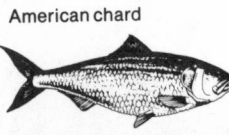

fuel, fingerling fish, and other miscellaneous items.

While these sums are a substantial outgo, let's take a look at the profit factor. A normal yield from a twenty-acre fish farm would be about 30,000 pounds of fish. At a conservative wholesale price of fifty cents per pound, the annual gross income would be $15,000 or two and a half times the total cost of operation. It is obvious that a fish farm of this type would soon be able to pay off the initial investment. From then on a minimal number of hours per day would ensure a very handsome cash income, total independence and the privilege to go fishing any time one wished. Compare this return on investment with some urban operations and you'll start throwing rocks at nearby cities.

Getting Started

One of the easiest fish to grow is native American catfish. They are well suited to first-time fish farming since they are less sensitive to temperature changes as are, for example, trout. Furthermore, they grow rapidly and make a good sport fish. As with any farm operation, it is best to start small and increase the size as you gain experience. That's the beauty of fish farming . . . you can have a one-acre pond, a 40-acre pond or any size in between.

Since virtually any land would be suitable to build a pond, your first consideration is water. Your water supply must be considered both as to quantity and quality. It's easy to figure the amount of water you need since pond volumes are measured in acre feet. An acre (about 200′ x 200′) equals 43,560 square feet. An acre-foot means 43,560 square feet, one foot deep. There are 326,000 gallons in one acre foot.

From this basic data you can determine if your well,

spring or other water supply is sufficient to fill the pond and keep it filled despite leakage and evaporation losses. Water quality must be high. The best way to check this is to have a chemical laboratory, County Agent, or state or federal biologist assist you. They can determine water quality and advise needed remedial measures. As an ex-urbanite, you may have had experience tending a home swimming pool. Thus you know that a large quantity of water can change qualitatively in a short time.

The temperature of your pond water is important. If it measures 70° F or more, your catfish will grow rapidly. Below this temperature growth is slow. Thus, it is obvious that most of the growth of your fish crop will occur in the warm months of the year. Low temperatures won't harm catfish but they simply won't grow as fast. One advantage here is that when the water is cold you can feed a smaller amount of food.

First Time Farmer's Guide

Lower Right: A typical
pond layout using
gravity flow from exist-
ing creek

If your farmstead has a natural declevity, then you will only need to clear the grass, trees and shrubs from the proposed pond area. If you have no low spot, then you can use a bulldozer, skip loader or other piece of earth-moving equipment to scoop out your pond. The pond need not be deep . . . two or three feet deep at the shallow end with a slope to five or six feet at the outlet end would be adequate. Where winters are severe, a depth of eight feet will prevent loss of fish due to cold weather.

Another way to create a catfish pond is to dam a small stream or creek. Before building a dam, ask some of the old-timers if the creek or stream has been subject to severe flooding. Too much water at one time could take out your dam, your fish and your high hopes.

The best bet for a small-scale start is to buy stock from another catfish farmer. Get in touch with your County Agent and ask him the location of the nearest sources of supply. If he doesn't know, write your State Agricultural Experiment Station, your State Fish and Game Commission or write the Information Division of the U.S. Department of Agriculture, Washington, DC 20250. The best time to stock your pond is in early spring. Then you'll be sure that your catfish will grow to eating size by autumn. The number to stock per acre depends on the size desired at the end of the growing season. Medium-size (4-6 inches) fingerlings stocked at 1500 per surface acre usually average slightly more than one pound in a 210-day growing season.

Good catfish feed should contain 28 to 32 per cent protein, no less than 5 per cent fat and 10 to 16 per cent fiber. A minimum of 8 per cent of the ration should be from fish meal. The rest of the ingredients may vary according to availability. Feeds are sold as finely ground mash and as floating or sinking pellets. Floating pellets cost more but enable you to observe whether the fish are feeding. As with any form of livestock, feed only enough to satisfy, i.e., feed your catfish the amount that they clean up in about thirty minutes.

It's worthwhile to mention that overfeeding farm animals often causes more problems than underfeeding.

For a small fishpond, you may want to harvest the fish with bait and tackle. However, if you're in a hurry and want to sell a batch of them, use a net—one-inch, bar mesh nylon available from any fishermen's supply store.

As with any new venture, the greatest expense will come the first year. However, the USDA calculates maintenance cost for your pond at about $20 per acre per year. If you have your own water supply from a well, then you can figure on pumping costs of about $10 to $15 per

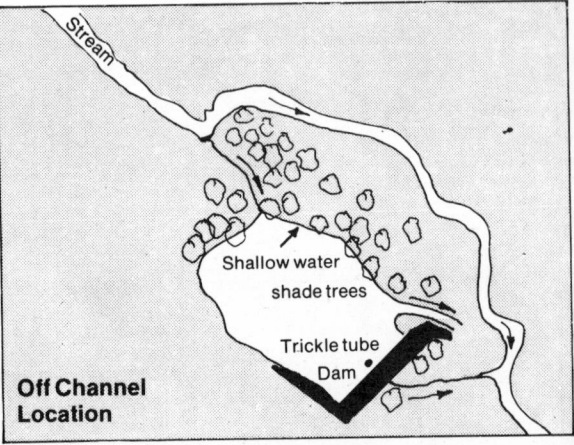

Stream

Shallow water
shade trees

Trickle tube
Dam

**Off Channel
Location**

First Time Farmer's Guide

acre foot of water. Feed will cost between $100 and $150 per ton, depending on the amount you buy, how far it is shipped and whether it is the floating or sinking type. About 3,000 pounds of feed is needed to produce 1500 pounds of fish. Analyze all costs before you start—taxes, labor, pond construction and maintenance, water supply development including pumping and quality control, harvesting, and marketing. If all of these elements appear favorable, then go! Keep in mind that as time goes on, your market for catfish or any other type of fish you raise will increase. Furthermore, your markets are varied.

As you become more experienced, you may enter some or all of the following markets:

Fingerling and brood fish—These can be sold to other fish farmers.

Fee fishing—This could be the most profitable aspect of your fish farm enterprise. It's reasonable to as-

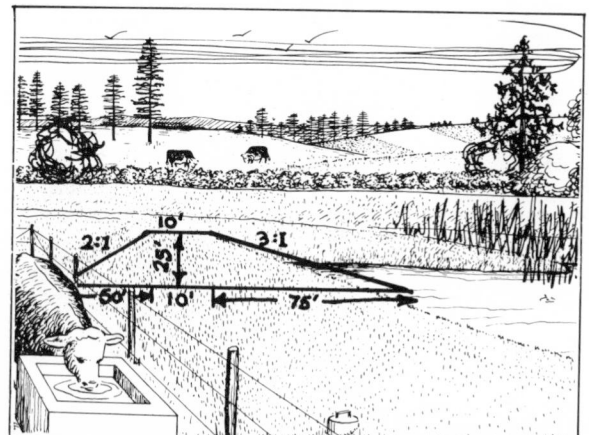

sume that you could obtain a dollar each for fish that you let your customers catch themselves. Thus, 1500 pounds of fish would more than cover all of your costs and leave you a profit.

Wholesale and retail markets—With the demand for *quality* food growing every day, you can sell your fish to wholesalers or market them yourself on a retail basis.

Best of all, if you enjoy a big mess of crisp, fried catfish with a heap of tasty french-fried potatoes, you may not need anyone to help you and your family enjoy the results of your fish farm enterprise.

Fish Farm Case History

Here's an example of how you can become a 'first-time-farmer' on land that *no one else would consider suitable for farming!*

An enterprising couple purchased several acres in a rugged canyon below the tall peaks of the Sierra Nevadas. With this land came spectacular trees, one reasonably level building site for a log lodge and a cascading stream. This stream originated from the melted snow of the peaks above and thus had the icy coldness needed to grow trout.

The trout farmer created some small pools with natural rock and built a small rock and cement dam. The small pools are used for propagating the trout while the largest pool behind the dam, several hundred feet long and more than fifteen feet deep, is used to bring the fish to maturity. It's quite a sight to see the swift flashing bodies of thousands of rainbow trout slicing through the crystal clear water.

The trout are fed commercial feed until they reach marketable size . . . about a foot long. They are caught with large brails or dipping nets, dressed and packed for

Diagram shows the approximate ratios and dimensions of a typical pond dam

air express shipment to gourmet restaurants all over the country. This trout farmer says that there is always a ready market for fresh, high quality trout. He points out that the main thing is to have a plentiful supply of fresh cold running water.

For more information about trout farming, write to the Superintendent of Documents, Government Printing Office, Washington, DC 20250, and ask for the booklet on this subject.

Extra Benefits

You will recall we discussed the principles of companion cropping in the Vegetable Garden Chapter; for example, growing fast radishes between slow lettuce or cabbage. This companion cropping principle applies to trout farming too. As long as you have a pond, why not consider growing bullfrogs? Frog legs are more delicious than chicken and frogs require virtually no care. The USDA has a pamphlet on the raising and breeding of frogs.

Another companion crop for your fish farm is turtles. Both turtle meat and turtle eggs are considered culinary delicacies. Again, the USDA provides a useful pamphlet.

Then there's the possibility of using your fish farm as a headquarters for a duck and goose enterprise. Both of these goodlooking farm birds will enjoy eating aquatic plants and present a traditionally beautiful picture while smoothly skimming the surface. Get the USDA pamphlet on how to raise these fowl.

In the summertime your pond will probably be warm enough to use as the 'old swimming hole', while in winter it may freeze over to provide you and your children with a skating rink!

Diagram shows control system for input and output of fish pond water. Lower drawing indicates the natural way for pond to exist ...cattails, reeds and shallow spots for turtles, frogs and other waterbased creatures

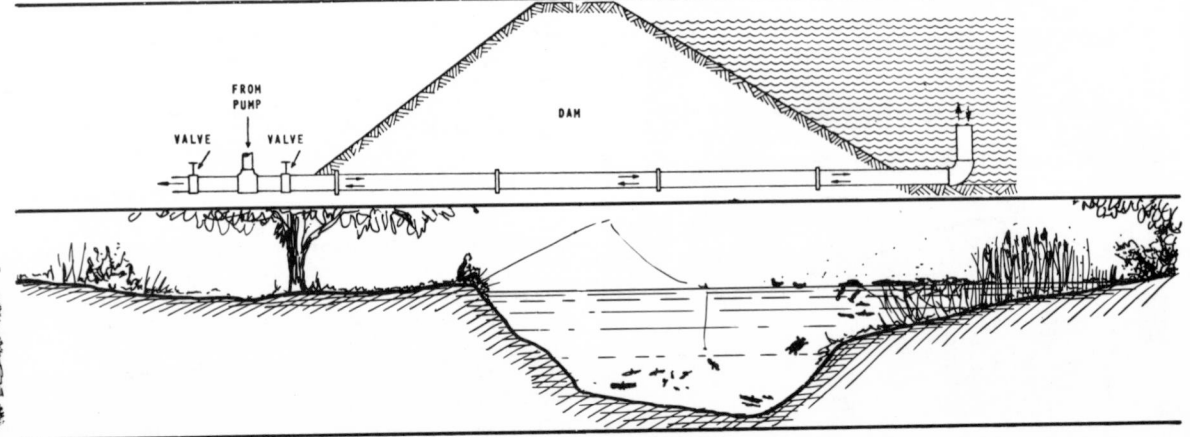

FROM PUMP

VALVE   VALVE

DAM

A pond will also act as a reservoir for fire protection as well as a hedge against prolonged drought. Probably nothing you add to the farm will produce as many benefits as your farm pond . . . food, recreation, beauty, all in one wonderful natural entity.

Your pond can include ducks, geese, turtles, frogs, etc, not to mention your own children in the summertime

Fish Farming

223

Free Foods

'Remember this — that very little is needed to make a happy life.'
— *Marcus Aurelius*

Indians subsisted for centuries on this widely distributed nut...

Try acorn bread—half whole wheat flour, half acorn flour.

With the surge of interest in independence, first-time farming, and just plain survival, a number of old books plus several new ones on the subject of wild foods have become available. Here's a list of some of the best:

Stalking the Wild Asparagus — Euell Gibbon
Stalking the Healthful Herbs — Euell Gibbon
Free For the Eating — Bradford Angier
More Free For the Eating — Bradford Angier

As all of the books agree, it is virtually impossible to starve to death on this planet if you have some knowledge of what foods are good to eat. There is the story often told of a British flier who bailed out of his un-flyable plane and landed in a large bed of purslane. Unaware that he was in the middle of a nutritious wild salad bowl, the pilot, regrettably, starved to death. In the event that you have to bail out of a British fighter plane some day, purslane is illustrated on page 73.

While a diet of purslane alone would become rather tiresome (especially without roquefort or a good vinegar and oil dressing), it would still provide much of the vitamin and mineral needs of the human body. So, to accompany this basic salad material, we've selected some of the best, most nutritious, easily found and quickly prepared wild foods. Added to your farm production of fruits, vegetables and meat, they can provide much variety, interest and fun, not to mention cash savings.

Acorns

Before all those people came over here on the Mayflower and assorted ships and ruined this country, other people with a sense of oneness with nature enjoyed a healthful diet that fell out of trees. Acorns were one of the basic foods for many Indian tribes. They are as nutritious today as they were ten centuries ago and no more difficult to prepare. There are many types of acorns, ranging from the big sweet nutmeats that fall from Eastern oaks to the small, bitter acorns of the Western live oak.

Sweet acorns can be consumed as is, just like any nutmeat. However, if there is any bitterness to any of the acorns that you collect around your farm, just do this. Boil them for two hours and pour off the water. Soak again in cool water with occasional changes. If there's a stream running through your farm, put the acorns in a mesh sack, anchor them to the sandy bottom with a big rock and let the flowing water do your work.

After a few days, grind the acorns into a paste. This paste may be made into a mush by mixing half and half with water and cooking it. Adding wild blueberries or blackberries plus a little thick cream makes this a fine dish for breakfast, lunch or dinner. If you can't eat it all at one sitting, spread the paste out on a clean board or

First Time Farmer's Guide

rock and let it dry. You can then re-grind it as acorn flour. Use this flour in the same way as any conventional flour.

Cattails

This plant, which is also called elephant grass (typha), has been called by wild food expert Euell Gibbon 'the supermarket of the swamps'. Cattails are distributed worldwide and grow along the shores of lakes, ponds and the backwaters of rivers. Nineteenth century American living rooms always sported four or five of the handsome seed spikes as a decoration.

Virtually every part of this friendly plant can be eaten. The young growing shoots are succulent and nutritious when eaten raw or boiled like gourmet asparagus. The root stalks are the most nutritious part of the cattail. The best time for collecting these goodies is late in the fall and through the winter to early spring. At this time the

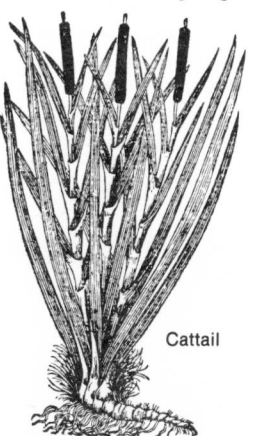

Cattail

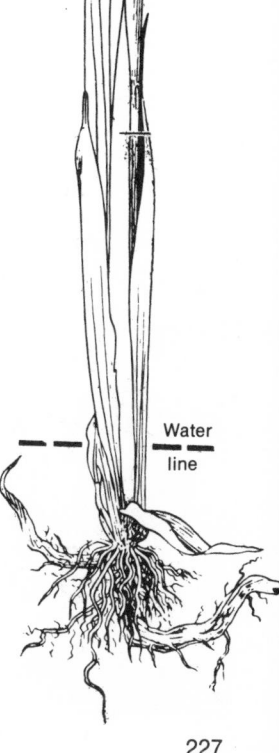

Water line

How to reap the
harvests of Johnny
Appleseed

roots have the most food value. To prepare the root
stalks for food, peel off the outer covering and grate,
chop or grind the white inner part. You can eat them raw,
or boiled and served with lots of butter and a bit of sesame salt and pepper.

The yellow pollen which appears at flowering time
can be cooked as a cereal, mixed with water and baked
as small cakes or steamed as a far-out, primitive but delicious bread.

Wild Apples

Wild apple trees are abundant throughout many
parts of the United States. The majority are trees that
grew from seeds scattered by pioneers who tossed their
apple cores out of their wagons or by birds who ingested
a seed or two and then seeded from the air. Other sources
of wild apples are from abandoned orchards which may
be found frequently by the back country roamer. Wild
apples don't look anything like the big, well-preserved,
and preservative-coated specimens you find in super-
markets. They are usually small, dotted with insect holes
and slightly tart. But they are free, can be gathered in
great quantities if you take a gunnysack with you on your
wild apple tours, and when cooked up into apple pie,
jelly or butter, they'll taste better than anything you've
ever purchased from a market. You can use all of the
recipes in your *Boston Cookbook* that apply to apples
when you cook your wild finds.

So there are some basic free foods, first-time
farmers—acorns, cattails and wild apples. With these
three easily found and used free foods, you can eat well
without even farming. But there's lots more out there in
the wilderness and here is a partial list of the many wild
foods that are waiting to be picked and eaten for free.

21 THE WORLD

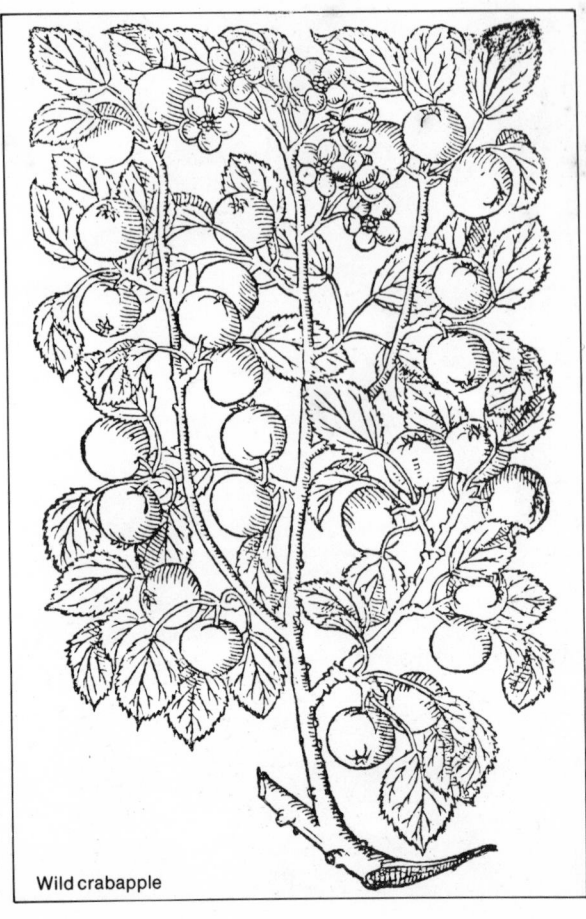

Wild crabapple

First Time Farmer's Guide

When we say many more, we really mean it because out of the some 300,000 plants that grow on spaceship earth, more than 120,000 of them are edible.

Other Edibles

According to the Air Force Survival Manual, wild grapes the world over are not only edible but delicious. Being rich in natural sugars, they should be one of the wild foods that you seek diligently. Incidentally, if you're out searching for wild foods and get thirsty, you can cut a grapevine stem and collect fresh water from it with any container.

Edible pine nuts are one of the most subtly delicious of wild foods. Peasants in Siberia have been known to subsist on pine nuts as a sole source of food in winter. The nuts are produced in woody cones which appear at the base of the cone scales. When the nuts are mature,

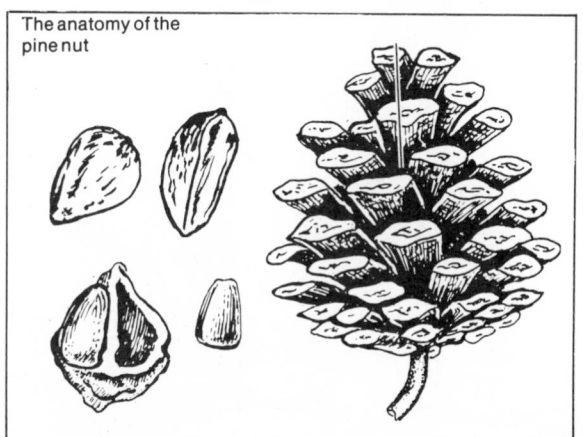

The anatomy of the pine nut

Below: the wild grape

they will fall out of the cone if you shake it, and may be
eaten raw or roasted slightly over a hot outdoor fire.

Wild onions emit a characteristic oniony odor, so it's
easy to distinguish them from other kinds of bulbous
plants. They occur widely throughout North America in
both moist and arid regions. They may be used just like
the onions you grow on your farm. Sliced and fried with
potatoes, you'll find wild onions a rare and appealing
treat.

Would you like something sweet and delicious and
healthful that you can gather free? OK, gather the edible
young shoot of the agave or century plant. It grows in
many desert and semi-tropical areas. Cut off the new
shoot and roast it . . . you'll find the molasses-colored
layers as delicious as anything you've ever eaten. If you
find lots of them, slice them in one inch pieces, dry in
the sun and they'll keep for years.

Early in the chapter we mentioned the plight of the
British flyer who didn't know about the nutritional
values of purslane. This small, unassuming little plant
could be easily overlooked. You can identify it by its red-
dish hue and small yellow flowers and the fact that it
never grows more than six inches high but grows along
the ground. You can enjoy every part of this plant except
the roots and it may be eaten raw with vinegar and oil
or other salad dressing, or lightly steamed like spinach.

A gourmet treat that sells for unbelievably high
prices is wild rice. It grows in swampy, marshy regions
and is easily identified by its broad, rough leaves and the
hairy, straw-colored cover out of which the wild rice
grains shatter when ripe. In fact, even experts have
trouble gathering quantities of wild rice because the
grains scatter in all directions when the mature plant is
touched. It's usually gathered by canoeists paddling be-

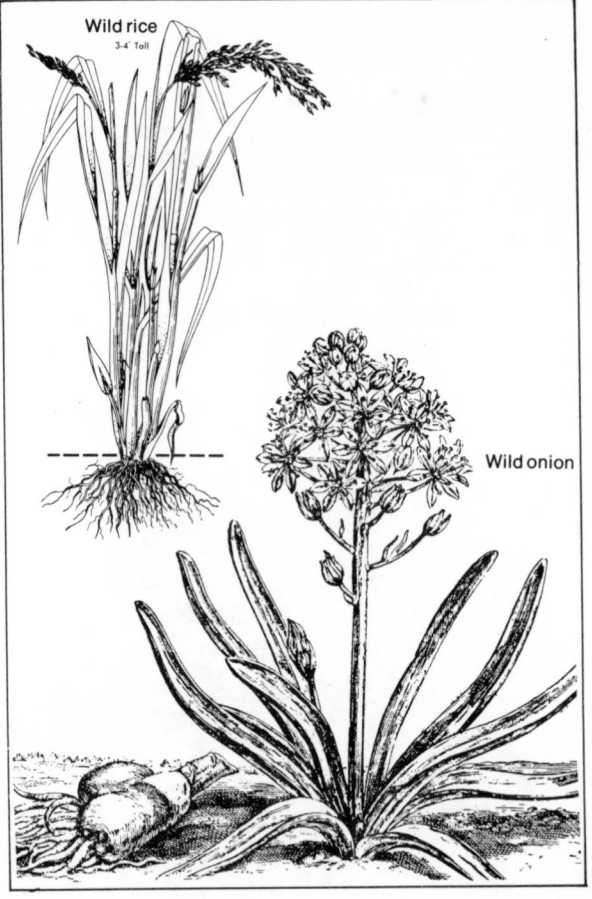

Wild rice
3-4' Tall

Wild onion

First Time Farmer's Guide

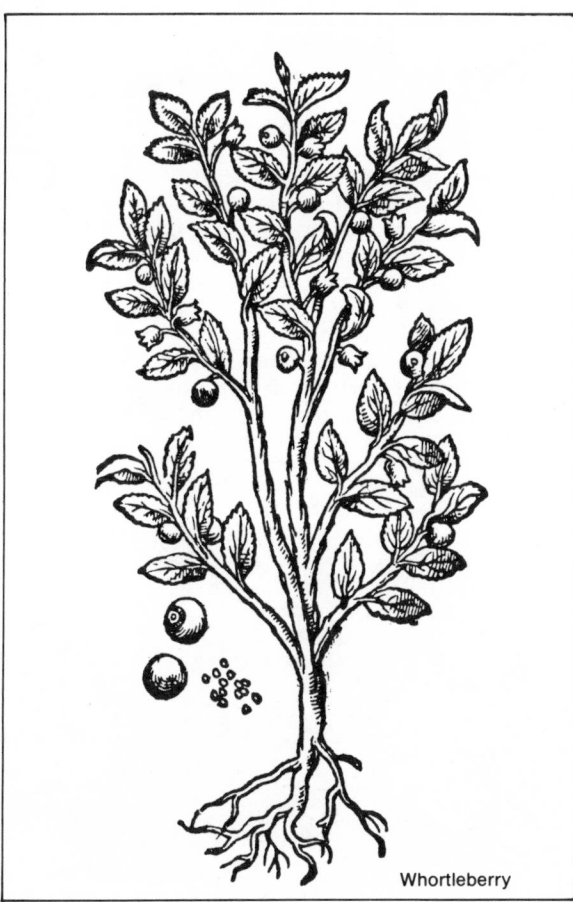

Whortleberry

tween stalks and bending them into the canoe to harvest. Wild rice may be used in every way that domestic rice is prepared. An additional benefit is that when dry, it will keep for many years.

Almost everyone — urban, suburban or denizen of the loneliest reaches of the wilderness — has seen the magnificent spreads of wild blackberries. But there are other berries that many people ignore. Of these, the huckleberry, and its close relatives, the blueberry and whortleberry, are quite common especially in forested areas. All grow on shrubs about six feet high and when ripe are blue, black or red. If you can resist them long enough to get some home, they can be made into a most delicious farm-style jam or jelly. If by some miracle there's still some left after this kitchen task, dry them in the sun and eat them like raisins. Did you know that flies only zoom around at altitudes of 20 feet or less? You can use this bit of knowledge to keep flies away from drying blueberries or other fruit by placing the fruit on a tray on top of your barn or at the end of a 20 foot stick.

If you live in a region where citrus fruits are hard to come by, don't worry about your vitamin C source . . . it can be easily filled by gathering and eating the fruit of wild roses. There edible fruits, called rose hips, are produced at the tips of branches in clusters. Rose hips are usually red or orange and more or less bottle-shaped. You may eat them from late summer to autumn and they're best when quite soft. They remain on the bush nearly all winter. Look for wild roses on the edge of woods or in fields. During the flowering season you can recognize them by their beautiful red, pink and yellow flowers. These make nice adornments for your farm kitchen table.

Wild berries abound in many parts of the US . . . especially in the New England states and the Pacific Northwest

Make Frontier Cobbler with whole wheat batter, honey and plenty of wild berries.

Wild rose

Free Foods

231

Harvesting meat that
didn't grow on your
farm

Hunting And Fishing

A small farm family in Northern Montana never worries about their meat supply. Father farmer bags a big elk as winter draws close. The neatly-packaged elk steaks, roasts and ground meat are stored in nature's own freezing plant — an outdoor locker, where it remains safe and ready for use throughout the long cold winter months.

One rancher whose 40-acre spread was only an hour's drive from a large city, lowered the meat bill for his family to the vanishing point. The deer that invaded his cornfields were quickly dispatched. Virtually the only meat expense this rancher incurred was for beef fat which he used to alleviate the characteristic leanness of venison. A dollar's worth of suet ground up with 40 or 50 pounds of deer burger meat made lots of practically free hamburgers for his three hungry sons.

Many homesteaders in Alaska and Canada are able to live on their small farms quite comfortably by taking advantage of forests filled with bear, moose, deer and caribou.

One orange grove owner has kept his family supplied with rabbit meat for years. He walks down the rows between the trees and harvests (euphemism for 'shoots') the mature rabbits which live on the grass growing around his trees.

Acquiring wild game for the rural homestead has been a longstanding tradition. It continues today in all of the still-untroubled wilderness regions of America.

Hunting

If you are a vegetarian or you have reasons of your own for not wanting to kill an animal for food, go on to the next chapter. However, if you are a first-time farmer who needs a source of high quality animal protein, it would be illogical not to consider the wild animals around your farm.

For large game, you have a choice of heavy caliber guns, .30 and up, or the newer small caliber, high velocity rifles, such as the .223. A popular gun that many people feel is adequate for both big and small game is the World War II model M-1 carbine in .30 caliber.

Many people consider hunting a sport and go at it with that thought in mind. However, if you are hunting solely to get food for your family, you can employ more direct methods. Waiting by the trails or water holes used by deer and similar animals is probably the simplest and most successful form of hunting. Even if you don't live in big game areas, there are lots of smaller animals that are easy to hunt, quick to prepare and tasty to serve on your table. Examples are rabbits, woodchucks, squirrels,

Take care to shoot
to kill instantly; kill
for food only, and
avoid all endangered
species, which in-
cludes most of the
predatory mammals

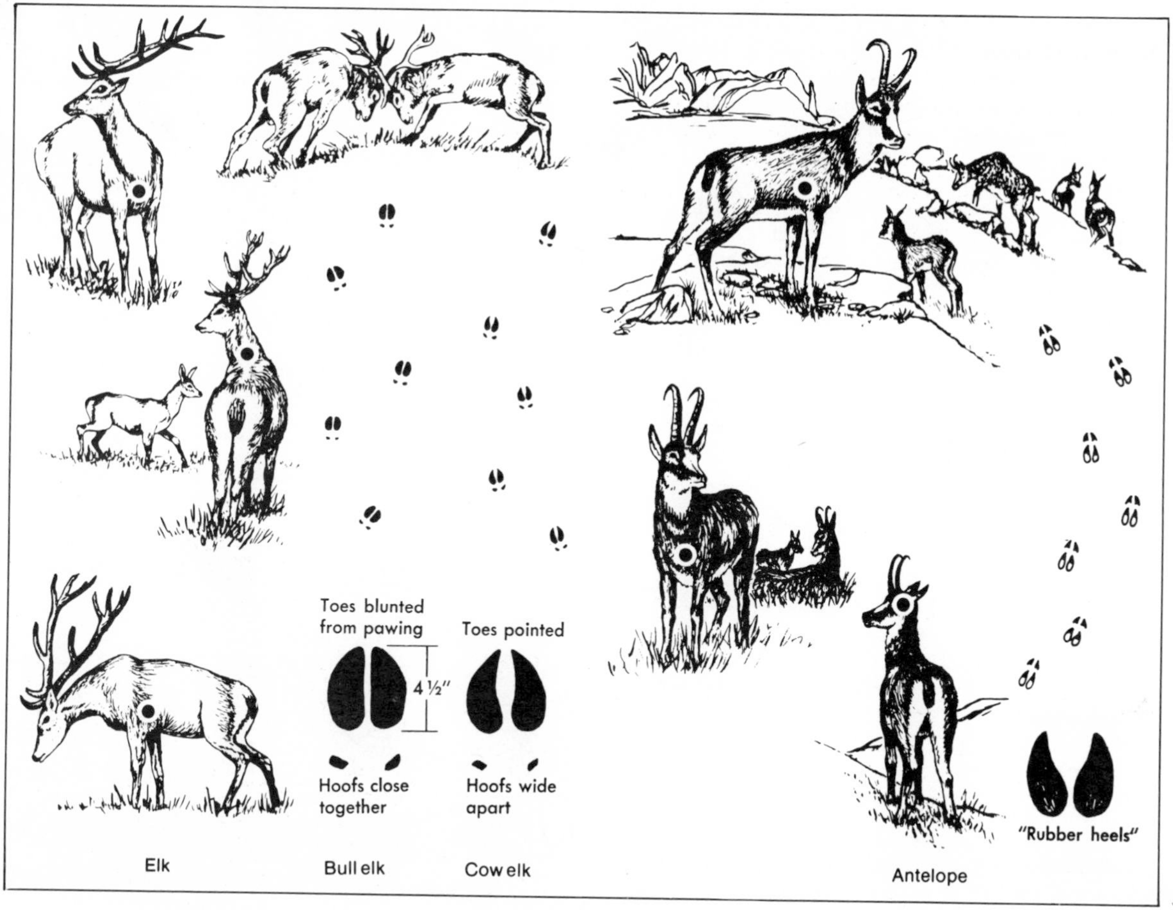

Toes blunted
from pawing

Toes pointed

4 ½"

Hoofs close
together

Hoofs wide
apart

"Rubber heels"

Elk

Bull elk

Cow elk

Antelope

Making meat jerky with
Wild Willy's One Dollar
Smoker (top). Bend four
coat hangers into
rectangular box. Add
rack and cover with
aluminum foil. Smoke
meat strips over cool
smoky fire of hickory
or other hard wood
chips

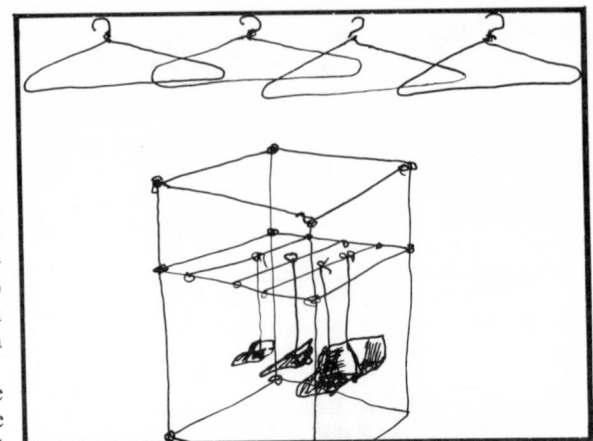

coons, beavers and possums. For these animals a .22 rifle, or a light shotgun (20 or .410 guage) is adequate. If ammunition is too expensive, cut a fork from a tree and make yourself a slingshot using an inner tube for the elastic. A slingshot loaded with old ball bearings is an effective and inexpensive short range weapon. The new air guns are also powerful and economical.

Dressing wild game is similar in technique regardless of size. Hang the animal by its hind legs from a tree branch or fence. Make a slit from vent to throat and remove the entrails. It improves the flavor of wild game to protect it from flies and let it hang for several days in a cool place. This is especially true of animals that have a 'wild' taste.

There are many books on cooking wild game but one fundamental fact can be related here. To make wild game more palatable and eliminate its wild taste soak it in salt water and then marinate it in wine or water in which you place your favorite spices.

Almost all of the meat that you acquire can be made into jerky. Simply cut the meat into thin strips and hang in a sunny place to dry. It takes about a week in hot weather. You can keep flies away by covering it with a fine netting. Alternatively, you can smoke it using Wild Willy's one dollar smoker. Another way to keep your meat free from insects is to salt and pepper it. Cover it at sundown so that it doesn't get damp from dew. That's all there is to it.

Fishing

Fishing requires even less equipment than hunting but caloriewise produces less. If you are gathering food for real, remember that a full-grown trout will only deliver about 200 calories. This is far less than the caloric

value of an equivalent amount of, say, bear.

You can take your cue from Huckleberry Finn and his friend Tom as far as fishing is concerned. Just buy a box of fishhooks appropriate to the size of fish you propose to catch. A spool of fishing line appropriate to the hook is the only other item you'll have to purchase. When you get to the river or lake, cut yourself a slender sapling, tie the line to the narrow end and put a hook at the other end of the fishing line.

Earthworms that you can dig out of your own garden are one of the best baits to use. If you don't have a lot of time to spend fishing, try this method. Make up a fishing line with five or six hooks spaced at one-foot intervals. Tie one end to a one-gallon can with the top tightly screwed on and the other end to a large rock or heavy weight. Now bait all the hooks and lower the rig into the water, rock end down. Anchor the can to a nearby branch and you can go on about your corn shucking. The fish will catch themselves while you work on other tasks. This method is called *setline fishing* and is used extensively by people who fish for food rather than sport. It works well in both fresh and salt water.

There are several other ways of fishing that don't even require hooks. Make yourself a spear from an old broomstick and a commerical spearhead. Go down by the river at night with a flashlight. The curious fish will gather under the light where they are easy to spear. Not much 'sport' in this from a sportsman's standpoint, but then the fish never have called fishing a sporting proposition either.

Two men with a small net can wade up a stream and drive the fish in front of them. When you reach the rapids or a cul de sac, lift the net and you've got your haul.

A no-work method is fish trapping. You can make your own trap out of willow branches like the Indians did, weaving them in a cone shape, or you can buy a commercial model which will last for many years. Fish trapping makes lots of sense if you own your own fish pond or your farm is on a riverbank. But do one thing before you try any of the methods, including hook and line. Check the local rules and regulations. The methods we have given you are suitable for what we call fishing 'for real', i.e., fishing to get food for yourself and your family rather than merely for sport.

Preparing fish for cooking is very simple. Turn the fish over on its back and cut straight down to the backbone below the head. Next make a cut at right angles from this cut to the tail. Reach in and grasp the fish's entrails and with one motion, pull them down and out. Wash and dry the fish. As with wild game, there are many fine books on preparing all kinds of fish. To preserve fish, the best methods are freezing and smoking. To freeze, merely place in a suitable wrapping and drop in your freezer compartment. To smoke fish, lay or hang the small ones whole and the large ones in pieces from the rack of your Wild Willy's one dollar smoker.

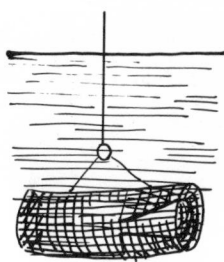

Wire fish and crab trap

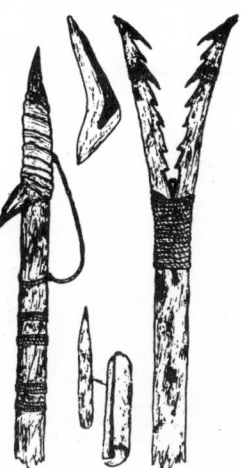

Below: the bone spear, very effective if you've the time...

How to Grow Money

Love is our law — Truth is our worship —
Form is our manifestation — Conscience
is our guide — Peace is our shelter —
Nature is our companion —Order is our
attitude — Beauty and perfection is our life

The Patriotic Diggers!

None other than E.B. Weiss, a most aware marketing prognosticator, predicts that the desire and need for good, healthful, organic-type food will skyrocket in the '70's. This points up the fact that if you need a little bread to buy a 100-pound sack of brown rice and another one of soybeans, a simple way to earn this money would be to operate a roadside stand at which you would sell the surplus produce of your farm.

Achieving some degree of economic self-sufficiency, even at the risk of being called a straw-hat capitalist, makes lots of sense. You can grow five dollars worth of strawberries (about 20 boxes) on a very small patch of ground. This same five dollars could be exchanged at the local feed store for *100 pounds of whole grain wheat.* Thus, you would be essentially bartering a small fruit delicacy, raised in odd moments, for enough basic food to make *hundreds* of good breakfasts. One hundred pounds

of wheat cooked up produces 500 pounds of good food. This is *one-third* of the food requirements for a 150-pound man for an entire year! So to get the cash you need for those things that only cash can buy (salt, nails, thread for sewing) consider a small-scale, totally relaxed week-end stand.

Did you know that strawberries were the most popular item sold by roadside stands, and that apples are second? This tasty bit of knowledge was obtained from a survey made of farmers operating their own road-side stands in the Eastern United States. The survey also revealed that out of 3,000-odd roadside stand owners, 300 of them found business so good they were able to spend the off-season (October through June) vacationing in popular resort areas.

The Roadside Stand

As the survey indicated, strawberries and apples would be winners. But what about big, red beefsteak tomatoes, giant Hubbard squash and the all-time favorite, fresh picked corn? Surely these items would stop the cars meandering down your lane.

Here are some of the advantages of roadside selling;
It's an easy venture to start.
It requires a small capital outlay and only limited risk.
Promotes self-proprietorship and family employment.
Brings in additional income from your farm operation.
It serves as an outlet for surplus production.
Provides the opportunity to live on a farm.
Is a seasonal occupation.

It's possible that the main reason that many small farmers start a roadside stand is to profitably dispose of surplus farm produce. As a first-time farmer, you will find that it is virtually impossible to predict how much to

Douche en pluie, cercle et jet.

First Time Farmer's Guide

grow for your own needs. Even experienced farmers can't predict with great accuracy.

For example, you may hit a great tomato year in which your vines explode into the nearby shrubs and trees and produce overflowing bushels of gigantic, irresistible beefsteak tomatoes. You eat, the wife cans and freezes, the children consume hundreds of bacon and tomato sandwiches, but despite this mighty effort your family can't make a dent in the output of these prolific plants. On another occasion you may plant some banana squash over an old wood-ash pile (as the author once did) and have the heavily-laden squash vines threaten to take over the entire neighborhood (with one squash plant darkly eyeing the whole world). In both instances you'll be in that delightful position of being able to make money from something that you grew all by yourself and that would ordinarily go to waste.

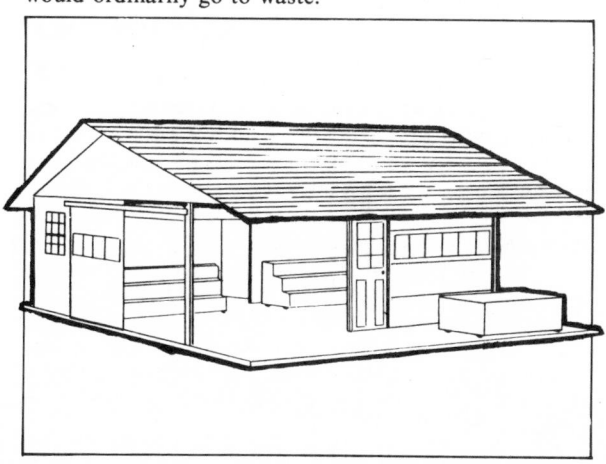

For a temporary roadside stand, here are some suggestions. If your roadside business looks like it's going to be a permanent fixture, then you may want to build something more permanent and elaborate like this model. Here's a USDA plan for a large permanent roadside stand. For one of this size, a business netting a substantial profit would be necessary to warrant the initial cost and upkeep.

Pricing the merchandise that you sell will be based on a number of elements:

The amount of merchandise to be sold.

Its keeping qualities.

Number of customers anticipated.

Competition.

Miscellaneous factors like weather, special demand merchandise, holidays, etc.

One interesting aspect of merchandising farm produce is the growing demand among consumers for vegetables that are organically grown: tomatoes, celery, lettuce, apples, peaches, pears and all types of fruits and vegetables, that are free of chemicals and pesticides.

A way to create year-round sales is to take the name and address of each of your customers. This is done most conveniently by placing a guest book on your counter and inviting everyone who stops to sign your book. To make this even more appealing, provide a small sign that tells the guest that he will be placed on your mailing list for occasional specials that can be purchased in person or by mail. Once you have developed a fairly substantial mailing list—two or three hundred people—you can prepare a mimeographed bulletin which tells about what you have for sale at the stand or what you could provide them on a mail order basis. This latter consideration will be discussed in detail later in the chapter.

Diagram of a USDA Design for an elaborate roadside stand

How to Grow Money

What to sell and how
to sell it . . . To be
successful, keep
your overhead low.

Buying Extras For Your Stand

It is obvious that you won't have fresh fruits, vegetables and other produce to sell all year long. Therefore, you might consider buying organically grown goodies from other sources. For example, there is a company in Sacramento, Sierra Natural Foods, 2408 - 26th Street, Sacramento, California 95818, that sells in both small and large quantities. If you want to stock a nice supply of sun-dried figs, prunes and raisins, here are some sample prices per case:

Choice black Mission figs, 30 lbs., $10.20
Extra large organic sun-dried prunes, 25 lbs., $12.25
Quality Thompson seedless raisins, 30 lbs., $11.70

These prices are freight collect. It would take some experimentation to determine whether purchasing in these quantities plus paying freight and re-packaging would produce a profit. However, it's worth a try on a small scale.

One should be cautious about buying any type of outside merchandise and here is the reason. You are striving for repeat business—tourists that take a drive into the country on a regular basis. If you ever disappoint them on product or price, they not only won't come back, they'll tell their friends. Conversely, if you treat people fair and square, give them good value for their money and do it with honest cheer and a warm heart, you may end up as successful and rich as Walter Knott.

Here's a mini-encyclopedia of ideas from which to choose when you set up your first two barrels crossed by a 2" x 12" x 10' pine plank:

Sell homemade pies, cakes, cookies and breads made from whole grain, honey-sweetened, totally organic ingredients. Smash your grapes, crush your apples and sell delicious fresh fruit drinks in ice cold mugs for ten to twenty-five cents. Even more inviting, prepare them while the customers wait.

SPRING WATER—ALL YOU CAN DRINK, FREE. A great sign to put out on a hot day to get people to stop.

Everyone loves a genuine, home-made king-size dill pickle. Grow your own cucumbers and dill and make cider vinegar and you've got all that's necessary.

Buy a secondhand windmill and put it next to the road. You can make it pump water by putting a concrete cistern beneath it and let the free breezes pump the same water over. If you're an authenticity bug, go ahead and drill a well and let it *really* pump water. Many men are windmill buffs and cannot pass one under any circumstances.

Pick pears, peaches, apples, plums. Make homemade jams, jellies, juices and syrups and stick on homemade, woodblock-printed labels. (Hide a few jars for yourself because these always sell out, especially around the holidays).

Lots of blackberries in your vicinity? Cut off a few thousand pieces and root them in discarded tin cans. Then put up a sign 'Wild Blackberry Vines—Ready to Plant in Your Garden'. This could also apply to dogwood, small evergreen or desiduous trees, herbs, wildflowers and shrubs, plus seed stock and such ornamentals as holly, mistletoe and pine cones.

Draw an original map of the region surrounding your farm. Put up a sign 'Free Map of This Valley'. Give one to every customer. Other printed items to give away or sell would be a Farm Recipe Book, a Guide to Historical Points or a little booklet on how *you* became a successful 'Ex-Urbanite, Easy-Does-It First-Time Farmer'.

Handmade items—make them or buy them. Aprons,

afghans, bed spreads, knitted wool hats. This would be a nice winter-time 'cottage industry' activity. If you have a couple of sheep and you incorporate some of your own home-grown wool, be sure to say so.

Handmade baskets have universal appeal. You can buy them through importers on either coast. Obtain the yellow pages for San Francisco and New York from your telephone company and look under 'Importers'. While you're considering baskets, look into a line of appropriate rural orientation imported items like small carvings, handwoven fabrics, unique metalwork and rugged ceramics.

By creating an early- and late-bearing strawberry patch, you can offer this delicacy practically all year. Let customers pick their own at a reduced price.

Make and install free-use picnic tables near your stand. Invite people to stop and picnic under your 'spreading chestnut tree' (good name for the stand, by the way).

A wheel like this is not hard to build. It's an old-fashioned, overshot water wheel. A small water pump will keep it revolving and we defy tourists with small children to pass it by.

Speaking of water wheels, why not install an old-fashioned stone grinding mill. Buy your grain by the sack and grind fresh whole wheat flour by the pound while the customer waits. Start with a simple hand mill like the Corona ($12.95 postpaid from John Shuttleworth, PO 38, Madison, Ohio 44057).

There's one item that seems to be sold only by roadside stands . . . that's a date shake. So what's so hard about blending milk, ice cream and dates for thirsty/hungry travelers?

Here are some references that can give you more

Some ideas on how to appeal to the hungry traveler...

Letting the mailman do
most of the work for
you...

information about this fascinating field.

Directories

Two comprehensive reviews of roadside publications have been prepared. Each report summarizes the contents of a number of publications.

Ransom A. Blakeley, *An Encyclopedia and Bibliography on Roadside Marketing,* Cornell University, Department of Agricultural Economics, A.E. Res. 114, May 1963, 83 pages, (lists 55 publications).

J.E. Jeffries and M.E. Cravens, *A Review of Roadside Marketing Literature,* Ohio State University, Agricultural Experiment Station, A.E. Departmental Series 362, May 1964, 99 pages, (reports on 27 publications).

Recent State Bulletins

Since the above directories were prepared, several additional state bulletins have been issued. Some of them are listed here.

Ohio State University

M.E. Cravens and J.E. Jeffries, *Analysis of Roadside Marketing in Franklin County, Ohio,* Research Circular 125, November 1963, 27 pages.

Cornell University

Ransom A. Blakeley, *Suggestions For A Beginning in Roadside Marketing,* Department of Agricultural Economics, RAB: 64:2, January 1964, 10 pages.

Description and Price List of Plans for Storage and Market Stands for Fruits and Vegetables. Agricultural Engineering Extension Bulletin 851-S, 8 pages.

Pennsylvania State University

Charles Porter, *Guidelines to Successful Roadside Marketing,* Extension Service, Special Circular 70, 1964, 7 pages.

Delaware Bulletin

The Modern Farm Roadside Market, (Articles on Recommended Management and Merchandising Practices), Food Distribution Section, January 1961, 39 pages, (50¢).

Conference Proceedings

Two states, Ohio and New York, have prepared proceedings of their annual roadside market conferences. The first conference was held in Ohio in 1960 and in New York in 1964.

Mail Order Marketing of Farm Products

Supplementing your cash income through a mail order business operated from your farmstead is a good idea for the following reasons.

Mail order is a growing business. More people find it convenient to send away for products.

A mail order business allows you to work when you please or when you have time.

Farms and rural regions are productive of many of the most successful mail order items—seeds, botanicals, plants, herbs, food products of all kinds, handicrafts and seasonal items.

People enjoy buying from a rural address.

Your mail order business can be as large or as small as you wish.

The whole operation is tax deductible.

The mail order business is really fun . . . there's hardly a business that produces so much excitement as seeing what the postman brought you in the way of orders, checks, cash and inquiries.

What To Sell

It is generally agreed that the most successful mail order operations are based on creativity. The item or items that you sell by mail should be unique and original. They should also possess as many of the following characteristics as possible:

They should have a high profit margin . . . preferably five times their cost packaged.

They should be light and durable. Seeds are ideal (70,000 celery seeds weigh one ounce).

Whatever product you select, it should be of high quality and real value to the customer.

They can be specialty items since many successful mail order firms operate with a small group of *aficionados*.

How To Sell

Here's a good rule to commit to memory before you begin to sell.

'Start small, use imagination instead of money, drop losers (unsuccessful items) immediately, follow through with potential successes'.

Here are some ways of getting your mail order products before potential customers that cost little or nothing:

Send a notice of the availability of your product to the editors of magazines that are circulated to your potential customers. It is optional, but a photograph of your item would contribute to the effectiveness of this method. Editors of Trade, Special Interest and Consumer Magazines are always happy to bring this kind of information to the attention of their readers. For example, you can send news (and samples) of a new type of ornamental corn that you have grown on your farm to the editor of farm, home and garden publications.

Prepare an article about yourself and your product and submit it as a cost-free manuscript to appropriate publications. Your local and regional newspapers would welcome this type of story if written from a general human interest standpoint.

As we mentioned under Roadside Stands, you can acquire a mailing list of potential customers by having those who stop at your stand sign a guest register. A simple mimeographed bulletin of your mail order product(s) can then be mailed to these people who already know of you.

As a last resort, since it costs money, and when you have exhausted all of the potential of the above methods, think about taking a small ad in a publication that has readers who may be interested in what you are selling.

Treat your customers right. Answer all correspon-

Start small, use imagination rather than money, drop losers . . .

People expect bargains at small stands so give them some. You'll make the difference with greater volume.

dence within 24 hours. If anyone complains, take care of their complaint promptly. Mail refund checks airmail. Write as many personal letters as you can, particularly to those who have a question or a special problem. For others, a form letter may be adequate, especially where you are receiving many inquiries of the same type.

Remember that repeat orders and the expansion of your business are based on giving people more than they pay for.

Keep accurate records.

Never stop experimenting or diversifying. Although some product lines have a long life span, others are much briefer. Thus, you must continually work at your business to ensure a steady income.

Don't give up easily. Many mail order operators have tried for years before hitting on a successful product and method of sale. Keep in mind that every failure is merely a permit granting you another opportunity.

Demand Items

Here is a list of items that have been successful and some that could be.

Seeds and stock.

Lightweight goodies from your farm: organically grown fruits, all kinds of nuts — hickory, butternuts, chestnuts, beechnuts, pine nuts, pecans, peanuts, English and black walnuts.

Maple syrup and sugar. Again these products bring good prices and justify the high cost of mailing.

Hickory chips. If you live in a region where this tree grows, buy a shredder and make chips from fallen branches.

Handicrafts. From children's rockers to leather goods there is an unlimited potential in this era of the de-sire for handmade goods.

Seasonal horticultural products. These include pine cones, holly, mistletoe, wreath materials, yule logs, pumpkins, etc.

Non-seasonal natural items. There are many decorative items in this category which have year-round appeal, such as ornamental gourds, corn and dried flowers.

Pamphlets, booklets and books on subjects that pertain to your farm experiences.

A very successful mail order operator, the Nichols Nursery in Albany, Oregon, puts out 150,000 mimeographed catalogs per year! While the catalog is very plain, it is packed with exciting information about their products and homey little tips that establish a strong rapport. Incidentally, this farm has been very successful in offering their catalog accompanied by a sack of hops for $1. Their ads appear in many mail order oriented magazines.

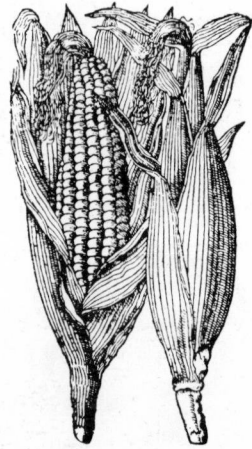

Power

'I wouldn't mind living in the wilderness, Wilbur, if I could
just take my kitchen appliances along.'
— **The Everyday Housewife**

So there you sit, brooding about how you can bring electricity into a northern British Columbia homestead when the nearest power line is 166 kilometers away. What if we were to tell you that your little wilderness homestead could have electricity, heat and refrigeration . . . all homegrown? You'd probably say we'd been smoking a strange pipeful.

One hundred years ago much of the work done on farms, small or large, was accomplished by human and animal muscle power. It is from these days of heavy labor that the reputation of a farm being akin to a Siberian labor camp became firmly established. During the next hundred years, power came to farms relieving both animals and men of the necessity of exerting themselves strenuously. Power came in many forms but eventually found its focus in the internal combustion engine. It is a rare farm today that does not have several gasoline- or diesel-powered pieces of equipment. While it is true that petroleum-fuel power-sources are quick, convenient and efficient, it is also true that they add to the pollution of our planet and can be a significant expense item in your farm budget. Although there are many tasks on a modern small farm that can best be done by an internal combustion engine, let's look at some alternate power sources.

'Of all the forces of nature, I should think the wind contains the largest amount of motive power.'
Abraham Lincoln in an Address in Springfield, Illinois in 1859.

Wind

Did you know that in the wind that blows over every single acre of the Western prairies there is more power than in Niagara? Did you know that a ten-foot windmill turning in a 22-mile an hour breeze would develop

The Eclipse Wind Engine at right is turning a grinder, mixer, polisher and other tools for the happy farmer.

Wind Powered Generator

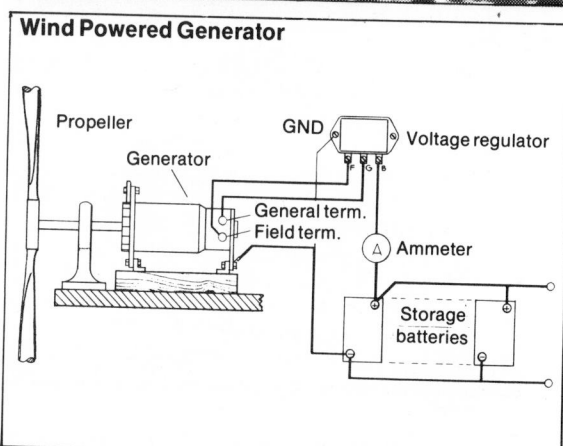

Propeller
Generator
GND
Voltage regulator
General term.
Field term.
Ammeter
Storage batteries

enough horsepower to pump more than 2,000 gallons of water per hour 100 feet straight up?

Many farms are located in regions where the winds blow steadily and fairly predictably the year round. If your first-time farm falls into this category, you should consider harnessing this almost-free, non-polluting power. We've discussed the usage of a windmill for pumping water in a previous chapter. However, there are other applications of windpower. During the Great Depression, many small farmers hooked an automobile generator to a makeshift propeller and produced enough current to run a few lights and a radio set. These units are still in use in many parts of the world. The author found one whirling away on the roof of a small shack in Baja. If you're handy with tools and know something about electricity, write to Mother Earth News, PO 38, Madison, Ohio 44057, and ask for the latest information on home-made wind chargers. There is a commercial unit available called the Windcharger. It is available from Dyna Technology, Inc., Sioux City, Iowa 51102. The price is about $400.

An analysis of the cost vs. the usable electricity generated per month indicates that electrical power from your local power company would be lots cheaper. However, if you live far beyond power lines, consider this unit for low-draw electrical equipment. One great advantage of this unit is that the electrical power can be stored in the same kind of batteries that are used in your car. If you have lots of batteries you can store lots of electricity, thus if the wind doesn't blow for a while, you'll still have power for your radio, lights or other small equipment. If you wanted enough electricity to operate electrical motors and large electrical appliances, you would need a big unit. If this is the case, you have a choice: make your

If the wind always blows from the same direction, you can use this simple mill. Shield the lower half from the wind.

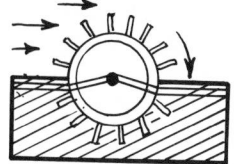

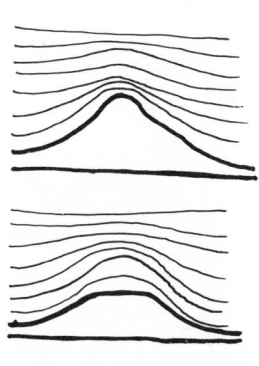

Wind, water and
electricity, plus some
ingenuity

own unit from a generator that you could buy surplus, or purchase a commercial one. Elektro, GMBH of Winterthur, Germany, has units with capacities up to 5,000 watts and voltages to 110V.

In the era before the rural electrification program got underway and small internal combustion engines appeared on many farms, wind power was used for many tasks—grinding corn, powering saws, grinders, churns, corn shellers and many other handy farm tools and equipment. The Eclipse Company went out of business in 1908 but they left behind the rare old engraving (p. 248) of their famous Eclipse Wind Engine taking most of the hard labor out of farming. To the natural-born handyman this drawing will be both a challenge and an invitation.

Secondhand windmills, including the tower, are available in many rural areas. Sometimes you can have them free for your service of removing the unused mill.

From then on it's up to your ingenuity and ambition. For example, you could use an old windmill water pump to generate electricity as previously discussed. A system of belts and gears could be rigged to provide house current whenever the wind blows. There would be lots of problems to solve, but a first-time farmer with curiosity and ingenuity would enjoy the adventure.

Aside from using wind power to propel tools or generators and pump water, it could be used to pump water from a lower level to a higher level on a continuous basis. This water could then be used to generate electricity as it flows downward through a hydroelectric plant. All of which brings us to our next non-polluting power possibility . . . water.

Water

If your farm is located on a river, stream or creek where the flow is significant, it is very possible that you can use this power effectively and inexpensively. Many years ago, water power was harnessed extensively for milling grains. The varieties of overshot and undershot waterwheels made for much charm in the rural scene, not to mention the tremendous saving in human and animal muscle power. Today, however, water power is most frequently applied to the generation of electricity. A number of firms supply small hydroelectric generators, such as this one. One of the best features is that their life is virtually unlimited and the power is as steady and reliable as the water flow adjacent to your farm.

A man who has a small, part-time farming venture in addition to his duties as the caretaker for a private water system, generates all the power he needs at practically no cost. He purchased a surplus generator unit and

The turbine and
generator, the most
expensive parts

converted it to water flow propulsion. As the water from
a reservoir flows through his premises on its way to customers, it expends some of its energy in generating electricity which costs our friend practically nothing and
takes nothing from the eventual users of the water.

You have more than one reason to be pleased if you
live on a stream or river, especially if you are far from
conventional electrical power and the cost of fossil fuels
would be high or their use against your principles. In
these instances, even a very small water-power site could
make your farm independent.

The cost of developing a water power site can be
quite small. Let's say that you live on a stream that is
about ten feet wide and flows steadily all year. With the
help of some friends, you could build a simple dam at a
convenient point. A canal could lead the water from this
dam to what is called a headrace. This takes its name
from the fact that water that is higher than its ultimate
destination has head. The race comes from the fact that
the water will flow rapidly down to the point where it is
going to power a water turbine. From the headrace, the
water is piped to a turbine where it does its work and is
then released into the tailrace for its quiet return to the
river.

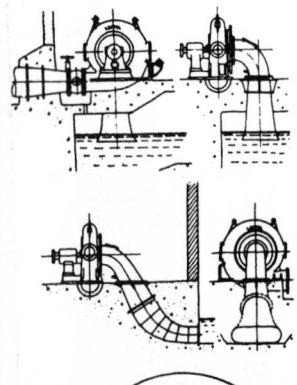

This type of installation is simple, effective and
actually a miniature of such gigantic hydroelectric projects as Hoover Dam. Best of all, everything we've
described can be built from native salvage or used
equipment:

The dam can be of river stone.

The canal can be simply an earth ditch. Later on you
may want to cement it for appearance and clean flow.

The headrace can be made of native stone and sand
plus a little cement.

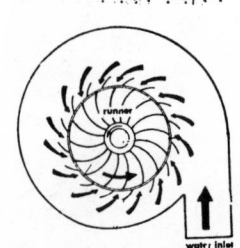

The turbine penstock can be an old piece of steel
pipe . . . the type that can be found in many wrecking
yards or even lying by the side of the road.

A turbine and generator would be the most expensive item. However, units like this can be found secondhand in marine salvage yards and similar places. Or you
could build your own water wheel using wood and have
it drive a surplus generator unit directly, through gears
or belts.

The tailrace would require only native materials.

Wiring, voltage regulators, switches, etc. can be purchased either new or used from electrical supply companies.

Although the demand for small water powered turbines has declined in the last twenty years, there are
three firms that still manufacture them; James Leffel &
Co. Springfield, Ohio 45501 is one of them. Their booklet, Leffel pamphlet A, 'Hints on the Development of
Small Water Power', is available on request. It is a very
useful supplement to the information in this manual. Its
description of Leffel's small vertical Samson turbine is
very complete. This turbine is available in sizes from 3 to
99 horsepower. The company maintains an Engineering
Department which stands ready to assist in planning and
design of the entire installation.

This company also manufactures a complete unit
called Hoppes Hydroelectric Unit, which is useful in
isolated locations where the demand is small. It comes in
sizes of 1 to 10 kilowatts. A Leffel bulletin describing this
unit gives complete instructions on submitting the information necessary for ordering it.

The other two firms are located in Europe. The
Michell (or Banki) turbine is manufactured exclusively
by the Ossberger-Turbinenfabrik of Weissenburg, Bavar-

ia, Germany. This turbine is made in sizes ranging from 1 to 1000 horsepower. The company has an impressive record of installations, many in less-developed countries. Ossberger-Turbinenfabrik is very responsive to requests for information. It furnishes without charge a considerable amount of data, translated in English.

A third company which manufactures turbines and governors for turbines is the Officine Buehler, Taverne, Canton Ticino, Switzerland. They are in the small turbine field, and they manufacture all types except Michell. Their workmanship is of the highest quality, and their engineering is superb. Like the other companies, they assist prospective customers in planning their installations.

If the thought of being free of dependence on a power company turns you on, then water power development is probably a good way to go. Remember that even if you don't generate electricity with water power, you could use a simple water wheel to power a corn grinder in the same way it's been done for many centuries before you made the scene. A very fine book is available from VITA (Volunteers for International Technical Assistance). Write them at College Campus, Schenectady, NY 12308 and ask for the current price and availability of 'Low-cost Development of Small Water Power Sites' by Hans W. Hamm. In addition, the 'Village Technology Handbook' also produced by VITA has drawings and information on the construction of simple water wheels. This book also explains a reciprocating wire power transmission for small water wheels that has been used for many years by the Amish people of Pennsylvania.

The Leffel water-powered electric generator installed. Note the small amount of water needed to power this unit

The Sun

'The roof of the average home receives about 100 times as much energy from the sun as could be used inside for lighting, cooking, heating, air-conditioning and heating water.' — *(E.A. Farber, University of Florida.)*

When you were living in the suburbs, did you ever turn on your garden hose and have the water pour out so hot it almost scalded you? If so, you've already had experience with a solar heating system. Just for fun, imagine that your first-time farm has a spring 100 feet up the hill behind the farmhouse. The water from the spring is piped down to the roof of your house. There it travels back and forth through an ordinary garden hose that is laid out in a pattern to give maximum length in minimum space. The water then goes into an insulated holding tank in your attic.

So all day long the sun heats the water in the hose and whenever you turn on the faucet, hot water comes out of the storage tank and is replaced by water in the hose. A separate cold water line is piped direct to the spring. With this simple, inexpensive system you can eliminate the need for gas or electric water heating in your farm home. This simple example is one of many that prove the usefulness and practicality of solar heating systems.

The climate of Japan is quite wet, especially in summer and for this reason the Japanese like to take hot baths. But fuel costs are comparatively high in this tiny overcrowded nation. Thus, it is logical that there are more than one million solar water heaters in use in Japan. There are a number of types but the most popular is one that consist of a three by six wooden frame lined with black vinyl. A piece of glass covers the top. In its

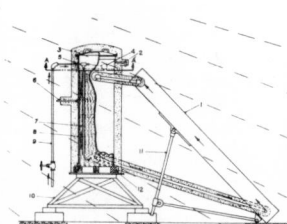

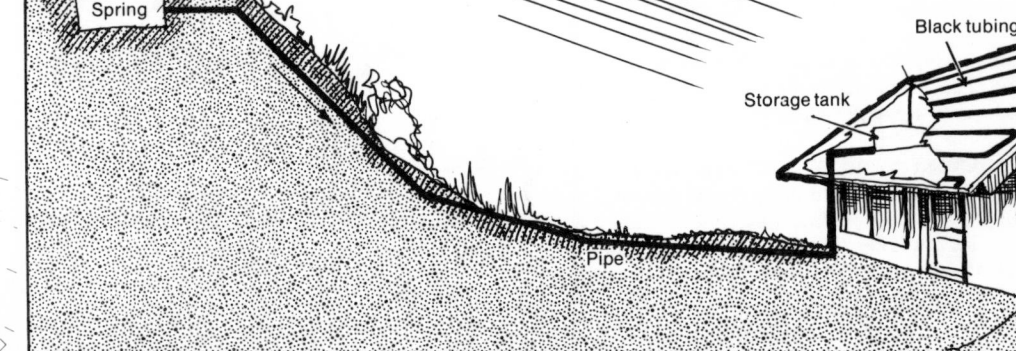

simplest form, you just pour in the water and drain it out when it's warm. The cost is about $20 for the commercial unit, but it could be built for lots less on a materials-only basis. Life span is about ten years.

There is no reason why you couldn't provide hot water in abundance for your farm as well as use hot water for heating purposes if you were to use a battery of these simple open-type heaters. Here are some facts about solar water heating that can help you determine whether it would be practical for your farm.

The efficiency of solar water heating varies with the weather, the area of the absorber, the flow rate, the type of heater, the air temperature, the temperature of the water supplied, the wind conditions, etc. For example, on an average day in December in most of Florida, a standard absorber will heat a minimum of 1½ gallons of water per square foot per day from the air temperature to 140 degrees F. The heat loss from the surface of the storage tank is the main factor to be considered. The loss in a day amounts to 15-20 percent of the day's solar heat input. A layer of glass wool insulation 4 inches thick would reduce this loss.

As an interesting side light, a large scale solar heater with a 66 sq. m absorber has been constructed in Tokyo to supply hot water for more than 100 university students. It supplies 7,000 liters of water at over 50 degrees C except during the winter, when auxiliary heating is used.

The cost of energy from a solar heater depends on just two things: the smaller the angle between the sun ray and the surface of the glass cover, the more short-wave radiation is reflected. Clear, untinted glass is best, since constituents like iron (greenish tinge on the breaking edge) reduce the transmission of short-wave radiation. Most absorbers are about 21 square feet in area, so this can be deemed adequate for the average family. Most authorities figure about 20 gallons of hot water per person per day, so for a family of four, you'd need an 80 gallon storage tank, plus reserve for cloudy spells.

Experimenters are making increasing use of plastics in solar heaters. But other materials used in tests have been copper, aluminum and galvanized iron. Polyethylene sheets and polyvinylchloride sheets are among the promising new materials being tested, and someone has also proposed plastic coated iron sheets for heat absorbers (to avoid corrosion).

There are other ways to use heat from the sun directly. For example:

To heat greenhouses.

To warm animal quarters through glass or translucent plastic skylights.

To aid in sterilization of dairy floors by means of sliding roof panels.

To dry fruits, vegetables, meats, fish or grains and other cereals.

Take advantage of sunshine . . . it could be one of your most valuable allies to help you operate a successful small farm.

Solar absorbers:
The Kawai absorber
Pan-type
Sinusoidal tube
Straight tube/duct
Flat plate type

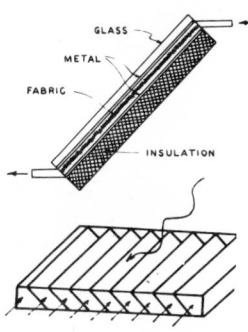

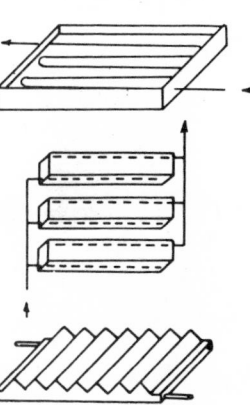

Power for Your First-Time Farm

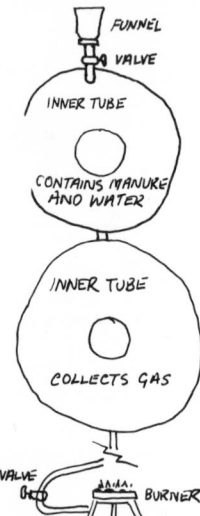

Here's a system that has lots of promise

FUNNEL

VALVE

INNER TUBE

CONTAINS MANURE AND WATER

INNER TUBE

COLLECTS GAS

VALVE   BURNER

Power From Pigs

After World War II, a British pilot, John Fry, relocated his family from London to a pig farm about eight miles outside of Johannesburg, South Africa. Things were just dandy until the city fathers of Johannesburg told John that when the wind was right (or rather wrong) the odor from the several thousand pigs and their daily manure output gave Johannesburgians minor fits. They told him to eliminate the odor or shut down.

John did some fast research and came up with a methane digestion system. The output of his digester went into a 15,000 watt generating plant. With this much electricity available, his family never turned out the lights and they enjoyed the sight of a huge splashing fountain in the middle of their swimming pool. In addition, Mr. Fry used the digested manure to 'power' his private cornfield. Thus he had a complete, organic cycle going. The corn to the pigs, pigs producing manure and the manure producing power for John and more fertilizer for the corn to restart the cycle. Oh, yes, once the plant was in operation, the city fathers of Johannesburg were happy to point out John's farm as one that could be called 'a model of sanitation'.

In its simplest form, here's how a methane power plant works:

Manure from animals is piped into a tank with a quantity of water.

Due to the presence of bacteria which can decompose manure anaerobically (without air), the manure decomposes into ordinary water, an inert, odor-free sludge fertilizer, and methane gas. The latter is similar in chemical composition to the gas that comes out of your stove burners. This gas can be used in every way that you have been using natural gas in your home. It can be burned for heating, used in a gas refrigerator or piped to an internal combustion engine, which in turn can propel an electrical generator. So not only do you derive the benefit of virtually free fuel, your manure problem disappears at the same time you receive the by-product, — a usable fertilizer for your garden.

Here is a diagram showing the basic structure of a methane plant. Construction of the unit is straightforward. It is no more difficult or expensive than building a conventional septic tank where the methane gases are simply vented to the atmosphere and are wasted. The only additional costs are the container to act as a gas holder and odds and ends of pipe and fittings. Anyone handy with tools can construct one from plans which may be obtained from the following sources: 'Mother Earth News', Issue No. 3 ($1), P.O. 38, Madison, Ohio 44057 and World Health Organization, Washington, DC.

Once your system is built, you can acquire a second-hand Diesel engine equipped to burn methane gas directly. Alternatively, you can purchase special carburators that will allow you to make the conversion yourself. For sources of supply for this equipment, see your local Diesel engine dealer. They have the catalogs that refer to this type of equipment. A unique method of utilizing the methane gas would be to burn it in a steam boiler which just happens to be our next topic.

First Time Farmer's Guide

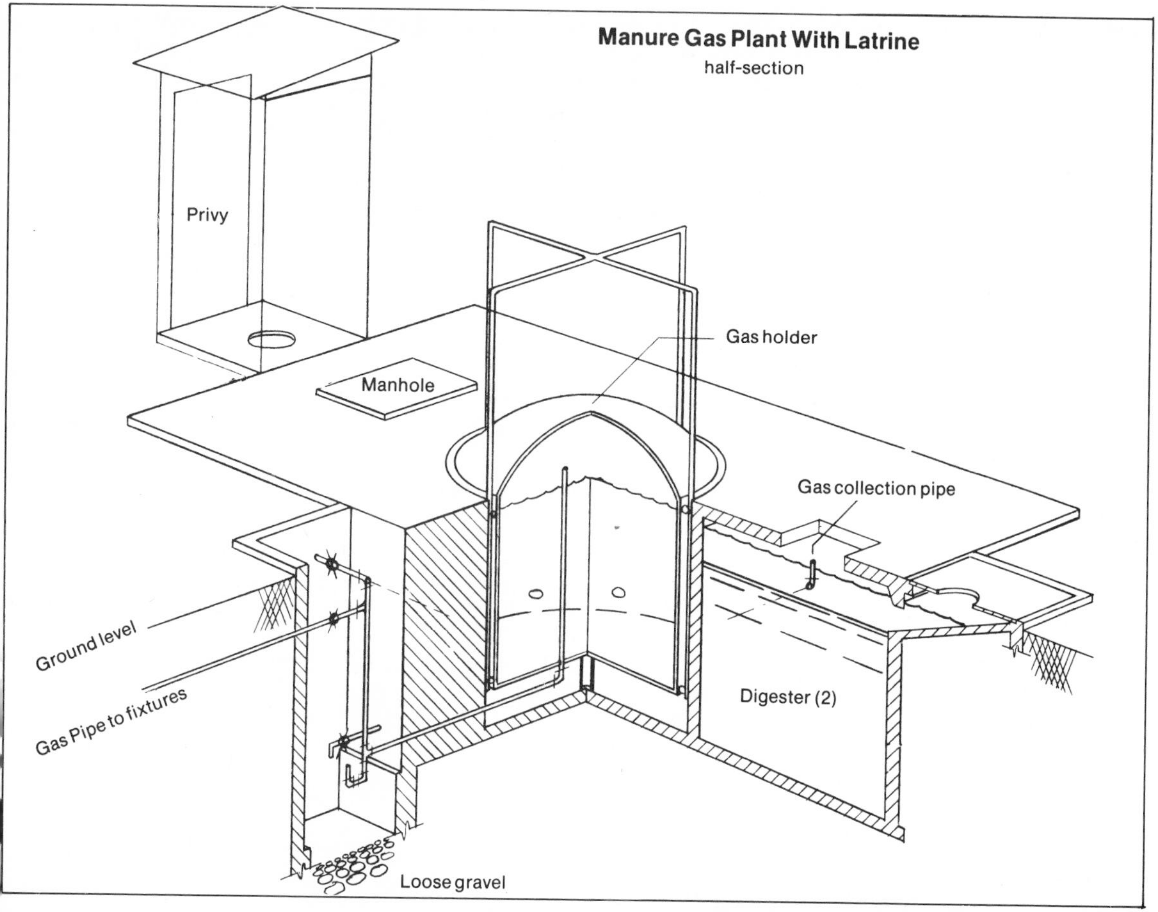

Manure Gas Plant With Latrine
half-section

Privy

Manhole

Gas holder

Gas collection pipe

Ground level

Gas Pipe to fixtures

Digester (2)

Loose gravel

Basic components of a manure gass plant

At far left—a simplified version of a gas plant. It consists of two inner tubes. Add manure-water mixture to one, connect to other by a hose. From the latter direct to a gas plate.

Steam

There has been a lot of discussion lately about steam cars. Many people have been interested in how the use of steam engines (external combustion engines) can help lessen the pollution which plagues our poor planet. It does ones heart good to look upon the brochure of the Semple Engine Company, P.O. 8354, St. Louis, Missouri 63124. They are manufacturing and selling a beautiful, up-to-date steam engine complete with boiler. Although the intention is to sell these engines for marine use, there is no reason in the world why they could not be used for all kinds of tasks around your pollution-free farm. After all, an electric generator, a power saw or a big grain grinder wouldn't know what sort of torque is being applied, would it? Thus, a power system which could use wood, coal or even the methane gas described in the previous section would be ideal. If you are not familiar with steam power, here are some of the advantages:

They produce no more pollution than simply building a fire.

They can be put into operation in 14 minutes (the Semple unit).

Steam engines last virtually forever.

They are quiet and have minimal vibration.

No clutch or transmission is needed since a steam engine can start easily under a heavy load. Those of you over 40 may recall steam locomotives shuffling out of the station with no strain.

Fuel can be anything you want to use. For example, if your farm was near a lumber mill, you could probably acquire truck loads of sawdust free and prepare a simple feeding arrangement to burn it in the steam boiler.

Steam has been around for a long time and all the bugs have been worked out of steam systems.

Very little training is needed to operate a steam power unit.

You can buy various sizes . . . up to 20 horsepower from Semple and even larger sizes from other firms or surplus marine dealers.

With all these benefits you'd expect that the system would be quite expensive. Actually, considering its longevity and the fact that you may be able to get fuel nearly free, the price tag of about $1300 for a complete engine, boiler and accessory unit is not out of sight.

There are a number of books and publications about steam and here are a few:

Books:
New Catechism of the Steam Engine, H. Hawkins (Audel)
Audels Engineers and Mechanics Guide Volumes 1, 2, 3.

The above books are out of print but are readily available from your used book store.

Magazines:
'Steam Power Quarterly', 12010 Rives Avenue, Downey, California 90242, $6.00 a year.
'Light Steam Power', Kirk Michael, Isle of Man, G.B., $5.80 a year.
'The Iron Men Album', Enola, Pennsylvania, $3.00 a year.

First Time Farmer's Guide

A typical steam engine unit . . . simple, long lasting, low polluting characteristics

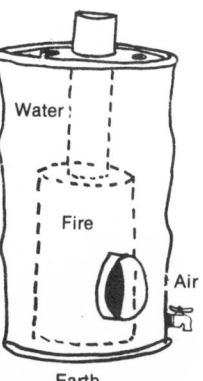

Power for Your First-Time Farm

It all started with
horsepower. Perhaps
that's the way it will
end

The Horse

Would you like to have a traditional farm? One with a windmill, big field of corn and hollyhocks standing against the white picket fence? If you're a purist on your first-time farm, then you should consider a form of power that is as old as it is reliable.

Surprisingly, thousands of horses are still being used on American farms. Here are some of the reasons why:

They're fun! If your only experience with horses has been to rent one for a couple of hours, you cannot imagine what it's like to have your own horse to ride off into the sunset whenever you wish. And if you think you'll enjoy that ride, think of the fun your children will have!

Horses can be a part of your balanced farm. They will eat grass and hay and return valuable manure to your fields.

You won't find any system of power less polluting to your fresh farm air than old Bess. Harnessed to a plow, cultivator or small reaper, a horse can do all of the work that a noisy, polluting gas engine can do. Not only that, they'll walk between the rows of corn with minimum guidance from you.

Horses, as we've described in the chapter on livestock, require minimum care. In fact, many people consider them one of the easiest animals to maintain . . . in a class with pets like dogs and cats. So if tradition means a lot to you, the two or three hundred dollars that an ordinary farm horse will cost, could be a most worthwhile investment.

First Time Farmer's Guide

Pest Control

'Here is no place to sit down in, but you must rise
as soon as you are set, for we have gnats in our
chambers, and worms in our gardens, and spiders
and flies in the palaces of the greatest Kings.'
— from *Holy Dying,* Jeremy Taylor

Right: The hungry
grasshopper on a corn
stalk

'Modern agricultural chemicals are ecologically crude in their effect on insect components in the environment. These chemicals are designed to kill off 100 to 1,000 species, including the beneficial insects. (Remember, there are nearly 700,000 known species of insects—and one of people.) Chemical sprays as they are used today create an insect vacuum for a time. Then, all the old pests come roaring back at a level increased 15 times. It's a disruption of the natural balance—and it's happening all over the world.'—*Dr. Robert van den Bosch, Head of the University of California's Division of Biological Control at Albany.*

About the only way that you and your family can avoid eating pesticides in your food is to grow your own food without the use of pesticides. More and more organic gardeners are doing just this. There are, fortunately, a number of simple and effective ways for the home gardener to protect his fruits and vegetables. These include:

Keeping plants as healthy as possible.

Natural, non-chemical insecticides.

Mixing one plant with another, companion planting.

Selecting insect-resistant varieties.

Using insects as helpers or 'bug eat bug'.

Have your feathered friends help you.

Toads, bats and lizards.

Miscellaneous insect remedies: hand removal; high pressure water; greenhouse growing.

Keeping Plants As Healthy As Possible

In his famous book *The Vegetable Garden,* the English agricultural authority, E.R. Janes, wrote:

'Feed the soil so that plants are in sturdy health, because all the remedies in the world are useless if the

The hungry grasshopper on a corn stalk

First Time Farmer's Guide

underlying cause is repeatedly neglected.'

This makes lots of sense in this era of 'drown all the bugs in chemicals'. When plants live in poor soil, they develop into weak specimens just as people who eat nothing but hot dogs and cokes are easy marks for the first bugs that invade their domain. Thus, building up your gardens and orchards with natural compost, bringing in earthworms, using mulch and maintaining the right amount of moisture can do more than any remedial methods in limiting insect attacks.

Natural, Non-Chemical Insecticides

If you're a hot chili pepper fan, you are well aware of the digestive penalties that come from over-eating these tasty little items. Believe it or not, chili peppers have the same effect on bugs. One gardener discovered that by grinding up a few hot chili peppers, mixing them with water and a little soap to make it cling, the resultant spray drove all of the caterpillars, worms, spiders and ants from his vegetable crops. So simply plant a few dozen hot pepper plants (They are available through your seed catalog), let them mature and then make your own totally natural insecticide. Incidentally, you can pick these hot peppers and dry them for future use. Or, make up a concentrate by boiling a number of peppers and then simply diluting this essence of hot peppers to drive away the but invaders when necessary.

In addition to peppers, much success has been obtained by grinding up green onions, garlic, mint, sweet peppers, parsley, wild mustard and other spicy or aromatic plants. This is a great opportunity to let your imagination roam. Perhaps you'll be the first-time farmer who discovers that ground up flowers of dried wild lilac is the anathema of the entire insect world. In

Hot peppers and the insect invaders

Spearmint

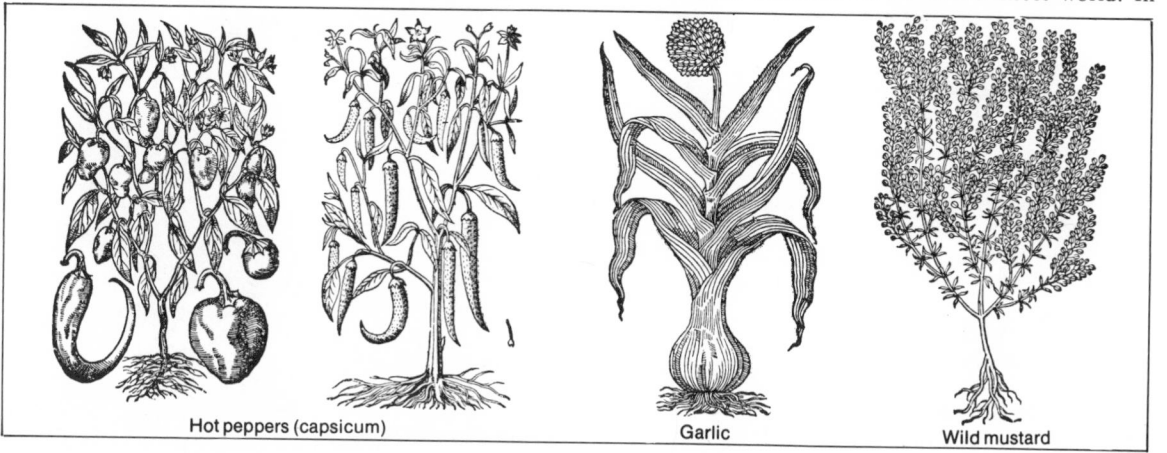

Hot peppers (capsicum)   Garlic   Wild mustard

Natural pest control
devices. (Grow some
extra plants, give them
to the bugs with your
blessing)

all seriousness, experiment with natural substances that grow in or around your farm. There are some natural organic supplies available, i.e., the ground roots of a plant called rotenone, the ground flowers of chrysanthemum and the ground stems of ryania are typical. They are sold under a variety of trade names either by themselves or in a mix.

Companion Planting

Organic gardeners have discovered that you can keep aphids away by just planting plenty of chives in your garden. So not only do your plants go untroubled by aphids, you reap a continual harvest of the tender tops of fresh chives for use in cottage cheese, omelettes, salads and soups. The idea of planting a highly aromatic plant to ward off insect attacks on the crops you're growing is currently being developed with great interest and enthu-

siasm. Here are some specific instances of success in the field of insect protection through companion planting: fast-growing, bright orange nasturtiums can be planted between fruit trees, small fruits and vegetables to keep away many types of bugs. Other flowers equally useful are geraniums, marigolds, calendulas and chrysanthemums.

Along with chives, a number of other herbs have worked well. These include sage, coriander, fennel or anise, savory, wormwood, tansy, onions and garlic. A peach grower in Iowa plants garlic cloves around his trees as close to the trunk as possible. It has prevented peach borers from making a free lunch of his infant trees.

In a real display of plant world cooperation, tomatoes grown near asparagus help fight off asparagus beetles. An even better example is demonstrated by the green bean which keeps potato beetles away while in turn

Chives

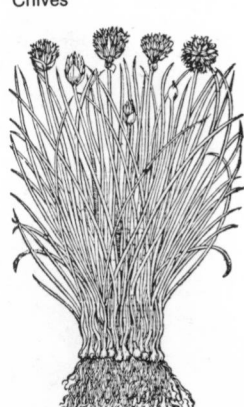

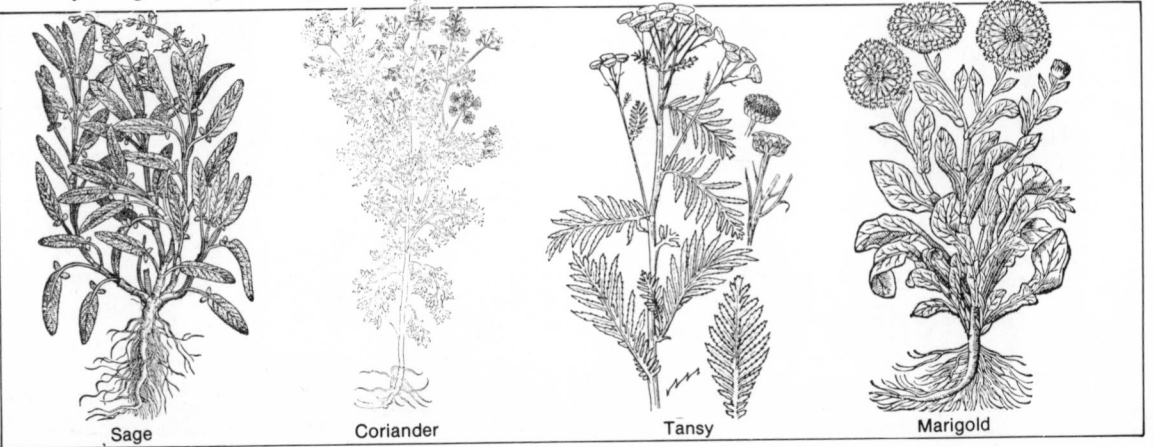

Sage   Coriander   Tansy   Marigold

First Time Farmer's Guide

the potato plant keeps the Mexican beetle from attacking the bean plant. There are lots of opportunities for first-time farmers to discover their own insect protection methods by mixing flowers with vegetables, herbs with trees, and whatever other botanical combinations that may prove effective.

Selecting Insect-Resistant Varieties

Pick up a couple of seed catalogs and read what they say about certain varieties. In many cases they will point out that a particular hybrid or new variety will be resistant to diseases or pests. Tomatoes, a formerly highly vulnerable field crop, now have been bred to resist a great variety of tomato-loving insects. So, to minimize pest problems, you have another valuable and efficient ally . . . the better seed, courtesy of the hardworking and resourceful seed companies.

Using Insects As Helpers

Many years ago citrus growers in California were troubled by several varieties of small insects. Since orange trees frequently grow in almost solid masses making it difficult if not impossible to spray, someone got the bright idea of hiring some very small workers. The

Tomatoes—a highly disease resistant vegetable

Have lots of flying insects? Then grow root crops.

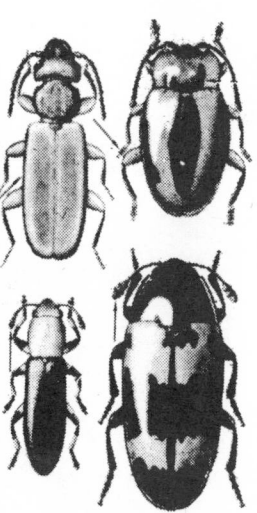

The orange growers
friend . . . the ladybug,
and the strange but
helpful praying mantis

workers? — ladybugs. These brightly colored, super neat insects that most people love to see and play with, came to the orange grower's rescue by gobbling up all of the anti-orange pests. The method was simple . . . large quantities of ladybugs were placed in every affected orchard.

To give you some idea of the economy and efficiency of this method, we'll tell you that there are more than 100,000 ladybugs in a gallon of ladybugs. Each adult eats four or five dozen aphids, mites and scale insects per day. Thus, just one gallon of ladybugs in your garden or orchard would eliminate a million smaller insects in 48 hours. Two additional benefits — ladybugs are harmless to your fruits and vegetables and they cost less than $10 per gallon.

A strange insect with a penchant for eating almost any other insect is the praying mantis. These friendly insects grow to be quite large, as shown here. Just a few

of them will do a great job of keeping your garden free of insect pests. Two other helpful insects are green lacewings and trichogramma wasps.

Purchasing bug allies is as easy as buying seeds. Here's a list of suppliers for each of the insects we've mentioned:

Ladybugs:

Bio-Control Company
Route 2, Box 2397
Auburn, California 95603

L.E. Schnoor
Rough & Ready
California 95975

Praying Mantises:

Eastern Biological Con Co
Route 5, Box 379
Jackson, New Jersey 08527

Gothard, Inc.
P.O. Box 332
Canutillo, Texas 79835

Robert Robbins
424 N. Courtland, E.
Stroudsburg, Pennsylvania 18301

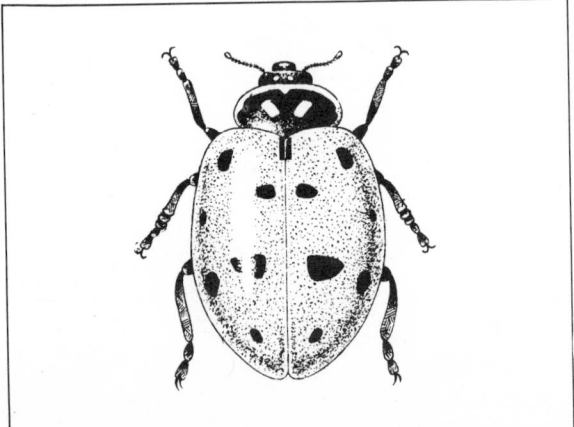

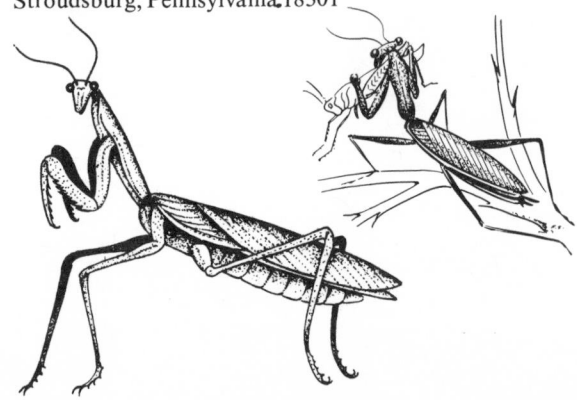

Lacewings (Aphid Lions) and Trichogramma Wasps:

Trik-O, Gothard, Inc.
P.O. 370
Canutillo, Texas 78935

Milky Spore Disease:

Doom, Fairfax Biological Lab.
Clinton Corners, New York 12514

Bacillus Thuringiensis Disease:

Thuricide	Biotrol
International Minerals	Kobes Dist., Company
& Chemical Corp.	Orange City, Iowa 51041
Crop Aid Products Dept	
5401 Old Orchard Road	
Stokie, Illinois 60076	

Feathered Friends

'Birds contribute three hundred million dollars worth of help in combatting insects'. — *USDA Report.*

That grasshopper that's eating away in your cornfield is considered by the meadowlark out in your pasture to be a real rib-sticking lunch or dinner. Chimney swifts like mosquitoes and woodpeckers dote on snails. Wouldn't it be great if you could invite these birds to come and live in your garden and orchards? Fact of the matter is, you can and here's how.

If you are fortunate, your farm already has an average supply of native birds. Even city birds recognize the tap tap tap that denotes a woodpecker or the joyful, clear song of the meadowlark. However, birds like barn swallows, phoebes, brown thrashers and finches would be less familiar. But whatever the type or your recognition of them, most all are helpful in controlling the number of insects on your property. Here is a list of birds that prefer an all-insect diet. Obviously these feathered friends should receive the warmest invitations to come and live on or near your farm: warblers, gnatcatchers, flycatchers, brown swallows, chimney swifts, house wrens, brown thrashers and phoebes.

To attract these varieties and others, here's what you can do.

Provide food and water. Food can be in the form of kitchen scraps, breadcrumbs, suet and millet. Planting shrubs and trees that produce berries and seeds is an ornamental way of attracting birds. These would include pyracanthus, bush cherry, snowberry, holly or winterberry and mulberry. A bird bath, which can be as simple as a large dish placed so that your cat can't catch the drinking or bathing birds. If you own a pond, lake or

Pest Control

Lacewings or aphid lions work for you without W-2 forms

Worms eat your root crops? Grow stalk and vine types.

stream, this service is already provided.

Birdhouses can be built unless you have trees and outbuildings that provide good nesting places. Here are some birdhouse designs that are suitable for various species.

To keep birds living on your farm, make nesting materials available to them. In early spring put out odds and ends of rags, string, bits of cotton, feathers or paper scraps to make it easy for them to build their nests. Placing these items near food supplies makes their procurement that much easier.

It's a good idea to keep your barn cat well fed so that he won't be tempted to eat your bird friends. In the same manner, keep your bird friends contented with native natural foods (they really prefer bitter or sour fruits anyway) and they'll leave your ripening peaches, apricots and cherries alone.

Bird house designs

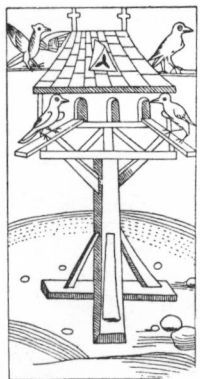

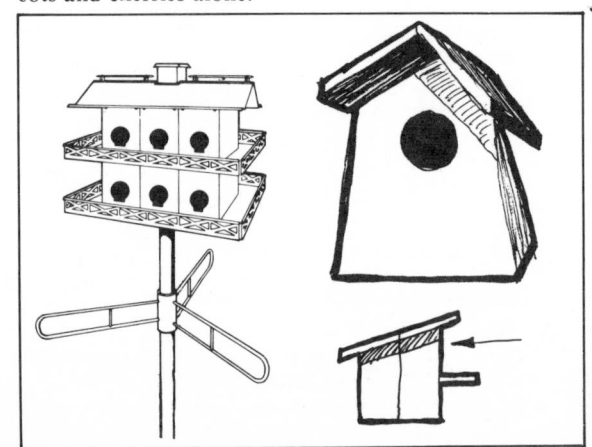

House Martin

Swallow

Swift

Pied Flycatcher

Wren

First Time Farmer's Guide

Toads, Bats and Lizards

It's hard to believe who kept count but it is claimed that a toad will eat about 3,000 insects a month. With an appetite like this, toads should be actively encouraged to come and live on your farm. Toads can be obtained by poking around in nearby swamps, marshes or pounds. They feed at night, so if you carried a flashlight, you would find them hopping about devouring insects. Gather a dozen or two and bring them back to your farm. Keep them penned up with some chicken wire for a few weeks so that they can get used to your spread. Then you can encourage them to live permanently by placing a board over a shallow trench with a narrow opening. During the day they will sleep there, enjoying the cool dampness. A great place to keep your toad allies would be near your farm pond, an over-flowing water trough, a leaking windmill pump or a shallow, slow-moving stream. Instruct your cat and/or dog to leave them alone. From then on your toads will eat up their 100-insect-a-day ration at no further expense or trouble to you.

There is not much you can do to control bats or lizards on your farm. Just make it a point to let them live where they wish and they'll join the birds and toads in keeping the farm insect population reduced to an acceptable level.

Miscellaneous Insect Remedies

Hand removal—If you don't grow too many tomatoes, just walk down the rows and pick off the hornworms. Feed them to your grateful chickens.

Many people have had great success by simply hosing off insect pests whenever they appear. They fall on the ground and either drown or are unable to re-climb the plant before they are consumed by your insect-eating allies.

If insects really prove troublesome, then grow your most troubled plants in a greenhouse.

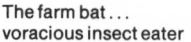

The farm bat . . . voracious insect eater

Short-eared Bat

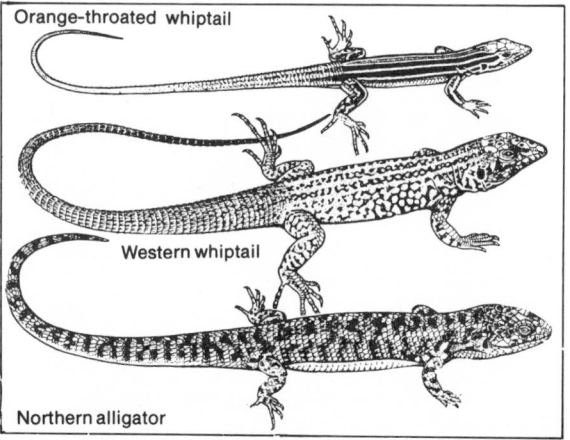

Orange-throated whiptail

Western whiptail

Northern alligator

Western toad

A summary of insect control methods that avoid polluting chemicals

A butane or blow torch is a fierce but effective way to control insects.

A Pesticide You Can Eat

Remember the diatomaceous earth that you may have used in your swimming pool filter? If you don't, we'll explain that it's a flour-like natural earth product that consists of fossilized skeletons of diatoms or small creatures that lived on the bottoms of ancient seas. Under a microscope the particles appear as tiny jagged fragments. Because of this characteristic, diatomaceous earth constitutes an excellent, totally organic pesticide (in fact, you can even eat it without harm).

To use it, simply sprinkle it wherever small crawling pests are a problem. Here's how it works: the insects cut themselves on the sharp particles and become dehydrated and die. Diatomaceous earth is available from swimming pool supply companies, many nurseries, or from rock, sand and other natural mineral suppliers.

Alternatives To Pesticides

The table which follows summarizes alternatives to harmful pesticides. The pesticides with formidable names like pyrethrum and nicotine sulphate are actually vegetable-based products and can be used with the assurance that you won't poison your environment.

To use this table, check your plants to see what kind of bugs or disease is harming them. Use the numbers which follow each listing to look up the method of control.

Method of Control

1. **Pyrethrum:** dried, ground flower of oriental chrysanthemum. Also known as Dalmation powder.
2. **Rotenone:** Powder from roots (tropical) containing rotenone.
3. **Soap Spray:** 2 tablespoons soap flakes (not detergents) in 1 quart water.
3a. **Nicotine Sulphate:** add 3 above. Bought as Black Leaf. Follow directions on label.
4. **Dusting Sulphur:** never use against house or fence as discolors paint.
4a. 4 above used with Pyrethrum.
5. **Water:** use as a fine strong spray, preferably in hand sprayer. Care not to flood.
6. **Mineral Oil Spray:** 3 parts oil/100 parts water.
7. **Wood Ash:** around base of plants to discourage cutworms.
8. **Epsom Salt Spray:** 2 ozs. salt, 2 gallons water.
9. **Beer:** stale or with molasses in saucer in garden.
10. **Ryanta:** root & woody stem of South American plant.
11. **Pepper:** (hot peppers in water), or Cayenne pepper. sprayed when plants wet with dew.
12. **Bordeaux Mixture:** can be bought ready mixed.
13. **Borax and Icing Sugar:** mix together in equal parts, sprinkle on ground or rocks.
14. **Tomato Leaves Spray:** crush and soak in water, strain.
15. **Rhubarb Leaves:** boil 3 lbs. leaves in 3 qt. water. Strain, add to 1 oz. soap flakes dissolved in 1 qt. water.
16. **Traps:** cutworms and millipeds come to surface at night. Use gloves and flashlight to catch them.
17. **Naphthalene:** dig into ground 2 oz/10 sq. feet.
19. **Trap for Grasshoppers & Ants:** Paraffin lined pill boxes or cans baited with sugar water, bacon rind, scraps. Drop filled traps in boiling water.

First Time Farmer's Guide

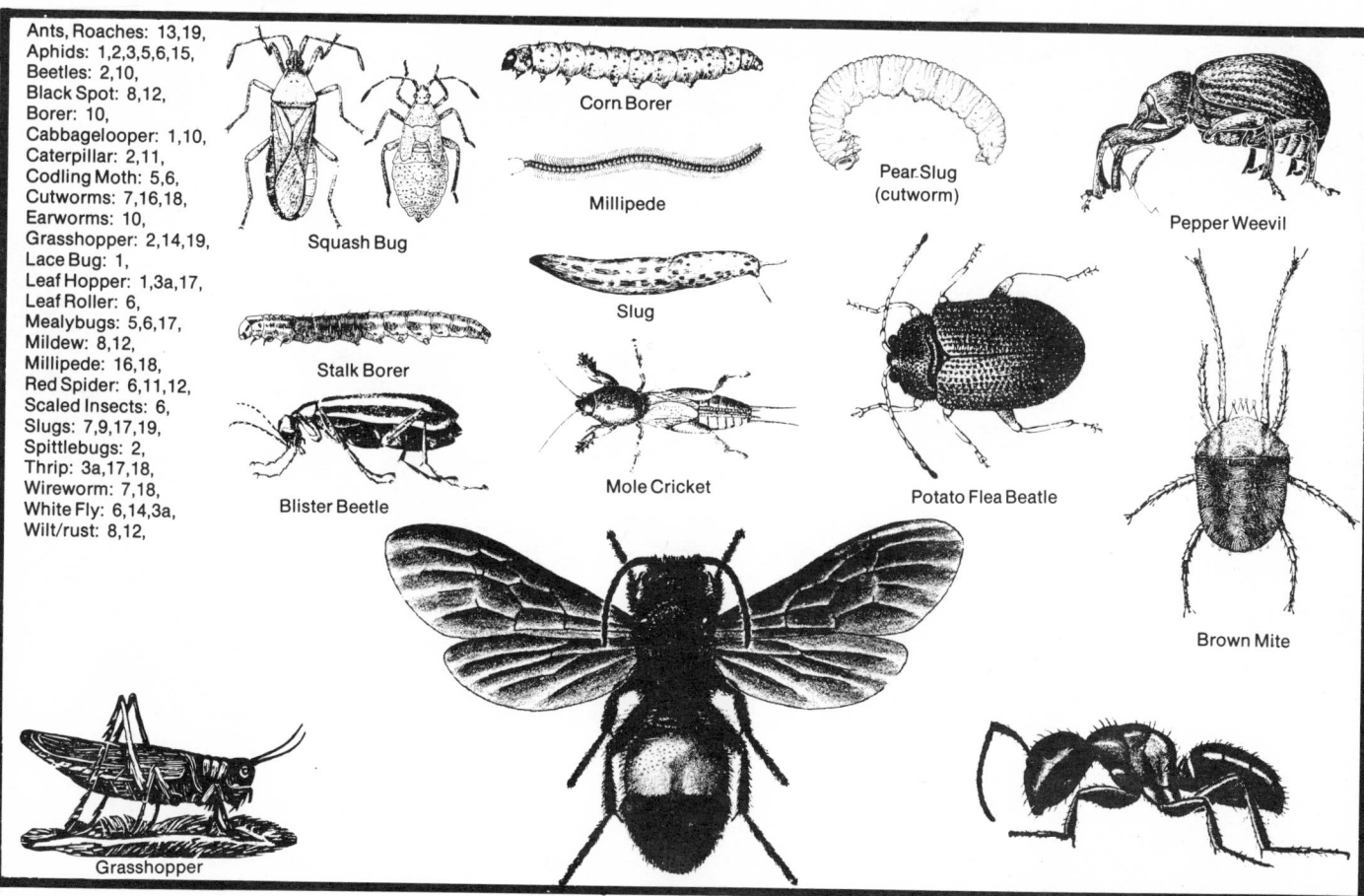

Ants, Roaches: 13,19,
Aphids: 1,2,3,5,6,15,
Beetles: 2,10,
Black Spot: 8,12,
Borer: 10,
Cabbagelooper: 1,10,
Caterpillar: 2,11,
Codling Moth: 5,6,
Cutworms: 7,16,18,
Earworms: 10,
Grasshopper: 2,14,19,
Lace Bug: 1,
Leaf Hopper: 1,3a,17,
Leaf Roller: 6,
Mealybugs: 5,6,17,
Mildew: 8,12,
Millipede: 16,18,
Red Spider: 6,11,12,
Scaled Insects: 6,
Slugs: 7,9,17,19,
Spittlebugs: 2,
Thrip: 3a,17,18,
Wireworm: 7,18,
White Fly: 6,14,3a,
Wilt/rust: 8,12,

Squash Bug

Corn Borer

Millipede

Pear Slug
(cutworm)

Pepper Weevil

Slug

Stalk Borer

Blister Beetle

Mole Cricket

Potato Flea Beatle

Brown Mite

Grasshopper

Farm Lore

'Who ever knew a good farmer of prudent habits to fail?'
— John Blake, 1850

A sleepy owl
introduces a wide-
awake section on
farm lore

Here are gleanings from many old farm books . . . things to make and things to do. They're mixed in with some more modern ideas using up-to-date materials and equipment. New or old, they will help you establish yourself on your first-time farm.

Useful Odds & Ends

There are many things that you can make yourself from ingredients readily available on your farm. Did you know that the ashes from your fireplace or outdoor burning pile can be mixed with grease, fat or tallow that would normally be thrown away, and that the result can be a pure and effective natural soap? Here's the way to do it.

To Make Soap From Ashes

To prepare a lye for soap, take a barrel without a bottom and place it on a board that has a trough to convey the water into another vessel. Cover the bottom with straw, then sprinkle over a couple of quarts of lime; fill the barrel with ashes; turn on the cold water, a pail at a time—slowly! Continue to turn on water, at intervals of 3-4 hours the first, third and fifth days. When the lye becomes strong enough to bear up an egg, add to 15 gallons of it 11 pounds of grease heated to the boiling point. Stir it for five minutes every day till it forms soap. If it doesn't in one week, add a pailful of soft water.

To Dry Corn For Winter Use

Sweet corn is the best. Husk it. Have a pot of boiling water, put your corn in and let it boil three minutes. Then cut it from the cob and put it in pans in a warm oven. It must be stirred frequently. When perfectly dry, put away in bags. When wanted for use, soak it all night, and next day boil it an hour with a little salt. Before serv-

ing, stir in a little flour, pepper and butter.

To Freshen Walnuts

When walnuts have been kept until the meat is too dried to be good, let them stand in milk and water eight hours and dry them. Fresh as new they will be.

To Make An Improved Candle

Make the wicks about half the usual size, and wet them with spirits of turpentine. Dry them in the sunshine before dipping and the candles will be more durable, and emit a steadier and clearer blaze.

Waterproof Boots

A pint of boiled linseed, half a pound of mutton suet, six ounces of clean beeswax and four ounces of resin are to be melted and well mixed over a fire. Spread this mixture plentifully over new boots or shoes with a brush while it is warm but not hot enough to shrink the leather. The leather remains pliant. This method has been in use among New England fishermen for over 100 years.

Inexpensive Plow Horse

Several years ago the Suzuki Motorcycle people built in 80cc two-stroke single that most people considered unkillable. No matter how much it was abused, it just kept right on running. Here's what you can do with one of these indominitable little machines, or its equivalent.

Put on a trail gear, i.e. a gear that will allow the engine to develop full power while going very slowly. This is usually done by putting on a very large rear wheel sprocket. Now put on the knobbiest, toughest trail-type tire you can find that will fit the rear wheel. If you can't find one, wrap some rope at right angles around the existing tire. In other words, let the bike develop maxi-

First Time Farmer's Guide

Watertank, cat, salt, maple sugar...useful hints

mum traction. Voila! You now have a no-cost mechanical horse that you can use to pull a cultivator, disc harrow or other gardening implement.

Low-Cost Water Tank

As an ex-urbanite you'll surely remember those inexpensive plastic pools used by children in the summertime. They range in price from about ten dollars up. Why not use one for your farm water tank? It would serve animals or, placed above your house level, would be a reservoir for your home.

You'll Need A Cat

You'll probably be storing wheat, corn and other grains on your farm as food for your animals, but rats and mice like these goodies too. Thus, your farm wouldn't be complete without a four-legged rat trap. Besides, a farm, first-time or last-time, wouldn't be a farm without a sleek pussycat to live in your barn and sleep in the hay.

Salt For Animals

Practically every mineral needed by herbivorous animals is provided by their feed. However, if your cow or horse begins nibbling the fences, get a block of salt ... it's the only mineral that farm feed doesn't provide.

Maple Sugar

While it's a romantic thought, making sugar from maple sap is largely a waste of your valuable time. It takes about 35 gallons of sap to make 8 pounds of sugar, not to mention the enormous amount of heat required to boil it down.

Thrifty Planting Tip

Start seedlings in eggshell halves filled with com-

Farm Lore

277

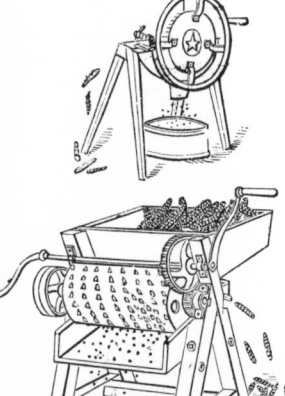

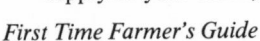

A must for your first time farm . . . a food grinder that you can use for many purposes — wheat, corn, chicken mash, etc

post. The shells can be stored in egg cartons and moved around to follow the sun. When you transplant them, put shell and all in the ground. The roots will break through the shell and the shell itself will provide needed minerals.

Bathtub Tip

To have more time to milk the cow and ride the horse, remove bathtub rings with a cloth moistened with kerosene or paint thinner. It will come off instantly and you can rinse off the odor with plain soap and water.

Cooking Hint

Farmers' wives use lard for greasing cake tins. The salt in butter causes cakes to burn and stick to the tin.

Farm Animal Advice

To calm an animal, speak to it before entering its stall. Gently stroke the animal's back to keep it relaxed.

How To Make Your Own Paint For Much Less Than It Costs To Buy

While it is fun to reach into the past for old time methods, here's one that's as up to date as a week from tomorrow . . . it's a formula for making your own paint. You can only have one color, but the paint is cheap and easy to make and will last a long time. It will keep your wood buildings in great shape.

Sodium Chromate: 6 pounds

Copper Sulfate: 1 pound

Concentrated Ammonium Hydroxide: 5 pounds

Dissolve the sodium chromate in five gallons of water. Then add the ammonium hydroxide slowly while stirring. Finally, add the copper sulfate and stir occasionally for several hours until all ingredients are dissolved. A plastic container would be ideal for mixing the paint.

Apply to your barns, fences or other wood surfaces

by dipping, brushing or spraying. Avoid contact of paint with skin and should it occur, wash with soap and water. The paint will cover at a rate of approximately 200 square feet per gallon and should keep the wood protected for at least four years. Cost?—about $1.00 per gallon!

Little Tidbits

For those unable to afford a flour mill, an old food mill—the kind everybody's mother has—can be purchased secondhand for less than a dollar, and is a pretty good substitute. The flour is like a combination of wheat germ and flour, makes an excellent bread, and is very economical. The grinding keeps you strong.

Weave rags and old clothes into rugs on a frame with nails on either end in lieu of a loom. Weaves up fast if cut in inch strips. Makes a beautiful covering for floors and walls and keeps out wind and wet. Using string for

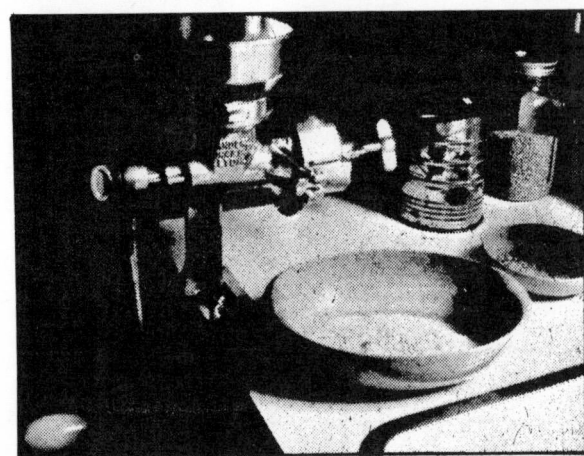

First Time Farmer's Guide

warp, cost is about ten cents a rug. Results with colors and designs unlimited.

Want to feel better fast? Give up all forms of refined sugar.

Next time you use a pumpkin, save the seeds, dry them, crack or crush and put them in water. The hulls will float and the kernel will stay at the bottom. Drain, dry a bit in the oven and eat. Voila, a delicious nutmeat, chockfull of vitamins and minerals.

How Much Food Do You Need

'The countryman has a provident and gainful family, not one whose necessities must be furnished out of a shop. His provision is always out of his own stores and agrees with the season of the year.' — *Don De Guevara, The Praise and Happiness of the Country Life, 1539.*

The average human being will eat about ten times his own weight in food per year. That means if you weigh 160 pounds you will eat a little over three quarters of a ton of food per year. Thus, if you use whole grains at four or five cents or even 10 cents per pound as a fundamental part of your diet, you won't need to grow a tremendous amount of food on your home farm. Keep in mind that whole grains when cooked will weigh four or five times their dry weight. This means that a 100-pound sack of whole wheat that costs you from four to ten dollars, depending on where you bought it, can provide you with about 500 pounds of ready-to-eat food. It's mind-grabbing, to be sure, that one-third of your annual diet can be obtained for less than a ten dollar bill! Potatoes are an extremely nutritious food and can be grown or purchased cheaply. A 100-pound sack bought from a nearby ranch or farm probably won't cost more than seven or eight dollars.

Some Ingenious Ways To Save On Food

A must for your farm is a big black cauldron . . . the type of pot that witches used for brewing up magic potions. They are available at many antique and plain old junk stores. Restaurants going out of business often sell big pots which are the modern counterpart to the cauldron. Use to boil up vast quantities of soups, stews, apple sauce or chili beans. A great companion container is a five or ten-gallon ceramic crock to store pickles or sauerkraut.

Speaking of sauerkraut, to make your own, simply shred the cabbage, sprinkle a little salt between layers, weigh it down with a press of wood and a rock in a crock and let it ferment. Store in a cool place.

Here are three things to do with leftover bread (never throw it away):

Dip it in an egg-milk mixture for french toast.

Cube it, sprinkle with melted butter and garlic salt and toast slowly in the oven to make croutons.

Toss it in your blender for crumbs to use in meatloaf and other recipes.

If you can locate a rotary meat slicer, you can make the toughest meats taste like T-bones. Just boil or roast meat slowly, then set the blade for the thinnest slice and go to work.

Worlds cheapest soup: Add a handful of broken spaghetti and all the water you dare (preferably the water you've cooked your vegetables in and saved in a jar in the refrigerator) to leftover spaghetti sauce. Presto, spaghetti soup!

Never forget, eggs have the highest quantity of high quality protein per pound.

For a great breakfast, boil whole wheat kernels in

The average human will eat ten times his own weight in food a year

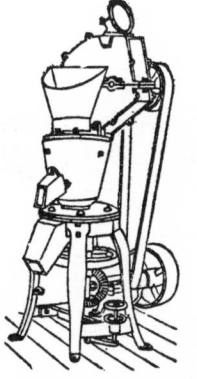

The preservation of
your fruit and
vegetables

salted water for about 20 minutes or until tender, adding raisins or dates toward the last. Serve with milk and honey.

Cheap source of protein: Boil chicken necks and backs till tender with rice, celery and salt.

Know what scrapple is? It's fried cornmeal or other cereal that has been leftover from the previous day. Slice it when cold, fry in butter or margarine and serve with syrup or honey.

Free tea — gather mint from any wild damp place, dry it and use like tea leaves. You can also add dried alfalfa.

Storage Of Foods

Almost as important as growing fruits and vegetables is their preservation. A very old book on farming reveals some almost-forgotten methods and here they are.

Fruits

All kinds of fruit may be stored in dry sand. The only qualifications are that the fruit must be clean, dry and sound when stored and the sand must be absolutely dry. A big bin of sand in the cellar of your farmhouse would be ideal. The chief advantages of packing in sand are the exclusion of air currents, the preservation from changes of temperature and the absorption of moisture.

Here's a method for drying apples that works well with similar fruits. Pare and cut the apples in slices. Many people leave the skins on. Spread them on cloths, tables or boards and dry them outdoors. In clear, dry weather this is the most expeditious plan. It is a good idea to use frames . . . simply four pieces of wood nailed together like a picture frame with loosely woven cloth tacked to cover the frame. Frames combine the most ad-

vantages with the least inconvenience since they can be used either for drying in the house or out in the sun. In pleasant weather the frames can be set outdoors against the side of the building and at night or in damp cloudy weather can be brought into the house and set near the stove or fireplace.

Apples, as well as many other fruits can be strung like beads on a piece of twine. This method is used in the southwest to dry chili pepper. The colorful red peppers hanging in long strands make a handsome display. If you are troubled by flies during the drying process, place the fruits at least 20 feet in the air . . . flies seldom reach that altitude.

Drying grapes is a simple process. The grapes are allowed to remain on the vine until they are a golden color and translucent. They are then picked and placed on wooden trays, two by three feet, which you can make yourself from scrap wood. Place the trays so they slope toward the sun. When half dried, they are turned by placing an empty tray on top and turning over both trays, thus transferring the contents from one tray to the other. They are then left to finish drying. Remove any green ones and store them in a cool place with sheets of paper between every 25 pounds of raisins.

To keep cranberries, put them in a tub of water and put the tub in the cellar.

To dry figs, pick them and lay them on dry boards in the sun. Those of better quality should be pulled and extended by hand during the drying process. Thus prepared, the fruit is packed in woven baskets or wooden boxes and stored in a cool, dry place.

To keep lemons fresh for months, put them in a clean, tight wooden cask and cover them with cold water. Change the water periodically.

Old-style drying rack
that you can easily build
(below)

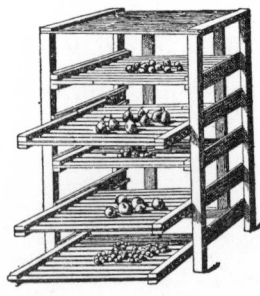

First Time Farmer's Guide

To dry peaches, let the fruit get mellow enough to be in good eating condition. Then put them in boiling water for a minute or two so the skins will peel off readily. Then quarter the fruit and place in the sun or near the stove to dry.

Vegetables

To enjoy wholesome and palatable vegetables during the winter months, proper care is essential in gathering and storing. As the cellars of most houses are too warm for proper preservation, the main supply should be kept in cool cellars, barns or in pits dug outside. A good plan is as follows:

Sink a barrel, box or cask (as many as you need) two-thirds of its depth into the ground. Heap the earth around the part projecting out of the ground with a slope on all sides. Place the vegetables in the barrel and cover the top with a water-tight cover. When winter sets in, throw an armful of straw on the barrel. Cabbage, beets, carrots and other vegetables will keep in this way as fresh as when taken out of the ground. Freedom from frost, ease of access, freedom from rot and freshness are the advantages of this plan. Here are some methods for other types of vegetables.

To dry lima beans, gather while green and tender and spread in the sun. String snap beans like beads and dry outdoors. In winter soak them and cook in the usual way.

To have bright, crisp parsley for winter, gather it and spread it thinly on a piece of paper. Place in a barely warm oven with the door left slightly open. As soon as dry, crumble it and put it in a bottle and cork it to exclude all air. Dried in this way, it will retain its color and flavor.

PLASTIC

BARREL

Here's a good way to dry pumpkins or squash. Cut them into small pieces, boil until soft, mash and strain through a colander as though you were making a pie. Spread this pulp on plates in layers about one-half inch thick. Then dry it in an oven at a temperature sufficiently low so as not to scorch it. In about a day it will become dry and crisp. The sheets thus made can be stored away in dry places and always ready for use for stewing or making pies.

To dry rhubarb, peel it, string it on a piece of twine and hang in the sun.

Sweet potatoes can be preserved just like fruit . . . in dry sand.

To keep tomatoes, pick them while green before the vines freeze. Put them in cool, dry place with free circulation of air, but above the freezing point.

Many vegetables like onions and turnips are best preserved by keeping them below 40 degrees F. If you live in a cold climate, store them in a corner of your barn and cover them with straw.

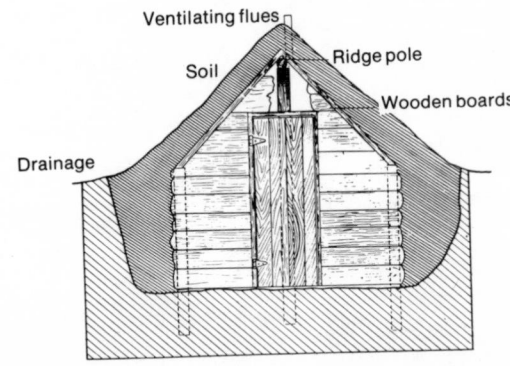

Ventilating flues
Ridge pole
Soil
Wooden boards
Drainage

First Time Farmer's Guide

Fruit or Vegetable Measure

Fruit or Vegetable	Measure	Weight	Quart Jars
Red raspberries	24 pt. crate	16 lbs	8
Strawberries	16 qt. crate	22 lbs	8
Peaches	1 bushel	48 to 50 lbs	25
Cherries	16 qt. crate	22 lbs net	12
String Beans	1 peck	6 lbs.	6-8 pints
Carrots	1 bushel	50 lbs.	40 pints
Corn	1 bushel	70 lbs.	16 pints
Tomatoes	1 peck	14 lbs.	7-9 pints

Farm Weights

Bushel	Weight in pounds	Bushel	Weight in pounds
Alfalfa	60	Wheat	60
Beans, Dry	60	Oats	32
Beets	60	Onions	57
Bluegrass seed	22	Peaches, dried	33
Clover seed	60	Peanuts, Spanish	30
Corn, Pop (Ear)	70	Pears	50
Corn, Pop (shelled)	56	Potatoes, Irish	60
Corn, Shelled	56	Potatoes, Sweet	46
Corn in Ear, Shucked	70	Rye	56
		Salt	50
Corn in Ear, with Husks	74	Sunflower	22
		Sweet clover	60
		Timothy seed	45
Hemp seed	44	Tomatoes	45
Hickory Nuts	50	Walnuts	55

Handy chart that will save much time and money

Farm Lore

283

Recipes

Here are several genuine old farm recipes that were copied from a yellowed book that was once on the bookshelf of almost every farmhouse, *Lee's Priceless Recipes*, published in 1895. It is a joyous occasion when one makes, for the first time, foodstuffs previously available only in packages from the super market.

Butter

If you keep but one cow, churn twice a week; and in dog-days, three times. Do it in the cool of the morning. If the weather is warm, set the churn into a tub of cold water; add ice if you have it, and put a piece also into the churn. Air is necessary to make butter come; therefore, if the cream flies out of the opening around the dasher, do not put anything round to prevent it. When the butter has come, continue the strokes of the dasher a few minutes to separate all the little particles from the buttermilk. This done, take it out into the wooden bowl with a ladle or skimmer. The bowl and ladle should have boiling water poured on them when you first begin to churn. After a few minutes it should be poured off, cold water should be poured on them, and they should stand till you are ready to use them. This is to prevent the butter from sticking to them.

Work the butter with the ladle, until the buttermilk ceases to come out; then sprinkle it with clean sifted salt, as that which was put into the cream will not be enough; work it in well, and taste it to see if more should be added. Observation and experience must teach you how much to use. Mould the butter, with the ladle, into balls or lumps of any form you prefer; put it into a covered jar or tureen and set it in the ice-house or cellar.

Cheese

A giant wheel of yellow cheese would be a marvelous hedge against diabolical happenings in the outside world. If your farm boasts a cow or herd of goats, then you already have the basic ingredient for making this time-honored food yourself. Here are the directions for cheese making:

Mix a gallon of fresh milk with a gallon that has rested overnight. Warm in a tinned or enameled pail to 86° F. Dissolve ¼th of a rennet tablet in cold water and add to milk maintaining the previous temperature. Let it stand until a firm curd forms . . . the curd is like vanilla pudding. Next, cut the curd into small cubes with a long knife. Then stir for fifteen minutes. Heat the curd to 102°F and stir frequently. Remove from heat and stir from time to time for about an hour. Now you can pour the curd into a piece of clean cheese cloth letting the whey run off. Add about one tablespoon of salt if you wish and mix the curd with your hands. Hang the cheese up to drain by tying the four corners of the cloth together. Now shape the cheese into a flattened cylinder six inches or so in diameter. Place a cloth around it to hold it in shape. Press the cheese between two clean boards using bricks or stones as weights. Coat with wax and allow to cure for a month.

Great Farm Beverage Recipes

Peaches, apricots, plums, apples and other fruits can be used to make delicious beverages. Stored in jugs and bottles in your cellar they can be brought out to lend cheer to a long winter evening.

Blackberry Wine

Gather when ripe on a dry day. Put into a vessel with the head out and a tap fitted near the bottom. Pour on boiling water, mash the berries with your hand and let them stand covered till the pulp rises and forms a crust in three or four days. Then draw off the liquor into another vessel and to every gallon add one pound of sugar. Mix well and put into a cask to work for a week or ten days and throw off any remaining lees. Keep the cask well filled, particularly at the commencement. When the working has ceased, bung the cask. Bottle after six months.

Authors note: The basic recipe can be used for gooseberries, elderberries, peaches, apricots and other fruits.

Cider Champagne

Good cider 20 gallons, spirits 1 gallon, honey or sugar 6 pounds; mix and let them rest two weeks, then fine with skim milk 1 quart. Bottle in champagne bottles. It opens very sparkling.

Home-Brewed Ale

Take 8 bushels malt, hops 12 pounds, yeast 5 quarts. The malt being crushed or ground is mixed with 72 gallons water at 160°, and covered 3 hours, when 40 gallons are drawn off, into which the hops are put to infuse; 60 gallons of water at 170° are then added to the malt in the mash tub and well mixed, and after standing 2 hours 60

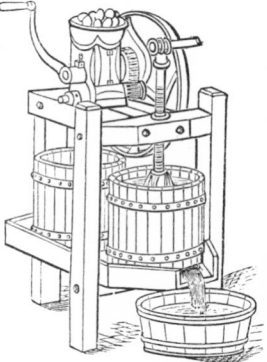

Farm Lore

285

gallons are drawn off. The wort from these 2 mashes is boiled with the hops for 2 hours and after being cooled down to 160° is strained through a flannel bag into a fermenting tub, where it is mixed with the yeast and left to work 24 to 30 hours. It is then run into barrels to cleanse; a few gallons being reserved for filling up the cask as the yeast works over.

How To Grow Bean Sprouts

Would you like a fresh vegetable that you could use in salads or cook in many different ways . . . one that would be available all year long? Surprisingly, there is such a vegetable. Not only does it meet the requirements we've just mentioned, it can be 'grown' indoors in three or four days, rivals even meat with respect to protein content and, in addition, contains enormous amounts of vitamins and minerals. Furthermore, it is easy to digest and is dispatched with gusto by every member of the family. Can you stand one more hosanna for this most rare vegetable? Ok, they are extremely economic.

What we're discussing are the sprouts of many kinds of seeds. You've undoubtedly eaten them already if you've ever dined at a Chinese restaurant. Bean sprouts (beans, of course, are really seeds) are an important and basic ingredient in many Chinese dishes, so doubtless you've enjoyed their crisp succulence and delicate flavor. Although you don't need to live on a farm to enjoy sprouted seeds, the availability of your own home grown seeds makes it that much more feasible and delightful. Also, you'll be sure that the seeds haven't been preserved with some foul chemical.

The simplest way to sprout seeds is to spread a piece of clean toweling on the bottom of a large baking dish. Cover the toweling with seeds and then sprinkle them

thoroughly. Keep the toweling moist until the seeds sprout . . . a matter of three days for soft-hulled types to a week or more for such tough ones as safflower. You can duplicate the professionals if you'll buy a large ceramic pot or crock — the type that are ordinarily used for planting ornamental shrubs. These pots have a hole in the bottom for drainage, which makes them suitable for sprouting seeds. First place a saucer or dish over the hole. Next pour in as many seeds as you wish to sprout, having soaked them in a bucket for at least 12 hours beforehand. From now on simply pour buckets of water over the seeds in the crock twice a day, or sufficiently often to keep them damp. Within three days the seeds will have sprouted and swelled up. Depending on the type, they should be ready to eat when they have reached a desirable size.

Among the many types of seeds that you can sprout

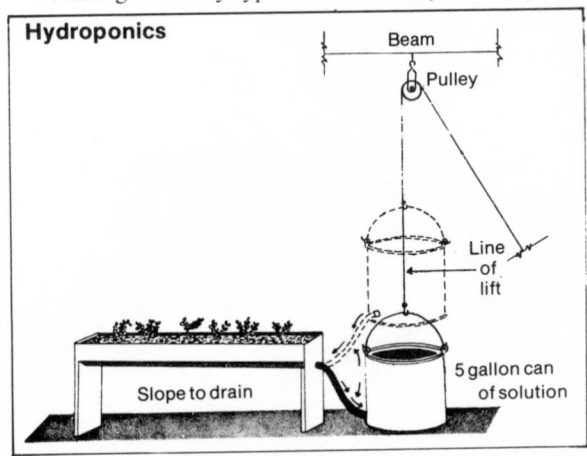

Hydroponics

Beam

Pulley

Line of lift

Slope to drain

5 gallon can of solution

First Time Farmer's Guide

are the following:

Mung beans (these become the Chinese restaurant bean sprouts with which you are probably already familiar).

All types of grains—wheat, corn, barley, buckwheat, millet, oats and alfalfa.

All kinds of beans, including soybeans (these are especially valuable from a nutritional standpoint) pinto beans, kidney beans, lima beans, navy beans and lentils.

Miscellaneous seeds such as safflower, sunflower, pumpkin, peanut, lettuce, dill, celery and parsley.

Experimentation with seeds and methods of sprouting will be most rewarding. As we said in the beginning, it's a great way to have fresh crisp salad makings and vegetables even when the snow is half way up the windmill tower.

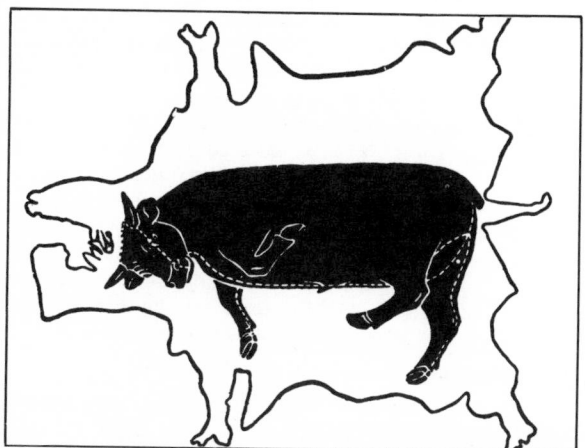

Tanning

An important activity of our pioneer forefathers was to convert the hides of both wild and domestic animals to useable materials—leather for shoes and harnesses and many other farm applications came from the 'sides' (split halves) of cattle. Warm clothes such as jackets and covers for otherwise icy beds were produced from woolly sheep and on a smaller scale, goats and rabbits. Wild animals . . . deer, elk, moose, bear and buffalo . . . also yielded useable skins and hides. Even small animals such as beaver, raccoon, hare and skunk could be tanned and sewn together to make all kinds of long-wearing, winter-fighting clothing and covering.

A not incidental benefit was the rugged good looks of a fresh deerskin jacket or a great sheepskin coat with the unshorn wool on the inside.

As a first time farmer, there's no question that you will want to make good use of all the products of your farm. With labor costs high and going higher, it is logical that if skins or hides are to be tanned and used, you will do the work. So here are some genuine, old-farm instructions on how to tan a fresh raw skin or hide into a soft, beautiful and useable material for clothing, bed or floor coverings and other uses around your farm.

Tanning With the Hair On

First scrape off all the fat with a blunt knife to avoid cutting the hide. This should be done on a log having a couple of legs on one end the other end resting on the ground. After the fat is cleaned off, take the brains of the animal, or of any other recently killed, and work them into the hide; this renders it pliable, Take 1 spoonful of alum, 2 of saltpeter; pulverize and mix; sprinkle on the

COON

Farm Lore

Nowadays it is not only
easy but exciting to
construct your own
home

flesh side. If the hair side is greasy, a little weak lye will take it out. Yellow ochre mixed with the brains gives a fine color to the under side. The whites of several eggs or the soaking of the skin ½ day in oil or lard is said to produce the same effect as brains. This process is good for deerskins, sheepskins and all small furs.

Tanning Without the Hair

Flesh it with a dull knife, and grain by scraping with a sharp instrument; then soak in pure water several days, and afterward in lime-water until the hair pulls out easily; remove the hair by scraping backward and replace the skin in fresh weak lime-water. Altogether the skin should be in lime-water 2 or 3 weeks, changing the water every 4 or 5 days. Take out, scrape, trim, rinse in clean water and put in a mixture of wheat bran and water; after 2 weeks transfer to a mixture of alum, salt and

water; stir well and replace for a day or two in the bran mixture; remove to a dry room; stretch for a while, and then soak in warm water. While soaking prepare a paste in the following proportions, increasing or decreasing quantity as necessary: Salt ½ pound, alum 1 pound 3 ounces, wheat flour 3 pounds, yolks of 16 eggs; mix with water, dissolving first the alum, then the salt. This is to be used in the next step, a little of the past to a great deal of the water. Place the skin in a tub of this preparation beaten to a froth; tramp and work well; then remove; stretch dry and lastly run over with a warm flat iron. This process, though slow, makes a splendid leather, and is good for all small animals — sheep, calves, etc.

Building Ideas

A comfortable place to live on your farm is of almost equal importance to having an adequate water supply. This is particularly true for the family man. His wife and children must have warm, pleasant, comfortable accommodations so that they will enjoy good health and the right outlets. One of the great advantages of rural living is that you can be as different, as creative, as innovative as you please (in most cases) since country farming laws are rather liberal. Cities and suburbia require that houses have a certain architectural style, height limit, setback, etc. However, if you live many miles from anywhere on thirty acres of wooded land, it's quite certain that you can put up a tipi, park a trailer or build yourself a three-story log cabin . . . or if the trees are big enough, put together a Swiss Family Robinson-type treehouse.

Build It Yourself

New materials have made it easy and exciting to build your own farm home. Not only that, there are new

First Time Farmer's Guide

Domes are possible in
an infinite variety of
shape and form

methods of using old materials. Here are two examples,
one for each of the statements we've just made. Extremely lightweight aluminum can be placed over a geodesic
frame to create a low cost, easily built, ultra-modern
home. For information on geodesics, write Sun Dome,
c/o Popular Science, 355 Lexington Avenue, New York,
N.Y. 10017. Information about machines to make blocks
of earth similar to the ancient method of adobe block-
making is available from VITA College Campus,
Schenectady, N.Y. 12308

If more conventional homes are your desire, pick
up a copy of Cabins and Vacation Houses. It's $2 plus tax
and shipping costs from Lane Books, Menlo Park,
California 94025 (frequently available from racks in
department stores and building material outlets). This
wonderful book has basic plans for very simple to very
elaborate rural cabins. One of the most interesting and
suitable for a person wishing to survive in the country is
the Teepee Cabin. It's only about 500 square feet on the
main floor but has another 100 square feet for a sleeping
balcony and another 100 feet in a third floor storage attic.
They figure the cost at between $4,000 and $5,000,
including foundation, fireplace, plumbing, kitchen and
electricity. If you were to rough it for a while, they figure
that the shell alone would cost about half this amount.

Another extremely interesting and practical design
is the expandable 'core'. This core can be built in a couple
of days and provides the absolute basics for cooking and
sleeping. It's intended, of course, to be expanded as
money and time permit. The cost of this core would be
about $400. This type of extremely rudimentary, low cost,
easy-to-build initial dwelling is highly recommended for a
survival-oriented, country-bound individual. It will give
you the chance to try your hand at building without mak-

First Time Farmer's Guide

ing too large an investment or too many construction mistakes. If the venture succeeds, then it would be logical to go on to further effort.

In another part of this comprehensive book on cabins, there is a review of how a cabin can be built in four stages. As the article points out, this is practical for several reasons. A cabin lends itself to stage-by-stage development, since liveability can be obtained at every stage. Also, rough construction (amateur hammer and saw work) is compatible with cabin appearance. Furthermore, lots of materials can be found right on site. The article goes on to point out that a five-year building program can be practical and specifies the elements to be completed at each given stage.

Another good basic book on log and frame cabins is *The Wilderness Cabin* by Calvin Rustrum. This one is available through 'The Mother Earth News', P.O. 38,

Domes, cabins, teepees, yurts, a bus—modify and adapt

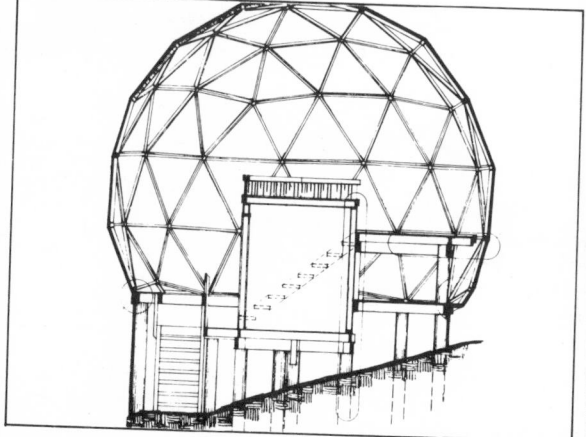

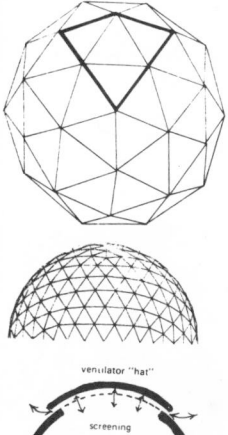

Farm Lore

Madison, Ohio 44057. Still another book, which is out
of print but may be found in used-book stores, is *How to
Build Cabins, Lodges and Bungalows*. This one has
heavy emphasis on log construction, which is a lot of
hard work but has been eased a lot by the use of chain
saws and other power tools. For 50¢ you can get 'Building a Log House'. Write Cooperative Extension Service,
University of Alaska, Anchorage, Alaska.

A gold mine of house plans, drawings of interiors
and building tips may be obtained from the following
organizations for free:

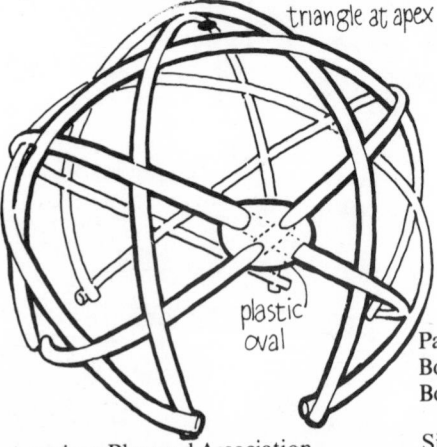

triangle at apex

plastic
oval

American Plywood Association
1119 "A" Street
Tacoma, Washington 98401

California Redwood Association
617 Montgomery Street
San Francisco, California 94111

Simpson Lumber Company
2000 Washington Building
Seattle, Washington 98101

Western Wood Products Association
Yeon Building
Portland, Oregon 97204

Pacific Shelter Domes
Box 279
Bolinas, California 94924

Cooperative Farm Building
Plan Exchange
Beltsville, Maryland 20705

Extension Agricultural Engineer
Oregon State University
Corvallis, Oregon 97331

First Time Farmer's Guide

There is a tremendous amount of material available for practically free on how to design and build your own country cabin. For example, if you'll write to the U.S. Government Printing Office, Washington, D.C. 20402, enclose a fat nickel and ask for Miscellaneous Publication No. 1074, you'll get back a sheet describing a picturesque cabin with a dormitory loft. The cabin has two bedrooms and a loft sleeping area. An open-type ceiling gives a feeling of spaciousness to the kitchen and living area and cuts construction costs. The cabin is intended to be framed with poles with a pole-supported deck and rough sawn native materials, such as bark slabs, are proposed for the exterior. This is one of those basic plans that you should have, whether you build this model or not. After reviewing the general idea, you can buy the complete working drawings from the Agricultural Engineer at the State University in your state. If there's a charge at all, it will be quite small (under $5 for sure). To find out the location of your State University Agricultural Engineer's office, simply send your request to Agricultural Engineer, Federal Extension Service, USDA, Washington, D.C. 20250. He will forward your request to the correct university.

The USDA has many other plans for rural buildings. Send for the list to the address given above. If you are a freewheeling far-out type, you may want to consider some of these ideas.

Tepees

If you've put all of your money in land and there's no house on it, here's a way to provide shelter for yourself and your family at the lowest possible price. If you've never been in a tipi, you'll be amazed at its feeling of solidity, warmth and coziness. The American Indians developed tipis to a high level of perfection . . . you

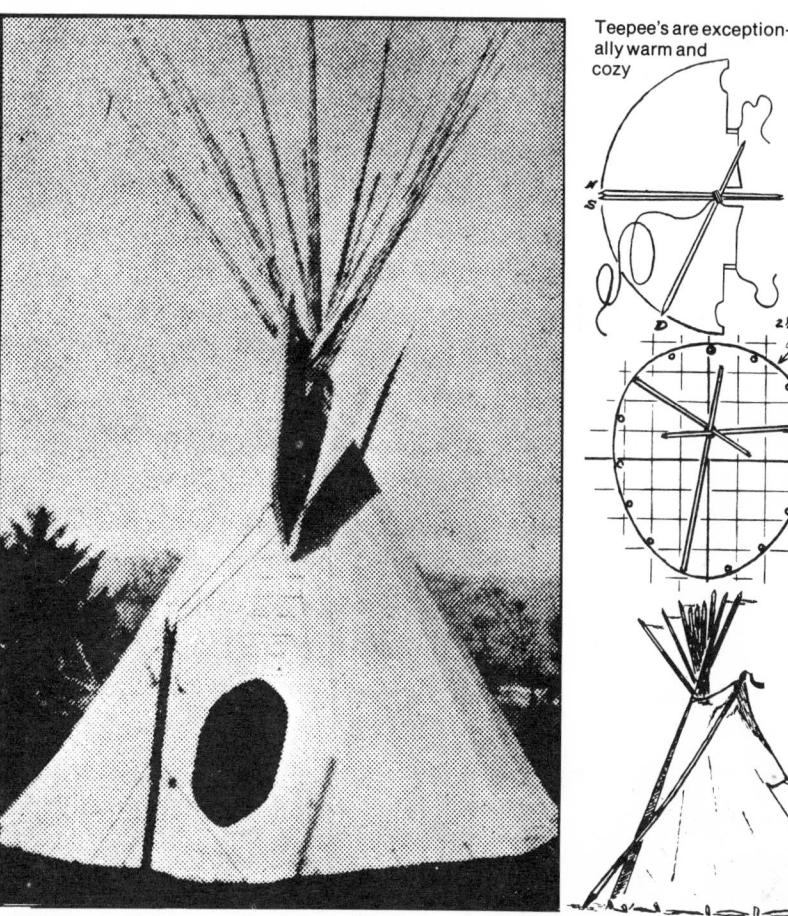

Teepee's are exceptionally warm and cozy

2½' x 2½'

can even cook inside of them and they won't get smoky. A system of double walls ensures comfort in cold weather. If you live in a wooded area, young pines or other straight evergreen trees would make fine tipi tent poles. These plus canvas and the plans puts you indoors at virtually no expense. Write to Mother Earth News, P.O. 38, Madison, Ohio 44057, and ask for a copy of the issue which contained plans for making your own tipi (one dollar).

Rocks From the Riverside

Many shallow rivers have an unlimited supply of smooth round cobblestones in various sizes. It's hard to visualize a more solid and permanent dwelling than one built of stones. A book called *'Living the Good Life'* by S. Nearing discusses stone houses at great lengths. You'll find the book in your local library. Why not? Cavemen did it. There's no maintenance to speak of on a house like this, and for sure you'll never have to patch the roof. One man in Topanga, California, bought a natural cave that contained a spring. He used it for years as a summer resort, but as he approached retirement, he built on a lean-to cabin and now has one of the warmest and most durable rural homes around.

If caves give you claustrophobia, then what about building yourself a treehouse? There are lots of advantages . . . the foundation and most of the framing is already in. Furthermore, you could live a dry, snug, camouflaged existence, free of termites, tax collectors and other parasites.

One man in Fresno decided that it was too darn hot to live above ground so he dug himself a domicile underground. It's now on public view if you happen to be passing through.

We could go on for several hundred pages about far-out-type rural dwellings. However, we want to leave some of the fun of creativity to your own imagination.

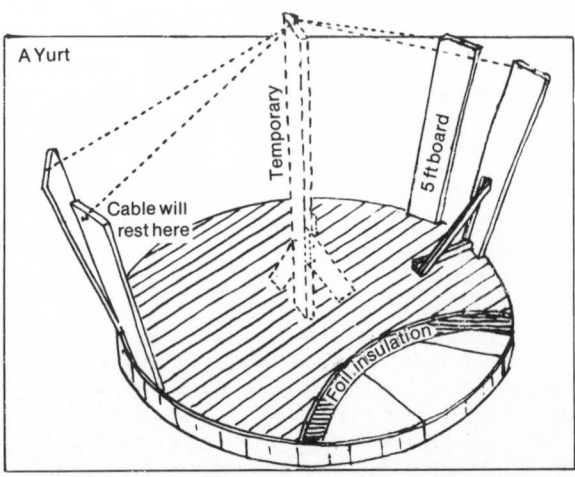

A Yurt

Temporary

5 ft board

Cable will rest here

Foil Insulation

First Time Farmer's Guide

Publications/Sources of Supply

'No man is born in possession of the art of living
any more than of the art of agriculture; the one
requires to be studied as well as the other. A man
can no more expect satisfaction from random
actions than he can expect a good crop from seeds
sown without regard to soil and season.'
— JC Loudon, *Encyclopedia of Agriculture*

Farm Periodicals

Would you like to know where you can buy a fine, healthy Nubian goat ready to milk? Perhaps your need is for a large quantity of ornamental seed corn, or you may be planning to build a totally self-contained, farm electrical system complete with a battery of wind generators. In each of these instances there's lots of help forthcoming for you from the hundreds of publications printed in the United States and Canada which are directed to farmers and dedicated to keeping fruit, nut and vegetable growers apprised of the latest developments. Here are some samples from each group.

General farm publications range from such giants as *Successful Farming,* which has a circulation of over one million and a quarter, to *Redwood Rancher,* which goes to about 6,000 farmers in northern California.

If you are in the beef business in Oregon, for example, you'd be able to keep up with what's happening through your subscription to the *Oregon Cattleman,* which goes to 3,000 readers.

If you've been putting all of your eggs in many baskets lately, then you would probably be receiving regular issues of *Poultry Tribune,* a publication out of Illinois with about 90,000 subscribers.

If peanuts are your bag, then most assuredly you'd be getting both the *Peanut Farmer* and *Peanut Journal and Nut World.*

These examples of farming publications are indicative of the tremendous material-in-depth available to help you operate an efficient small farm. This information can be so important to the first-time farmer that we are providing a selected list of publications that we believe can offer you the most pertinent information, and here it is:

Farm Periodicals

Buckeye Farm News
245 N. High Street
Columbus, Ohio 43216

California Farmer
83 Stevenson Street
San Francisco, California 94105

California Rancher
2900 Rio Linda Boulevard
Sacramento, California 95815

Capper's Weekly
616 Jefferson Street
Topeka, Kansas 66607

Colorado Rancher & Farmer
P.O. 1349
Denver, Colorado 80201

Cooperative Farmer
P.O. 1656
Richmond, Virginia 23213

Country Guide
1760 Ellice Avenue
Winnipeg 21, Manitoba, Canada

Farm Bureau Press
7th & High Street
Little Rock, Arkansas 72202

Farm and Dairy
Box 38
Salem, Ohio 44460

The Farm & Garden
260 Washington Street
Watertown, New York 13601

Farm Journal
230 W. Washington Square
Philadelphia, Pennsylvania 19105

Farmer's Friend and Rural Reporter
310 Pine Street
Green Bay, Wisconsin 54301

Farmland
P.O. 7305
Kansas City, Missouri 64116

Montana Agriculture
125 Mendenhall, Box 1207
Bozeman, Montana 59715

New Mexico Farm and Ranch
421 N. Water
Las Cruces, New Mexico 88001

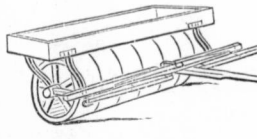

Specialized Periodicals

With an orientation exactly suited to the first-time farmer, a number of brand new periodicals have made their appearance:

'Mother Earth News' — It is published by a man who has devoted most of his life to the search for an alternate existence. John Shuttleworth is a knowledgeable editor who has acquired an enormous data bank of information relevant to the rural do-it-yourselfer. Write to P.O. Box 38, Madison, Ohio 44057.

'Countryside' — As editor and publisher, Jerry Belanger says 'it is published in the country by homesteaders whenever the other chores are done.' Measuring a handy 6 x 9 inches so you can stuff it in your overall pocket on your way to fiddle with something or udder. Write to 'Countryside', Marshall, Wisconsin.

Pennsylvania Farmer
P.O. 3665
Harrisburg, Pennsylvania 17105

Prairie Farmer
1230 W. Washington Boulevard
Chicago, Illinois 60607

The Progressive Farmer
821 N. 19th Street
Birmingham, Alabama 35202

Successful Farming
1716 Locust Street
Des Moines, Iowa 50303

Today's Farmer
201 S. Seventh Street
Columbia, Missouri 65201

Western Farmer
201 Elliott Avenue
West Seattle, Washington 98119

'Wood Heat Quarterly'—Published by Lowther Press, RD 1, Wolcott, Vermont 05680. In one of their issues, they show a photograph of a picturesque farmhouse and reveal that it is both the birthplace of their publication as well as their own homestead. Information that comes from sources like this just *has* to be authentic.

'The Whole Earth Catalog'—Virtually the originator of the publications which provide 'access to tools,' it is *an absolute must* for the first-time farmer. Here are a couple of addresses. You can write to either Portola Institute, 558 Santa Cruz, Menlo Park, California 94025 or 'The Book People,' 2010-7th Street, Berkeley, California 94710. (The Catalog ceased publication July 1971—as planned—and Bantam Books has published an edited collection.)

'Canadian Whole Earth Almanac'—the companion publication to the American original, it publishes thematic issues, regularly (food, shelter, industry & craft, etc), and in good order. $3.00 each from Book People, 2940-7th Street, Berkeley, California 94710.

Farm Books

Although it is impossible to find a book as complete as the one you are now reading, there are many hard cover and paperback books and booklets that are relevant to your new way of life. Books can be your best investment. If you only received *one* important bit of information from a book that cost five to ten dollars, this information could save you ten to a hundred to perhaps a thousand times the book's cost.

Ways to Obtain

Free lending libraries are the easiest and least expensive sources. Remember that if they don't have the book you want, they may be able to get it for you from another branch.

Used book stores are now prevalent in both urban and rural areas. Excellent books on old-fashioned organic farming methods can be purchased from 25 cents up.

Salvation Army and Goodwill stores frequently have large supplies of old books at extremely low cost. An unusual source of books on farming subjects is the Nature Consultant's Lending Library, Wright Road, Collinsville, Connecticut 06022. Judy and Hal Hinds thought up this idea and it's a good one. For a yearly membership of five dollars, they will loan you any of the books in their own library for a period of one month with no fines or further charges. They have many unusual, hard-to-get items. Write them for further information.

A valuable book that will give you the name, author, price and publisher of every book currently in print in the United States is *Books in Print,* published by R.R. Bowker, 1180 Avenue of the Americas, New York, New York 10036.

Another good information source book is *How to Find Out, a Guide to Sources of Information For All* by G. Chandler, Pergamon, Maxwell House, Fairview Park, Elmsford, New York 10523.

Back to the Land

The Have-More Plan for a Little Land, Ed and Carolyn Robinson, originally published by Macmillan, New York 10022. A reprint of the most salient parts of the book is available from Mother Earth News, P.O. Box 38, Madison, Ohio 44057.

How to Live in the Country Without Farming, Wilton Wend, Doubleday & Co., Inc., Garden City, New York. (Available in bookstores or from Nature Consultant's Lending Library.)

We Took To The Woods, L.D. Rich, Grosset & Dunlap, New York. (Try your library, old book stores or Nature Consultants.)

Soil And Cultivation

Plowman's Folly, E.H. Faulkner, University of Oklahoma Press, 1005 Asp Avenue, Norman, Oklahoma 73069.

Pay Dirt, J.J. Rodale, Rodale Press, Emmaus, Pennsylvania 18049.

Water

Village Technology Handbooks, VITA, College Campus, Schenectady, New York 12308.

Well-Drilling Operations, Government Printing Office, Washington, D.C. 20402.

Manual of Individual Water Supply Systems, Peace Corps, Washington, D.C. or GPO, Washington, D.C. 20402.

If you have problems ...write to John Shuttleworth of Mother Earth News ...the no shuck 'back to land' editor

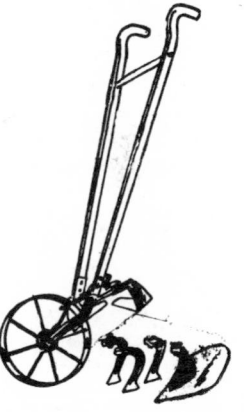

Foods For Free

Using Wayside Plants, N. Coon, Hearthside Press, 381 Park Avenue South, New York, New York 10016.

Anyone Can Live Off the Land, J. Johnson, David McKay Company, 750 Third Avenue, New York 10017.

Growing Things

The Sunset Garden Book, Lane Magazine and Book Company, Menlo Park, California 94025.

How to Have a Green Thumb Without an Aching Back, Ruth Stout, Exposition Press, 50 Jericho Turnpike, Jericho, New York 11753.

The Encyclopedia of Organic Gardening, J.J. Rodale, Rodale Press, Emmaus, Pennsylvania 18049.

How To Grow Vegetables and Fruits by the Organic Method, as above.

Anyone Can Have a Green Thumb, A.D. Pardee, Hearthside Press, 381 Park Avenue South, New York, New York 10016.

Cooking Things

Let's Eat Right to Keep Fit, A. Davis, Harcourt Brace Jovanovich, 757 Third Avenue at 47th, New York 10017.

Food is Your Best Medicine, H.G. Bieler, M.D., Random House, 201 E. 50th Street, New York, New York 10022.

The Natural Food Cook Book, B. Hunter, Simon and Schuster, 630 Fifth Avenue, New York, New York 10020.

The Complete Book of Food and Nutrition, J.J. Rodale, Rodale Press, Emmaus, Pennsylvania 18049.

How to Cook Fish and Game, W. Goddard, Tri-Ocean, Inc., 62 Townsend Street, San Francisco, California 94107.

Diet for a Small Planet, Frances M. Lappe, Ballantine Books, 101 Fifth Avenue, New York, New York 10003.

Valuable Guides for General First-Time Farm Use

Farmer's Almanac, T. Wheelwright, Crown Wheelwright, 419 Park Avenue South, New York, New York 10016.

Farming Programs for Small Acreage, E. Jurgenson, Interstate, 19-26 N. Jackson, Danville, Illinois 61832

How to Save Money on the Farm, B. Wilson, Van Nostrand-Reinhold Book Company, 450 W. 33rd, New York, New York 10001.

How to Make Wood Furnishings for Your Home, M. Dal Fabbro, McGraw-Hill, 330 W. 42nd Street, New York New York 10036.

How to Make Something From Nothing, F.B. Griffith. A. S. Barnes, P.O. 421, Cranbury, New Jersey 08512.

How to Fix Almost Everything, S. Schuler, M. Evans & Company, 216 E. 49th, New York, New York 10017.

How to Live on Nothing, J. Shortney, Pocketbooks, Division Simon & Schuster, 630 Fifth Avenue, New York, New York 10020.

How to Live in the New America, Bill Kaysing, Prentice-Hall, Englewood Cliffs, New Jersey 07632.

How to Live in the Woods on $10 a Week, B. Angier, Stackpole Books, Cameron & Kelker Streets, Harrisburg, Pennsylvania 17105.

Son of Hassle-Free Sewing, Sharon Rosenberg & Joan Weiner, Straight Arrow Books, 625 Third Street, San Francisco, California 94107.

Free and Nearly Free Information from Federal and State Agricultural Organizations

There is no question that the biggest bargains in small scale farming today are available from Federal and State government sources. The following are examples of some available from the Superintendent of Documents, Government Printing Office, Washington, D.C. 20402.

Wood Frame House Construction, 65¢, Catalog No. A 1.76:73.

A-Frame Cabin, 5¢, Catalog No. A 1.38:1093.

Building With Adobe, 5¢, Catalog No. A 1.35:535/2.

Know the Soil You Build On, 15¢, Catalog No. A 1.75: 320.

1½ Story Dwelling, Farm Building Plan No. 7179, 5¢, Catalog No. A 1.38:1034.

Planning the Electric Water System and Plumbing for Your Farmstead, 15¢, Catalog No. A 1.38:674/2.

Plumbing Manual, 40¢, Catalog No. C 13.29:66.

Farmstead Sewage and Refuse Disposal, 20¢, Catalog No. A 1.75:274.

Trout in Farm and Ranch Ponds, 10¢, Catalog No. A 9:2154.

Beekeeping for Beginners, 15¢, Catalog No. A1.77:158.

How to Buy Public Lands, 5¢, Catalog No. I 53.9:4/2.

Where and How to Get a Farm, Some Questions and Answers, 5¢, Catalog No. A 1.35:432/3.

Manual of Individual Water Supply Systems, 40¢, Catalog No. FS2.6/2:W29/2/963.

USDA

Another even more specialized branch of the Government from which you can obtain information is the US Department of Agriculture, Washington, D.C. 20250. Unlike the Government Printing Office publications, a large number of USDA publications are free on request. Just write to Information Division, USDA, Washington, D.C. 20250 and ask them to send you a catalog or list of publications in the field of your interest. Each year the USDA publishes their year book. The most recent edition, *Contours of Change,* 'attempts to tell where we are today and looks to the future'. The first

First Time Farmer's

part of the book discusses the agricultural revolutions. One of the articles has an arresting title 'One Man Feeds 5,000 Cattle or 60,000 Broilers'. The article describes how large scale farming functions. Well worth your time to read this as well as the balance of the book.

'Contours of Change' is but one of the many year books published by the USDA. In previous years the following typical titles appeared:

1969—Food For Us All
1967—Outdoors USA
1964—Farmer's World
1958—Land

The books are all hard cover, beautifully printed and many are illustrated in both black and white and color. The majority cost less than three dollars. In addition to the pamphlets, booklets and hard cover books, the USDA publishes a number of periodicals. They are both numerous and specialized. To obtain a list, write to Division of Information, Office of Management Services, USDA, Washington, DC 20250. These periodicals include:

Agricultural Handbooks—Information for ready reference, such as manuals, guidebooks, specifications, glossaries, and lists of plants or animals, for professional and technical workers.

Agriculture Information Bulletins—Subject matter of interest to people and groups throughout the American public—urban as well as rural.

Conservation Research Reports—Reports of conservation research, including reports on less complete research projects than are reported in the Technical Bulletin Series.

Farmers' Bulletins—Information on practical methods of applying the results of scientific research to farming in simple language.

You'll find most USDA year books in your local library

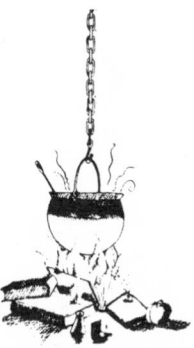

Home and Garden Bulletins — Information on home and garden subjects for use by town and city as well as farm residents.

A typical USDA periodical is 'Agricultural Situation'. It contains brief reports of current marketing and economic developments affecting farmers. It is available for 50¢ a year.

As with all publications which cost money, send your request and remittance to the Superintendent of Documents, Government Printing Office, Washington, DC 20402.

To obtain a list of all available publications of the USDA, send for List of Available Publications. It costs 45¢ a copy and you should send your money to the Superintendent of Documents, Government Printing Office, Washington, DC 20402 and request this USDA list.

In addition to all of these services, the USDA, through its Information Division, will provide answers to specific questions. Of course, in most cases the questions have been asked before and have been answered by one or more USDA publications. However, if you run into something that you feel the Department can help you with, don't hesitate to write them.

Agency for International Development

Another government office that can furnish information is the Department of State agency for International Development, Washington, DC. This Department also has responsibility for the Agricultural Technical Services Desk and the Agricultural and Rural Development Service. Therefore, it is a source of non-duplicated information on agriculture.

Agricultural Experiment Station

Almost every state has an Agricultural Experiment Station. Most of them will provide you with literature on all phases of agriculture and animal husbandry free of charge. This is their job as they are supported by taxpayers in their own state. Their objective is to help you do the best possible job in growing food and livestock for yourself and others. Obtaining information from a state agricultural facility is an excellent way to insure that the data is pertinent. Obviously the Federal Government information applies to all states in a general way, whereas, your own state will be able to pinpoint your problems and offer solutions. For example, growing musk melons in California would be quite different from the procedure to be followed in upstate New York.

While the US Department of Agriculture as well as other federal and state agencies provide much valuable information, you, as a first-time farmer, should be aware that many government agencies are subjected to external influences. For example, it is generally agreed that certain long-lasting pesticides, herbicides and fungicides should not be used any longer. However, in many publications of the USDA they still recommend the use of inorganic chemicals and pesticides which persist (are non-degradable). Thus it will be well for your own health

First Time Farmer's Guide

and welfare as well as the safety of your mutual environment to carefully consider various recommendations.

Learning to Farm by Mail

There is a fine book which may be had for 50¢ that lists correspondence courses in farming available from colleges and universities throughout the country. Write National University Extension Association, 1 Dupont Circle, Washington, DC 20036, and ask for *A Guide to Independent Study Through Correspondence Instruction.*

A typical college that offers courses in agriculture by mail is Pennsylvania State. Most of these courses cost less than five dollars. Here is a listing of some of them:

42. Sheep Husbandry. 8 Lessons. Cost $3.45.
68. Animal Breeding. 7 Lessons. Cost $3.05.
127. Animal Hygiene. 8 Lessons. Cost $3.45.
69. Milk Technology and Food Value. 11 Lessons. Cost $4.65.
134. Cottage Cheese Manufacture. 4 Lessons. Cost $1.85.
81. Canning and Food Preservation. 8 Lessons. Cost $3.45.
74. Orchard Fruits. 6 Lessons. Cost $2.65.
92. Poultry Keeping. 11 Lessons. Cost $4.65.

You can write direct to Pennsylvania State, 202 Agricultural Education Building, University Park, Pennsylvania 16802 and ask for a free copy of Correspondence Courses in Agriculture and Home Economics.

Red Birch Oregon Ash Dogwood Spruce Silver Fir Red Fir Hemlock Pine Elderberry

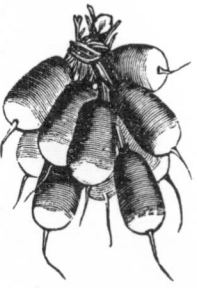

Sources of Supply

There are hundreds of thousands of manufacturers, wholesalers and retailers who can provide you with every conceivable piece of equipment or expendable item that you might need to operate your first-time farm. The catalogs, booklets and brochures of these firms will provide you with much valuable information. For example, seed catalogs often give instructions on how to grow plants. The booklets of the Purina Company have valuable pointers on the care of animals. These booklets are available, by the way, free at almost every country feed store that handles Purina products.

In addition to free literature, companies will send you plans, diagrams and answers to your specific questions. Just write them care of their public relations department for a prompt and courteous reply.

Farm Machinery of All Types

These are handiest sources for small-scale farming: Montgomery Ward, Oakland, California 94616 and Sears, Chicago, Illinois, or your local catalog store.

For larger equipment:
Allis Chalmers, 864-57th, Milwaukee, Wisconsin.
Case, Racine, Wisconsin 53404.
S.L. Allen Company, 5th & Glenwood, Philadelphia, Pennsylvania.
Domries Farm Equipment, 808 N. Brookhurst, Anaheim, California.
Lilliston Corporation, Albany, Georgia.
Waterloo Wood Bearing, Waterloo, Iowa.
Gravely Corporation, 1570 Gravely Lane, Clemmons, North Carolina.
Wiss & Sons, 33T-Littleton, Newark, New Jersey.
Deere & Company, Moline, Illinois.

Outdoor Equipment
Frostline Outdoor Equipment, P.O. 1378, Boulder, Colorado 80302.
L.L. Bean, Freeport, Maine 04032.
Herters, Waseca, Minneapolis.
Randall Knives, Box 1988, Orland, Florida.
Silvo Hardware Company, 107 Walnut Street, Philadelphia, Pennsylvania 19106.
Shotgun News, Columbus, Nebraska (not a catalog, but 50¢ will bring a sample issue listing many sources of weapons, black powder, flintlocks, crossbows, airguns — the full catastrophe).
Golden Age Arms Company, P.O. 83 Worthington, Ohio 43085 (typical weapons supplier).

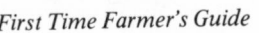

Basic Food Commodities and Food Equipment

Nomura & Company, 429 Beal Street, San Francisco, California 94105.

Modern Protein Food, 1800 Olympic Boulevard, Santa Monica, California 90404 (good source of inexpensive soybean-based protein).

The Wyne Table, P.O. 490, Norman, Oklahoma 73069 (wine and related beverage-making equipment).

Paprikas Weiss Importer, 1546 Second Avenue, New York 10028 (all kinds of kitchen equipment and if you have cherry trees, they have a automatic cherry pitter for $13).

Lee Engineering Company, 2023 W. Wisconsin Avenue, Milwaukee, Wisconsin 53201 (electric flour mill).

Smithfield Implement Company, 99 N. Mark Street, Smithfield, Utah 84335 (hand grain grinder).

El Molino Mills, 345 N. Baldwin Boulevard, Industry, California.

Yarn, Wool, Spinning Wheels and Other Do-It-Yourself Clothing Sources

Lilly Mills Company, Shelby, North Carolina 28150.

Made-Well Company, Sifton, Manitoba, Canada (spinning wheels and carding machines for playing with your wool).

Bonbazar, 149 Waverly Place, New York, New York 10014 (source of all kinds of burlap. Make your own drapes, sacks, lightweight horseblankets).

Cushings Perfection Dyes, Dover-Foxcroft, Maine (catalog of beautiful dyes for your wool, tie-dye, etc. 25¢).

You've never tasted real bread until you've ground your own flour

Some Rational Framing Systems

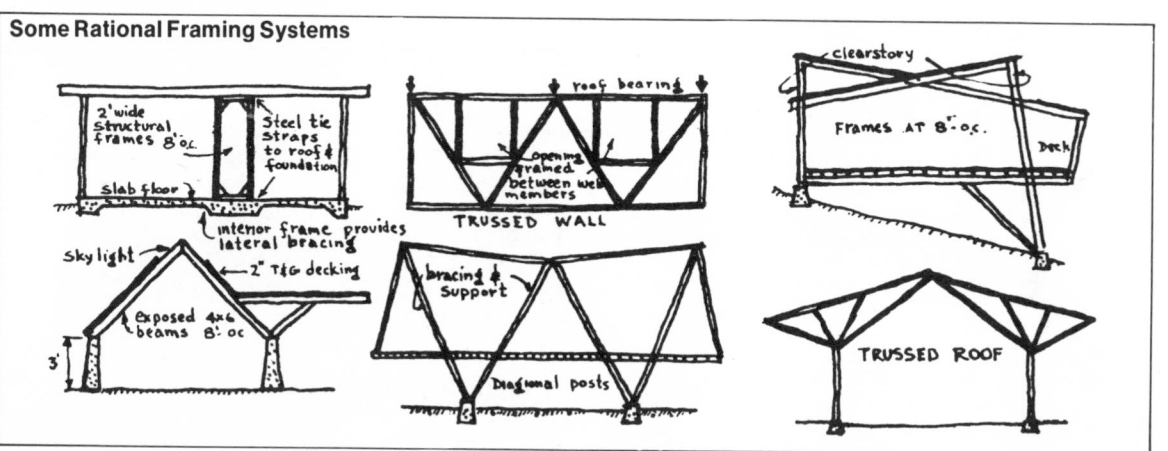

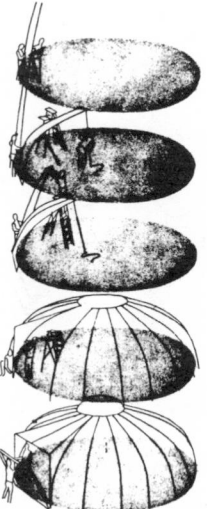

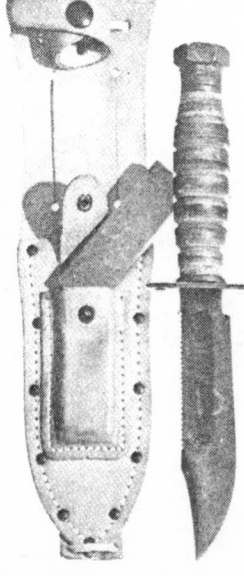

Miscellaneous
Surplus equipment
and other unnecessary items

Surplus Equipment

Many good buys in pumps, motors, farm-type machinery formerly used by the military:

Airborne Sales, 8501 Stellar Drive, Culver City, California 90230.

D.O.D. Surplus Sales, P.O. 1370, Battle Creek, Michigan 49016 (catalog of government surplus offerings like jeeps, trucks, etc).

Surplus Center, P.O. 713, Lincoln, Nebraska 68501.

Electrical, Optical and Scientific Items

Optics on a farm? Sure, see what the cows and sheep are doing from 2 miles away:

Edmund Scientific, 100 Edscorp Building, Barrington, New Jersey 08007 (many optical, electrical items to make your farm life more interesting).

Allied Radio, 100 N. Western, Chicago, Illinois 60680 (electrical and electronic gear).

Dunlite Electrical Company, 21 Frome Street, Adelaide, South Australia 5000 (wind generators).

Compact Water Pumps, Sanitation Systems and Lighting for Small Homes, Trailers, Tree Houses and Caves

Allied Trailer Supply, P.O. 806, Mountain View, California 94040.

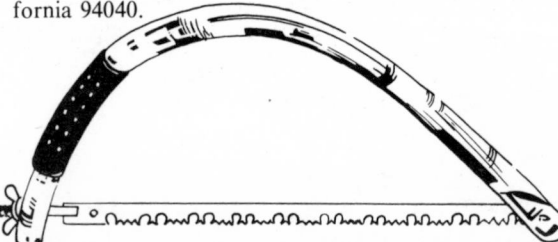

The Grab Bag

Miscellaneous items to make your first-time farm more fun, productive, far out.

The Smilie Company, 575 Howard Street, San Francisco, California 94105 (sheepherders' ovens, heavy griddles, 5-gallon storage cans for grain, catalog 10¢).

W.H. Zeller, 1415 Keil Highway, Hudson, Michigan 49247 (blasting fuse . . . might be useful to get rid of those old stumps).

Shaklee, P.O. 3625 Hayward, California 94544 (biodegradable cleaning products . . . by being a distributor you can get wholesale).

Griffolyn Company Inc., P.O. 33248, Houston, Texas 77033 (unusually strong plastic sheeting made to order).

Fleming, 2110 S.W. 173rd Place, Seattle, Washington 98166 (bottle and jug cutter to make glasses, mugs and vases from old glass bottles and jugs).

Bede Homebilts, 355 Richmond Road, Cleveland, Ohio 44143 (airplanes in kit form so you can live really far out).

Vita Green Farms, P.O. 878, Vista, California 92083 (vegetable and herb seeds, organic fertilizers by mail or truck, by ton or sack. Water purifiers, buglites, organic foods, free catalog).

J.C. Whitney, 1917 Archer Avenue, Chicago, Illinois 64616 (auto and truck parts).

Julius Roehrs, Ruterford, New Jersey 07070 (exotic plants, catalog 25¢).

Index

'When the sun rises, I go to work
When the sun goes down, I take my rest
I dig the well from which I drink
I farm the soil that yields my food
I share creation
Kings can do no more.'
—Ancient Chinese 2500 BC

Photographs and Credits

Robert Altman, 7, 84, 94, 147, 196, 197, 214, 251, 274, 281, 300, 304
M. Ballis, 162
Greg Brown, 29
Alan Copeland, 170
Clear Creek, 155
George Hall, 11
Ilka Hartmann, 105, 195
Mike Hinton, 229
Bill Kaysing, 277
Hank Lebo, 34, 103, 168, 182
Ira Lee, 107
Roger Lubin, 177
Marvel Comics, 20
Anthony Maine, 213
Steve Meltzer, 103
John Messina, 15
Mother Earth News, 120, 121, 227
Dan O'Neil, 64
Bill Owens, 262
John Pierce, 318
Rodale Press, 69
USDA, 12, 19, 45, 66, 87, 88, 89, 93, 148, 200, 224, 236, 238, 245, 246, 261, 296, 311, 312
And the *Handbook of Plant and Floral Ornament,* a Dover Book, for the many herbal & floral illustrations.

The power of the individual to conduct his own education, find his own inspiration, . . .

Index and Guide to Maps & Charts

Maps and Charts

First Time Farmer's Guide

Wire fences offer no wildlife cover; native shrubs improve wire fences

Living fences need no wire or posts; contour hedges save soil and game

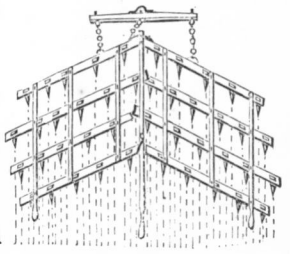

We hope you have enjoyed this book and, more than enjoyment, have been helped
to understand how really *simple* farm life can be. If one were to
state a basic principle of the agrarian way, it would be
this — just cool it and let Mother Nature do practically
all of the work for you.   Readers are invited to write, c/o Straight Arrow Books,
if they have any questions regarding the material
in this book. Also appreciated would be con-
structive comments and criticisms . . . after
all, everything is changing rapidly and we
would certainly like to include your advice and suggestions in
the sequel or revision to First Time Farmer's Guide.
Thanks for staying with us all of
the way to the end. — *Bill Kaysing*

BOOK DESIGN JON GOODCHILD

Editorial Assistants: Mickey Lapenta, Kathy Burlingham
Production: Vickie Jackson, Tom Hardy, Dian-Aziza Ooka,
Brec Brown, Carol Raskin
Green Thumb: Alan Rinzler